TAX675

The FOUNTAINHEAD Series

TO BE
  Identity in Literature
REALITY IN CONFLICT
  Literature of Values in Opposition
THE HUMAN CONDITION
  Literature Written in the English Language
OF TIME AND PLACE
  Comparative World Literature in Translation

MYTH, MIND, AND MOMENT
COMMENT
  An Anthology in Prose
TRAITS & TOPICS
  An Anthology of Short Stories
UPSTAGE/DOWNSTAGE
  A Theater Festival
SCIENCE FACT/FICTION
FANTASY
  Shapes of Things Unknown
I/YOU—WE/THEY
  Literature By and About Ethnic Groups
AMERICAN MODELS
  A Collection of Modern Stories
BRITISH MOTIFS
  A Collection of Modern Stories
MARQUEE
  Ten Plays by American and British Playwrights
THE LYRIC POTENTIAL
  Arrangements and Techniques in Poetry
PERSON, PLACE, AND POINT OF VIEW
  Factual Prose for Interpretation and Extension
LITERATURE FROM GREEK AND ROMAN ANTIQUITY
RUSSIAN AND EASTERN EUROPEAN LITERATURE
TRANSLATIONS FROM THE FRENCH
ITALIAN LITERATURE IN TRANSLATION
BLACK AFRICAN VOICES
LITERATURE OF THE EASTERN WORLD
FROM SPAIN AND THE AMERICAS
  Literature in Translation
TEUTONIC LITERATURE
  In English Translation

MYTH, MIND, AND MOMENT

EDMUND J. FARRELL
Associate Executive Secretary, National Council of Teachers of English.
Adjunct Professor of English, University of Illinois; formerly Supervisor of
Secondary English, University of California, Berkeley; formerly English
Department Chairman, James Lick High School, San Jose, California.

THOMAS E. GAGE
Consultant in English and Reading, Mt. Diablo Unified School District,
Concord, California. Formerly Chairman of English Department, Concord
High School, Concord, California; formerly Chairman of Humanities Depart-
ment, Fremont High School, Oakland, California.

JOHN PFORDRESHER
Assistant Professor of English, Georgetown University, Washington, D.C.
Editor, *Variorum Edition of the Idylls of the King,* Columbia University Press.
Formerly Assistant Professor of English, University of New Hampshire,
Durham.

RAYMOND J. RODRIGUES
Assistant Professor of Education, University of Utah, Salt Lake City, Utah.
Formerly Teacher of English, Robertson High School, Las Vegas, New
Mexico; formerly teacher of English, Edward W. Clark High School, Las
Vegas, Nevada; formerly President, Southern Nevada Teachers of English.

SCOTT, FORESMAN, AND COMPANY

Glenview, Illinois • Dallas, Texas • Oakland, New Jersey
Palo Alto, California • Tucker, Georgia • Brighton, England

To ascertain the tastes, the abilities, and the preferences of those for whom this book is intended, the following individuals read the many selections submitted to them, judged their appropriateness and interest, and solicited the reactions of young people. The authors and editors of MYTH, MIND, AND MOMENT wish to express their appreciation for this valuable assistance.

MARGARET S. DINN
Miami, Florida

DUDLEY CLINTON ENOS
Denver, Colorado

EVALEE HART
Cuyahoga Falls, Ohio

PHILIP A. LUM
San Francisco, California

PETER K. LYNCH
Long Island, New York

GUY MANN
Auburn, New York

BENEDICT OLIVER, F.S.C.
Pittsburgh, Pennsylvania

ROBERT C. SCHAPPELL
Lancaster, Pennsylvania

CAROLE SNYDER
St. Paul, Minnesota

RITA M. STONE
Fairfax, Virginia

Acknowledgements:
Cover: By Kristina Friberg, "Tankar." Courtesy of Tapestry Associates, (NY).
Frontispiece: Polish design (wycinanki). From *The Art of Stencil* by Norman Laliberté and Alex Mogelon.
Some Old Stories: "Arthur Sailing to Avalon." Biblioteca Nationale Centrale Firenze.
Mischief and Invention: "The Anti-Bird Ghost." Photograph by F. Willett.
Trials and Combats: "Cadmus and the Serpent." Detail from Laconian kylix. Louvre. Roger-Viollet.
Visions and the Other World: Engraving from *Illustrations of the Book of Job* by William Blake. The Cleveland Museum of Art, Mr. and Mrs. Charles G. Prasse Collection. Gift of Leona E. Prasse.
The End of Things: Dutch Apocalypse and Bible of the Poor. From *The Art of Written Forms: The Theory and Practice of Calligraphy,* by Donald M. Anderson. © 1969 by Holt, Rinehart and Winston, Publishers. Reproduced by permission of Holt, Rinehart and Winston, Publishers.
Some Newer Stories: "The First Eve." Reproduced from *The Art of Stencil* by Norman Laliberté and Alex Mogelon.

ISBN: 0-673-03410-0

2345678910-GBC-85848382818079787776

CONTENTS

CONTENTS

Unit **4.** Trials and Combats

Unit **5.** Visions and the Other World

Unit 6. The End of Things

Unit 7. Some Newer Stories

PREFACE

Until our time, when people talked about "myths" they referred to a series of Greek and Roman tales about the gods and their dealings with men. But about a hundred years ago the meaning of the word "myth" began to shift,—and for an exciting reason.

New versions of mythic stories began to appear, discovered in different places all over the world. Some were recent, some as old as human society itself. Explorers visiting remote tribes brought back ancient tales which had been handed down through the generations by word of mouth. People interested in folklore, visiting remote areas of the developed countries of Europe and America, collected and recorded old legends no one had considered important before. Students of ancient languages, translating manuscripts and stone inscriptions for the first time, discovered narratives which had been forgotten for centuries.

The most extraordinary thing about many of these newly discovered tales was that they told the same, basic stories the old Greek myths had told. But so diverse were the places and times in which these many versions of the same story appeared, that it was impossible to believe one telling could be the source of them all, and that the other versions were, essentially, copies. Instead, readers of myth came to realize that human beings tend, naturally, to tell certain kinds of stories over and over again. And that these stories deal with what matters most in life: birth, growth, the search for meaning, and death.

Here is one example of this discovery. For thousands of years Europeans had delighted in the Greek story of Orpheus, the wonderful harper who so loved his wife Eurydice that when she died he followed her down into the land of the dead and tried to bring her back to life. Recently we have learned that the same story is a favorite all over the world, and in every period of history. They told it in Babylon, there are African versions, and the American Indians too recount this same, sad tale. Neither time nor place limits the reappearance of this myth.

Myth, Mind, and Moment is an illustration of the discovery that certain elementary mythic stories appear everywhere in the history of literature. In it you will encounter clusters of stories selected from diverse places, peoples, and times. Some of these stories are just what you might think myths should be, the adventures of heroes and gods, battles with monsters, struggles with wily magicians, all set in a long lost world. Other selections might strike you, at first, as being non-mythic, because their settings are more modern and their characters more realistic. But a careful reading will show that, in a different way, each selection within a cluster embodies the same mythic tale. Consequently, reading through these clusters you will learn both the basic tales and the amazing variety of ways in which people have told them. You will learn that a myth can be embodied in a poem, a modern, realistic short story, a science fiction adventure, even in an essay. In fact, you will come to discover that myths represent a basic way of viewing life, and that this mythic viewpoint is very much a part of our modern world, and, though you may not have been aware of it, of the way you think about your life. So, in studying mythology through this book, you will not only learn more about literature, you will also learn more about yourself.

1

SOME
OLD
STORIES

THE MAKING
OF MEN

Leon Garfield and Edward Blishen

One Greek tradition says that the first ruler of the world was Uranus (yu̇r′ə nəs), the sky. With his wife Gaea (jē′ə), the earth, he had many children. Some were beautiful, but others were hideous creatures with a hundred arms or a single eye. Uranus imprisoned these monsters in Tartarus (tar′tər əs), the deepest abyss in the Underworld. Outraged, their mother aroused her other children, the Titans, to rebel against their father. Led by Cronus (krō′nəs), the youngest, they killed Uranus and Cronus ruled in his place.

The dying Uranus had prophesied that Cronus, too, would be overthrown by one of his own children, and so Cronus devoured them one by one as their mother Rhea (rē′ə) bore them. She concealed her sixth child, Zeus (züs), and deceived Cronus with a stone wrapped in cloth. When Zeus was grown he succeeded in giving his father a charmed drink which forced him to disgorge the other children. Zeus and his brothers then began a war with Cronus and the Titans which lasted ten years. One of the Titans, Prometheus (prə mē′thē əs), knew that Zeus would defeat them at last. When the other Titans ignored his counsel, he joined Zeus, who with his aid was victorious. Cronus and the Titans were banished and Zeus and the Olympians (see note page 70) ruled.

THREE BLIND, STONE-FACED beings crouched in the groin of a mountain. Robed in white, they were neither nymphs[1] nor goddesses nor the daughters of anything that had ever seen the light of day. From time to time, their thin arms and sharp fingers would reach out to fondle certain curious objects that were placed in their midst. A spinning wheel, a measuring rod—and a pair of shears. A short way below there grew an ancient thornbush against which the mountain goats would brush and leave clots of their hair. Whenever this happened, one of the blind three would rise and stumble to the bush, finger it over for wool and return to her sisters with her gleanings, which she would add to an already sizeable pile.

From THE GOD BENEATH THE SEA, by Leon Garfield and Edward Blishen. Copyright © 1970 by Leon Garfield and Edward Blishen. Reprinted by permission of Pantheon Books, a Division of Random House, Inc. and Jo Stewart, International Famous Agency.
1. *nymphs* (nimfs), minor goddesses, imagined as beautiful young women, who were the guardian spirits of springs or hills or groves.

Their names were as strange as their occupation: Clotho, the spinner; Lachesis, the measurer; and smallest yet most terrible, Atropos—she who cannot be avoided—the wielder of the shears.

They were the Fates[2] . . .

Suddenly, they turned their blind faces upward; and their sockets, half grown over, resembled irregular black stars in their heads.

Said Clotho, "A sudden brightness passed. At great speed—and very high. I felt it, sisters. . . ."

"It was a god," mumbled Lachesis. "I know the warmth and the scent of them. It was a god flying from Olympus toward Parnassus.[3] He will be there by now. . . ."

Then shrunken Atropos, forever playing with her shears, said shrilly: "It was Hermes,[4] sisters, it is the day we have waited for. Listen—listen—"

The three creatures bent their heads toward each other and began to smile, a faint but unmistakeable creaking sound was heard; the wheel had begun to turn.

The dreadful hands of Clotho and Lachesis reached out, and Atropos's fingers tightened over her shears.

Far, far aloft, immortal Hermes brushed a fold of cloud aside and looked down.

He saw the three white shrouded sisters sitting like maggots in the mountain's groin. Many times he had seen them before, but now there was a difference.

Their spinning wheel was moving, and the three sisters had leaned forward as if they were about to begin—What?

Hermes frowned—and sped even faster to Parnassus where all answers were to be learned.

He reached the mountain where the three grave Muses instructed the wild children of the wild nymphs. Once, these daughters of Zeus had been wild themselves, but time, responsibility and the dignified example of Apollo[5] had mellowed them into three goddesses as wise as they were respectable.

They drew their robes about them at the god's approach, endeavoring to conceal their beautiful limbs from the bright fire of his gaze. But Hermes was most studiously polite, and the gleam that had risen to the eyes of the once wild sisters died slowly away.

---

2. *Clotho . . . the Fates.* These three beings, more powerful than the gods themselves, controlled the destinies of all things. The first, Clotho (klō′thō), spun the thread of life; the second, Lachesis (lak′ə sis), measured it; and the third, Atropos (at′rə pos), cut it. **3.** *from Olympus toward Parnassus.* Mount Olympus (ō lim′pəs), in northeastern Greece, was the home of the major Greek gods. Mount Parnassus (pär nas′əs), in central Greece, was the home of Muses, goddesses of memory, of song, and later, of poetry, the sciences, and the arts. Their number was originally three. Later it was increased to nine. **4.** *Hermes* (hėr′mēz), the messenger of Zeus, celebrated for his cunning. **5.** *Apollo* (ə pol′ō), god of the sun, of prophecy, and of the arts.

Augury . . . prophecy . . . the future. He had understood from his friend and brother Apollo that he might learn it on Parnassus.

The Muses stared at the youthful god who stood so straight and bright in their quiet glade. So . . . so he had only come to learn. They sighed, recalling, perhaps, their old days when they led him to a stone basin filled with mountain water and showed him how to cast five white pebbles sideways into it.

"You must watch the way they dance, sweet Hermes. And mark how they fall. It is all in the pattern of their movement and the design of their rest. See . . . see. . . ."

They cast the pebbles, splashing one another as they did so—and gently shrieking; then inadvertently splashing the god and hastening to dry his fair limbs on their gowns. . . . "See . . . see . . . Like so!"

Hermes smiled—and learned.

Then they left him, for the god had caught the skill with wonderful speed.

They glanced back through the trees and saw him crouching over the stone basin with the pebbles held in his cupped hands.

He shook them, whispered to them, shook them again. "Who will inherit the earth?"

Then he cast them sideways into the water and watched them dance and fall.

What was their answer? Slowly, Hermes read it out. "It—concerns—Prometheus."

The god frowned in surprise. Again he shook the pebbles, whispered and cast them into the basin. "Why has Clotho's wheel begun to turn? What is she to spin? What will Lachesis measure—and what will Atropos cut?"

The pebbles rattled against the stone sides like frightened fishes; then they came to rest. "It—concerns—Prometheus."

Again, Hermes frowned, and for a third time shook the pebbles, whispered to them and hissed them on their way.

"When will this be?"

The pebbles dropped, rolled a little, then were still. Their answer was, *"Even now."*

Prometheus had a garden in Attica—a pleasant, cultivated grove in the lap of Mount Hymettus[6] where the wild bees made the honey from which the nymphs distilled the nectar for the gods.[7] Here, the Titan and his brother[8] grew such fruits as the earth would yield and had built

---

6. *Attica . . . Mount Hymettus.* Attica (at′ə kə) is the region around Athens. Mount Hymettus (hi met′əs) is east of Athens. **7.** *nectar for the gods.* Nectar (nek′tər) was the drink of the gods, which, together with their food, called *ambrosia* (am brō′zhə), sustained their immortal lives. **8.** *the Titan and his brother.* Prometheus lived with his brother Epimetheus (ep ə mē′thē əs). Their two names mean "forethought" and "afterthought," respectively.

themselves a house around an ancient fig tree. It had been Hestia[9] herself who had taught them the art of building; and wise Athene[10] had come often to sit and talk of how best to cultivate the soil while her beloved owl had perched in the wrinkled branches of the tree.

But now the Titans walked among their glades and across their close-cut lawns. Prometheus was troubled; his mighty head was bowed in thought. He feared for the lovely earth.

Little by little the brothers' shadows lengthened as the sun rode down into the sea. Prometheus was silent and Epimetheus, his brother, shrugged his shoulders and returned into the house. Of the two, he was the simpler and did not foresee, as Prometheus did, that present pleasure may be bought too dear.

Prometheus stared through the shadowy leaves of his orchards to the wide expanse beyond.

"All this," he whispered, "to no purpose? It cannot be!"

He raised his unhappy eyes and gazed toward Olympus. He tried to fathom what might be in the mind of almighty Zeus. He did not trust the god. He believed that sooner or later Zeus would beget a child and give it the world to play with. Even a child like murderous Ares[11] . . .

He shivered and knelt down. He took up a handful of the rich earth and crushed it in his fist. He opened his hand. The earth, moist from the rain, had taken the imprint of his fingers. He frowned and tried to mold it further, thinking of the marvelous coral nymph the ugly Hephaestus[12] had made under the sea. But he lacked the god's skill and his effort was vague and clumsy. Must the Olympians always be better than he? Angrily he threw it down and strode on to where a stream whispered lazily among tall reeds. Here the soil was heavy with clay and more obedient to the shaping hand. So Prometheus made a second image; and it looked like a little angry Zeus.

Prometheus laughed; then, suddenly, a strange excitement filled him.

He bent down and with both his vast hands gathered up more clay. He scooped out half the bed of the stream, so that the worried waters gushed and gurgled as if in a whirlpool.

Then, when the moon was gone into a cloud and the garden was in darkness, he hastened back to his home with the clay still dripping in his arms. He believed he had been very secret.

There was a room in the Titans' home that belonged to Prometheus alone. Its rafters were formed from the trimmed and polished branches of the fig tree that still grew from the middle of the floor. It was here that Athene had loved to sit and discourse with the profound Titan on matters of the universe, while aloft her owl made two orange suns with its eyes.

---

9. *Hestia* (hes ́tē ə), the goddess of the hearth. **10.** *Athene* (ə thē ́nē), the goddess of wisdom. **11.** *Ares* (ar ́ēz), the god of war. **12.** *Hephaestus* (hi fes ́təs), the god of fire and metalworking.

The room was rich and heavy with thought. It was here that Prometheus brought the clay and laid it on an oiled and polished bench that stretched for the room's great length.

Under this bench were several stone jars, well stoppered and sealed. No one knew of these jars but the two Titans who had guarded them jealously since the far-off days of murdered Uranus. One of them was cracked and skillfully repaired. The damage had been done during the wild war between the Titans and the gods. A mountain had crashed to blazing ruin and shaken the jar from a shelf. But Prometheus had saved it.

Now at last he broke the seal and opened it. Within was the divine substance of chaos from which all things had been created.

Prometheus had seen it, still ungrown, lying in a deep pit. It had glimmered and winked up at him. Eagerly he'd gathered it and stored it in the jars.

He poured it out. Everywhere in its shining bulk were the bright, immortal seeds trapped like fireflies in some black, festooning web.

Firmly and quickly the great Titan kneaded this ancient substance into the riverbed clay, till the precious seeds were evenly distributed. Then he set to work in earnest.

In the groin of the Fates' mountain the three blind sisters laughed aloud. Their wheel was creaking and grunting as it spun like a mad thing.

Prometheus shaped the clay into images of the immortal gods. His fingers grew more and more skillful as his great mind wrestled with the mysterious quest for form. His memory and imagination seemed to body forth shapes in the air, and swiftly he enclosed them in the curious clay.

Little Zeuses, Heras, Apollos and Poseidons ran from his fingertips; even a dark-browed Hades and a proud Artemis[13] with a wart on her knee where the Titan's fingers had fumbled.

Then he set the little godkins up before him and rested his mighty head on his aching hands. Already the immortal seeds had begun to stir and grow within the thick insensitive clay. Quietly, the Titan watched.

But he was not the only watcher. High among the crooked rafters perched an intent bird. It was a crane whose bright, bright eyes were the eyes of Hermes . . .

The clay was swelling, growing. Channels were being formed within it down which the burst seeds sent crimson tears to course, nourishing, coloring and warming into life.

Eyelids grew thin as gauze, flicked open to reveal strange little pools

---

13. *Heras . . . Artemis.* Hera (hir′ə) was the wife of Zeus and queen of the gods. Poseidon (pə sid′n) was the god of the sea. Hades (hā′dēz) was the ruler of the Underworld. Artemis (är′tə mis) was the goddess of the hunt, of the beasts, and of the moon.

of wonderment. Lips reddened, parted on white teeth . . . and tongues began to stir under the force of mounting breath.

And still they grew till their proportions were all but godlike. Everywhere in the vast room limbs were stretching, bodies twisting and hair stirring in the night breeze.

At last, they grew no more. The seeds had spent themselves; their task was done. The great Titan smiled.

"Go," he whispered. "Go seek your inheritance before it is too late."

His door was open and the starlight drifting in glinted on their sweet new limbs.

They turned their faces back to the vast dark room in which they had been made. Their eyes met the deep eyes of Prometheus. They smiled—and then they went out into the glorious garden of the night.

The Titan watched them and inexplicably his eyes grew full of tears and his huge heart ached with love and hope for the creatures he had made.

Suddenly, one gave a wild, wild cry and fell at the foot of a poplar tree. Prometheus hastened to his side; stared down, touched—then recoiled. His new-made child was cold and still.

In the groin of the gaunt mountain the three blind, stonefaced creatures laughed again. Atropos fingered her shears. The blades were sharp. To test them—just to test them—she had slit a new-spun thread.

Prometheus knelt beside his cold, quiet creation, not instantly knowing what was amiss, what had fled.

The watchful crane that had perched in the rafters was gone. Hermes the messenger had taken a shade to the echoing world of the dead. Alone and bewildered, it flitted on the farther bank of the River Styx.[14]

The first man had died.

"So frail a thread?" whispered Prometheus. "Was it the clay . . . or the seeds themselves? I had hoped—but it was not to be. What can you do against the gods and the Fates with the fragile, pitiful life I've given you?"

Then Prometheus buried his dead in the shadow of the poplar tree and mourned till it was light.

"My father bids me tell you to destroy them, great Prometheus; or he will do so himself."

Thus Hermes, messenger of the gods, as he stood, piercing bright, in the Titan's garden, washed by the morning sun.

"Why? Why? How have they offended? What is their crime?"

"Who knows what is in the mind of Zeus? Perhaps he is offended, Lord Prometheus? Perhaps he finds what you have made too close in

---

14. *Styx* (stiks), a river in the Underworld, across which were ferried the souls of the dead.

aspect to the gods? Perhaps he sees them as a mockery? Gods who are subject to the Fates. . . . Destroy them, Prometheus. So my father says."

"And you, good Hermes? Is it your wish, too?"

The god looked sideways, avoiding the Titan's despairing eyes; shifted from foot to winged foot and smiled as his shadow seemed to dance off into the trees.

"Between you and me, Prometheus . . . no. Not particularly, that is. I think they have a certain charm. Personally, I like them. I assure you, Prometheus, that such messages as, from time to time, I bring from this great god or that, do not necessarily reflect my own opinions."

Hermes, ever politic, ever unwilling to offend, watched the mighty Titan curiously; he continued, "Believe me, my friend—I understand your affection and your sorrow. When I summoned the shade of the one that died, I was troubled, Prometheus. As we entered the grove of black poplars, this shade and I, it asked me: Why, why? Prometheus. And I could not answer. Then, when I led it to the dark river and dragged it aboard the evil, rotting boat, and it saw there was no one else there but bony Charon,[15] again it begged me: Why, why?

"We came to the farther bank, and still there was no one else by. And so to the Field of Asphodel:[16] empty, empty. . . .

"It clung to me, Prometheus, as I left it, still begging me to tell it why.

"It knew nothing; had not lived more than the winking of an eye—yet it sensed the vastness of its loss. I looked back, and never in all the universe have I seen anything so lonely as that single, frightened shade wandering over the ashy ground and crying: Why, why?"

The Titan listened and groaned in anguish; then Hermes added softly: "They are so frail, Prometheus. Your creatures are so pitifully frail. Are they worth their labor?"

Eagerly the Titan laid his hand on Hermes's ribboned staff—as if to deflect or soften the god's terrible message.

"But I will strengthen them! I will refine the substance, purify it and pluck out the seeds that menace. I—"

"It is too late, Prometheus. They are doomed."

"By Zeus?"

"If not by my father, then by every wind that blows. How could they endure, never knowing when Atropos might take it into her blind head to slit the thread of their lives?"

How indeed? And the more Hermes argued, the more intolerable seemed the burden Prometheus's fragile creatures would have to bear.

Yet their very frailty stung the Titan's heart and strengthened his great will. He begged bright Hermes to plead with his father for a

---

15. *Charon* (kar′ən), the boatman who ferried the dead across the Styx. **16.** *the Field of Asphodel.* The asphodel (as′fə del) was the flower that grew in the Underworld.

little respite. If the creatures were destined to flicker out—then let them perish of their own accord. But spare them the dreadful thunderbolt. Let them see and love the gods, however briefly, and, maybe, find some favor in their sight—

Here, subtle Hermes pursed his lips and tapped his staff against his head.

"Between you and me, my friend, I fancy you've hit on something. I don't promise—I never promise—but if your creatures were to find favor in great Zeus's eyes . . . that is to say, if they were to go out of their way to please, then who knows? Think on that, Lord Prometheus; and I will undertake to delay my father's hand."

Between Arcadia and Attica, there was a place called Sicyon[17] where the creatures of Prometheus had begun to make a home. It was here, in a myrtle grove—once dear to Hermes—that Prometheus put it into men's minds to honor the gods. A rich, red bull, sleek and portly, was sacrificed and the Titan cupped his hands to his vast mouth and shouted up to Olympus for almighty Zeus to descend and be mankind's first guest.

"See, great god! My creatures honor you and worship you! Come down so they may behold you and give you the best of the earth!"

He shaded his eyes and stared desperately up toward the curtains of cloud that veiled the mountain's divine summit.

Even as he watched, a finger of lightning crooked around them and drew them briefly apart. Then came a roll of thunder. The god had heard. The god would come.

Eagerly Prometheus stripped the blood-dappled skin from the bull and divided the carcass, laying the bones and fat beneath one part of the hide, and the steaming flesh beneath the other; but in his haste he had not detached the stomach . . . Two portions, one for the god—and one for mankind.

Wide-eyed and innocent that they were, poised on the edge of extinction, the Titan's creatures watched as their great creator toiled and struggled to save them.

Suddenly they shrank back. A fearful radiance seared their naked eyes and scorched their skin. They cried out and fled into the shadows of the myrtles, hiding their faces in their hands. The blaze had been unendurable. It lingered on the inner eye where it burned its vision. Within the scalding radiance had been a shape. A shimmering fluent shape, part manlike, part immeasurably greater. Eyes had seen them— eyes like merciless suns.

It had been the god. . . .

---

17. *Between Arcadia . . . called Sicyon.* Arcadia (är kā/dē ə) was an area in the central Peloponnesus, the peninsula which forms the southern part of Greece. Sicyon (sish/ē on) was a town near the Gulf of Corinth, the body of water which divides the peninsula from mainland Greece.

"Welcome, mighty Zeus. Welcome, father of the gods, lord of the sky! Your feast is ready. Mankind awaits."

The Titan stood back as the fiery god stared around the grove. Then, seeing that Prometheus's poor creatures were blasted by his light, Zeus veiled his luster and smiled.

He saw the covered portions of the slaughtered bull. He nodded. They had not skimped their offering. The beast had been of the finest.

He touched one portion, lifted a corner of the hide. The stomach: it reeked of offal. He turned to the other. He glimpsed rich fat. Prometheus trembled; all-seeing Zeus nodded.

He pointed to the second portion.

"I have chosen," the mighty god decreed. "From now through all eternity, in feast and holy sacrifice, this portion is for the immortal gods, and that for mankind."

He flung back the skin he had chosen. Beneath the rich layer of fat lay nothing but the animal's wretched, meatless bones. The divine portion . . .

Prometheus bowed his head to hide a helpless smile. He awaited the enraged god's thunderbolt. But Zeus's anger took a subtler form.

"Let them eat their flesh raw," he said. "I forbid them the use of fire."

Without fire, they would die. Their slender limbs would freeze, their blood congeal and their bright eyes glaze and film like scum on a quiet pond. The angry god had doomed them as surely as if he'd hurled his thunderbolt and scorched them in an instant.

Prometheus wept slow, bitter tears. It had been his own smile that had brought it about: mighty Zeus had taken this way of punishing him. The smile of the father was to be the death's-head grin of his children.

For a while, fury took hold of him—and his gentle brother watched with terror and awe as great Prometheus paced their garden, bursting asunder the well-tended trees as if they'd been straw. Then the Titan passed into despair. War and violence had ever been hateful to him. The mighty struggles his nature demanded had all been in the mind.

He knew he could not storm Olympus and drag down the father of the gods. He lacked both Zeus's strength and Zeus's instant passion. Thinking had ever held him back.

For long it had preserved him—and saved him from the fearful fate of all his race. But now that power had reached its end—the limits of his mind. Thought stared into soul; and soul stared back at thought. They were the same; and the tragic Titan knew that he must destroy himself to save his children: men.

Some time during the night, mankind saw him shining among the thick trees that cloaked the northern slopes of Mount Olympus. His light pierced the branches so that it seemed as if some star had fallen and been caught in a vast black net.

Then his light was snuffed in a deep cleft in the rock, and the Titan mounted unseen.

An owl flew out of the trees, screeched several times, then fluttered uncertainly, hovering as if seeking its moment to pounce. It screeched again, and began to pursue a devious path in the night air, leading higher and higher up the mountain.

It was the owl of the goddess Athene.

The hidden Titan saw it and knew that the goddess had not turned against him. She had sent her owl to lead him secretly into the fortress of the gods. This was the most she could do for him. Mighty though she was, even she feared her blazing father's wrath.

Now came another bird out of the night. A crane perched in the Titan's twisting path. It stared at him with bright, inquisitive eyes.

"Though I will not help you, Prometheus," whispered the voice of cunning Hermes, "I will not stand in your path." The crane flew off and its soft cry came back to the mounting Titan. "There is what you seek in my brother Hephaestus's forge."

Flames gleamed and danced on the twenty golden bellows as they rose and fell like twenty gigantic beating hearts. They breathed on the forge, increasing its fire till the lip of its rocky prison shivered and ran.

Shadows loomed and lumbered against the huge smithy's walls. Rods and crucibles made the shapes of nodding beasts; and in their midst crouched the shadow of a misshapen monster on bird-thin legs that were broken sharply by the angle of the floor and walls. Hephaestus was at work. He was making a wedding gift for Aphrodite,[18] his wife. He scowled tempestuously as he beat out the gold on the black anvil with a loud, regular clang. He was fashioning the clasp of a girdle. . . .

Suddenly the god's heat-inflamed eyes quickened. A strange shadow had crossed his on the wall. It moved secretly among the beastlike shadows of the rods and crucibles which seemed to nod and swear at it, then crowd it under their own dangerous night.

Hephaestus turned. He saw a hand, holding an unkindled torch. He saw it reach forward, plunge in and out of the fire. The torch flared. It was alight.

The god looked up, Prometheus stood before him.

"For my children," whispered the despairing Titan. "For mankind."

The two great outcasts stared at one another.

"Take it and be gone," muttered the god.

---

18. *Aphrodite* (af′rə di′tē), the goddess of love and beauty.

For long after the Titan had departed, Hephaestus brooded over his anvil. His mighty hammer leaned against his knee . . . and the beaten gold grew cool. Then the god began again. His hammer rose and fell till fountains of sparks leaped up and seemed to engulf him in robes of broken fire.

At last he rested. The smithy grew quiet and the ugly god examined the clasp he had made. It was a golden hand holding a torch. It seemed to be caressing it, and the torch was spurting its vital fire. So delicately wrought was this hand that it seemed to tremble—to move, even with tenderness. . . .

The god nodded. Here in this eternal clasp was his own fierce love for Aphrodite—and Prometheus's aching love for mankind.

He fastened it to the girdle with rivets as fine as hair and hobbled off to the laughing goddess of his dreams.

Still Zeus did not strike the defiant Titan down. Prometheus had opposed him, set his command aside. Fire flickered below and strengthened the new, aspiring life.

Time and again Prometheus turned his eyes to heaven so that he might see his destruction blazing forth. But the lord of the sky seemed to have turned his back. Had grave Athene pleaded with her father? Had subtle Hermes put a case?

The Titan's uncertainty grew agonized as his time ran out. Nonetheless, he still labored for his creatures, teaching them what he could to widen their narrow foothold between the Fates and the gods. At night he brooded in the mysterious room where man had been born. Already he had begun to refine the precious substance of Chaos. Strange spots and scales he'd discovered on the bright seeds. These he scraped away and confined in a small jar which he sealed and hid. He suspected them to be some malignant rot. . . .

"Can you fashion a woman, my clever, ugly son? Can you make her as skillfully as Prometheus made his creatures below?"

The father of the gods stared down from his gold and ivory throne in the great council chamber. "Not of gold, nor silver nor imperishable bronze; but of the selfsame clay the Titan used—the soft wet clay of Attica?"

Hephaestus shuffled and blinked his reddened eyes away from Zeus's radiance. The fire of his forge was a night beside the blazing noon of Zeus.

"Fetch me the clay and I will make such a woman."

Zeus nodded, and swift as thought Hermes sped down, twisting through the cloudy swarms of bees that sang above the lower slopes of Mount Hymettus. Hephaestus waited, and presently, the thieving god returned with Prometheus's clay.

Then Hephaestus set about his task and Hermes, leaning against the lintel post of the smithy door, watched the great artificer at his work.

Unlike Prometheus, the god worked slowly. He seemed to seek the form within the dull shapeless clay. Even as Hermes watched, his burnt and twisted fingers probed and dragged at hair, cheeks, lips, breasts and limbs as if he were freeing rather than creating them. He tore the clay away from her eyes as if it had been a blindfold, and suddenly a woman stared at Hermes in the doorway. Even though he knew his ill-tempered brother's marvelous skill, Hermes was startled by this strange new evidence of it.

Her height was perhaps a finger's breadth below Aphrodite's, but otherwise her beauty was not of Olympus. It had the darker, richer colors of the earth. Hephaestus had fashioned a woman far beyond the Titan's skill.

She stood beside the mighty anvil and as the twenty golden bellows breathed on the fire, the heat drew tears of moisture out of the clay so that she seemed to be weeping before she had life. Then Zeus bade Aeolus,[19] warder of the four winds, breathe life into her nostrils and mouth.

She stirred; she moved; she stared about her with a sweet vacancy, understanding nothing—feeling nothing.

Being formed from unseeded clay, she had neither passions nor qualities.

So life-giving Zeus commanded the immortal gods to enrich her with their gifts.

First Hestia, gentlest of the children of Cronus, gave this woman a gentleness and generosity not unlike her own, and the vacant eyes took on a soft and tender gleam. But Ares, roughly elbowing forward, forced on her a touch of himself, so that behind the tender gleam there glinted the flicker of a savage fire.

Next great Apollo gave her sweet and tempting grace of movement—such as he himself delighted in, but straightway his moon-sister Artemis gave her defensive quickness, modesty and virginity.

Glorious Demeter[20] shook her head. Never quite in sympathy with Artemis, she blessed the woman with a richly fertile womb—and the knowledge of it. This knowledge now glinted mysteriously from under the downcast lashes that the mighty huntress's gift had imposed.

"And I will give her wisdom," said Athene suddenly. She had divined the danger there lurked in this woman, compounded as she was of so many opposing passions. "I will give her wisdom so that her gifts may be well used."

Zeus frowned, but could not deny the powerful goddess her right. So he bade Hermes give Athene's gift a double edge, with curiosity and deceit.

---

19. *Aeolus*, (ē′ə ləs). **20.** *Demeter* (di mē′tər), the goddess of the harvest and of marriage.

Now the woman turned and smiled gratefully at each of the gods in turn; her eyes seemed to linger so that her last look was always sideways . . . till imperious Hera hastened to cover her nakedness with fine, cloudy robes. This woman was curiously disturbing. Beside her, the nymphs were but as children—their amorous leapings and twinings as children's games. . . . Then Zeus gave her a name. Pandora[21]— all giving.

She bowed her head. "Great goddess," she murmured, raising her face now to lovely Aphrodite while her eyes lingered timidly on smiling Zeus. "Is there no gift from you? Are you displeased with me? Have I unknowingly offended you? If so, I beg forgiveness . . . and plead for your gift. For without it, I think, all would wither away unused."

So Aphrodite laughed—and lent Pandora the girdle that Hephaestus had made for her—the girdle that kindled desire.

"With such a piece of work," murmured the king of the gods as he brooded down on Pandora, "what need have I of thunderbolts?"

It was Hermes who led her down the slopes of Mount Olympus; and as the gods watched, none was sorry to see her go.

"What harsh message do you bring from Olympus now, Hermes?"

Prometheus and his brother were in their orchard, propping the well-filled branches, when the great herald rippled through the trees.

"No message, Lord Prometheus," answered the god courteously. He had plucked an apple in passing and now speared it idly on his ribboned staff. He stared at it as if surprised. "I bring a gift. Indeed, Prometheus, there is no need to look at me so angrily, as if you would refuse. The gift does not concern you. It is for your brother, Epimetheus."

He pointed his staff, with the red apple on its head, at the second Titan, the ever-gentle, not overwise Epimetheus.

"The gift of the gods is for you."

Epimetheus came forward with a pleased smile. His heart was open; his nature unsuspecting. Such happy beings as he are always the last of their race.

"Beware of gods bearing gifts," muttered his great brother whom he never understood.

Epimetheus looked uncertain. Hermes stretched out his staff. "Come," he called. "Pandora!"

She came from behind the trees in the cloudy gown of Hera. She walked with graceful yet uncertain steps. Her eyes were downcast— though from time to time they glimmered with a curious sideways glance that lingered in Epimetheus's heart.

"Here is your new gift, Epimetheus. Pandora—gift of the Olympian gods."

21. *Pandora*, (pan dôr′ə).

Epimetheus was entranced. Never had their orchard seen a richer fruit.

"Beware, brother—"

"Lord Prometheus, this is no concern of yours." Hermes spoke calmly, but there was an edge to his voice. Then he laughed disarmingly. "Epimetheus—your deep brother is too anxious. He mistrusts good fortune. Between you and me, I suspect a little envy. And who could blame him? See—"

He touched the trembling Pandora with his staff, laying its appled tip on her breast. She smiled timidly. "She bears the gifts of us all."

"She is the gift of Zeus, brother. Old Cronus once had such a gift. Do you remember a cup of honeyed drink—?"

Epimetheus hesitated; gazed uneasily from brother to the god. He avoided Pandora's eyes. He thanked Olympus, but begged time to consider. . . .

Prometheus smiled triumphantly.

"Do you refuse me, Epimetheus?" Pandora's voice was low . . . even pleading. The gentle Titan glanced at her. Modestly she cast her eyes down to Aphrodite's kindling girdle. Epimetheus felt desire rise like the all-covering sea.

Then briefly Pandora lifted her eyes and stared at Prometheus. Her look was still gentle and partly timid. She seemed to be bewildered and curious as to why this mighty being should bid his brother send her away. What had she done? Why did he stare at her as if to pierce her through and through? Why did his great brows furrow till his eyes were no more than pools of troubled shadow? Was it only because she had come between brother and brother? Was it as the bright god had said—that this vast soul was stabbed with envy for his brother's blessing?

If so, then it was not of her doing.

See—he was drawing Epimetheus aside, talking with him—while the god who had brought her looked on with the strangest smile. What was to become of her, with all her beauty and gifts?

Why had the gods made her so?

"Do not refuse me, Epimetheus," she pleaded, and such was her power that Epimetheus's heart faltered within him. She promised him such joy and fierce delight that even the gods would envy him. Epimetheus's eyes began to gleam. Whereupon the blessing of Hestia, momentarily conquering the passions of Aphrodite and Ares, prompted Pandora to speak of ease and sweet companionship, and the speaking silences of harmonious minds. . . .

"Can there be danger in such a gift?" asked simple Epimetheus of his brother.

"Nor will their lives be fruitless, Lord Prometheus," murmured

Hermes, drifting close and leaning toward the Titan's ear. "Glorious Demeter has blessed her, too. Even as your well-tended trees bear fine fruit, so will Pandora bear children to your home. Mark my words, Prometheus, her children will inherit our immortal gifts—for the gods' gifts do not die—and these children will mingle with mankind. Thus does my father mean well, Prometheus. He seeks to improve on your charming but fragile creation with some more durable qualities of the gods. Believe me, my friend—"

Suddenly the Titan turned with terror on the murmuring god of lies. His eyes were wild—his vast comprehension tilted so that all ran down into the pit of dismay. He had divined dread Zeus's purpose—and foreseen his own defeat. The creatures that he loved—the creatures who might have inherited the earth as neither gods nor Titans were permitted to do—were to be crippled before they had begun.

Even as in Pandora the passions of the gods opposed each other, so they would in men. All aspiration would be lamed, all achievement warped as man eternally fought within himself a battle that could be neither lost nor won.

Then the great Titan raised his eyes to Mount Olympus and cursed immortal Zeus.

He lifted up his voice and hurled his curses till they echoed in the far corners of the universe. Even in hateful Tartarus they were heard, like thin, high whispers over the ceaseless weeping and groaning of the Titans who were chained there.

Close by the dreary Fields of Asphodel, there is a pool beside which grows a bone-white poplar tree. It is the pool of memory. Here strayed the solitary shade of the man who had died. Vainly it drank of the pool: but what memories could it recapture of a life so fleeting, save an aching glimpse of a garden by night?

It heard Prometheus's curses and shook its thin head. "Why? Why?" it wailed—and flittered away into the lonely gloom.

Grim Hades in his palace heard them—and nodded in expectation of his vast brother's revenge.

As in a dream, Prometheus saw Hermes flicker away, and with a last stab of anguish he saw his brother and Pandora retreat with frightened faces, and run from the orchard. Their hands had been clasped—and there was no undoing them now.

Prometheus bowed his mighty head. He heard a rushing in the air. It was coming, and he was almost glad of it—the thunderbolt of Zeus!

The trees blazed, and for an instant their blackened branches reached up like imploring arms with fingers charred and flaming.

A radiance that seared even the Titan's ancient eyes stood in the ruined orchard like a fiery sword. Zeus in all his unendurable glory was come for his revenge.

Far, far to the north, amid the freezing mountains of the Caucasus,[22] there stood a tall, cold pillar. Chains of unburstable iron hung from its base and capital. Here the naked Titan was manacled by wrists and ankles, stretched so that he could scarcely twist his body or avert his head.

He waited—then a shadow fell across his face. He rolled his eyes to see what had come between him and the pale, bitter sun.

A vulture with hooked talons and greedy beak hung in the air. Its stony eyes met his. Then it swooped and the Titan writhed and screamed till the mountains cracked. His agony had begun. Again and again the hungry bird flew at him and tore at his undefended liver. When night came with biting frosts and whirling snow, the Titan's wounds healed and he grew whole again. But when the cold sun rose, the selfsame shadow fell across his face and the Titan waited for his agony to begin once more. Such was the punishment of Prometheus, maker of men.

Epimetheus, the last of the Titans, wept for his mighty brother— whom he had never understood. And in his great sadness Pandora comforted him. Little by little, Epimetheus began to think his brother had misjudged her. She was so quick to understand and minister to his every need. She never crossed nor questioned him; nor did she plead to enter his lost brother's mysterious room. For Prometheus, in his last moments of liberty, had charged his brother most urgently never to enter or disturb what he had hidden there.

Pandora nodded when charged to respect this wish. Though she had not liked Prometheus, she was sensible of her husband's affection and was anxious for him to feel that she was of a like mind. For a while it seemed that the gifts of Hestia and Athene were uppermost.

Then, thanks to the rich soil of Attica, the black scars in the orchard healed over, and the reason for the great Titan's fall faded from Pandora's mind. More and more she came around to the view that the whole unlucky affair had blown up out of jealousy. Why else had her husband's brother so taken against her?

She gazed at her reflection in a pool. Certainly she was beautiful enough to stir envy in any one. After all, the gods had made her. She sighed. It had been tragic; but jealousy was an evil passion and Prometheus had paid for it. She only hoped it would serve as a lesson.

She stood up and thoughts of Prometheus slid into thoughts of the forbidden room. What was so particular about it? She suspected jealousy was at the root of it again. A jealous spirit is jealous in everything. Most likely the room was very handsome and Prometheus had forbidden it to her out of spite. The more she thought of it, the

---

22. *Caucasus* (kô′kə səs), a range of mountains between the Black Sea and the Caspian Sea.

more she was convinced. It irritated her like a crumb in her bed. Wherever she turned for comfort, there it was, scratching away. Agitatedly she left the garden and entered the house. She paced the hall, pausing each time before the closed door. It was ridiculous. She felt she couldn't call her home her own. She laid her hand on the engraved bolt. Epimetheus would get over it. Naturally he'd be hurt at first and grieve for his brother again. But it would pass and then there'd be nothing to come between them. A shadow would have been removed. . . .

Pandora nodded. All in all, it would be for the best. She opened the door.

As she'd suspected, the room was the best in the house. A little dark, perhaps, and certainly dusty . . . but the fig tree and its polished branches gave it great character and atmosphere.

She ran her finger along the wide bench that stretched from wall to wall. Idly she drew the shape of a baby in the dust. She smiled. The room would make a fine nursery. . . .

No sooner had she thought of it than she set to work. She swept and polished and transformed the shadowy room into a shining joy. She cleared out the cupboards of all old stone jars—but did not open them.

Here she respected her husband's wishes; besides, the jars seemed quite useless.

Then, quite by chance, she came upon a smaller one, tucked underneath the bench. She held it up. It was a pretty jar. Cleaned out, it would hold jewels or perfume . . . She shook her head. No. She would defer to her husband's wish, foolish as it was.

Then she thought of Prometheus. How like him to keep such a jar for himself! What could he possibly want with it now? After all, it wasn't as though she intended to open *all* the jars.

She had her principles and would not have abandoned them for anything. She was perfectly certain that her husband would come to see it her way. He would admire her for leaving the other jars and so honoring his selfish brother's memory.

She shook the pretty little jar gently. There was something inside. She listened. It gave a dry rattling sound. She shrugged her shoulders. She'd put up with the sacred memory of Prometheus for long enough. She opened the jar.

She screamed; she shrieked; she dropped the jar. Gentle Epimetheus came running to her cries.

There seemed to be a cloud about Pandora: a whirling, malignant veil that glittered with ten thousand furious wings. They seemed to be insects of extraordinary venom and ferocity. They bit and stung and beat against his crouching wife; then they turned on him and he felt their wicked little spears in every part of his body. He cried out, "Prometheus, Prometheus! What have we done?"

Far in the north a fiercer pain than the vulture's beak stabbed at the chained Titan. From his icy place of punishment he saw what had befallen his children. His deep eyes filled with tears as a more terrible vulture tore at his heart.

Nor did this phantom bird depart with its bloody brother when healing night came. High in the freezing mountains, striped with the purple glaciers of his blood, Prometheus wept. His labors and his fall had been in vain.

The strange spots and scales he had imprisoned in the jar had been malignant indeed. Unhindered by the divine substance from which they'd been scraped, they had grown into hideous little furies. He had seen them fly out of his house in a wicked cloud to sting his helpless children. Madness, vice, old age and crippling sickness had been let out upon the world as a birthright for man.

Prometheus raised his eyes and stared across the world's night. His eyes met those of bitter Atlas,[23] and these two giants who had opposed the gods looked long and deep at each other from their separate high prisons of pain.

"Mankind," whispered great Prometheus, "forgive me—I have failed. Better that I never made you . . . for what is there left to you now?"

Pandora gazed down at the shattered jar. It was past repairing. She felt awkward. Her husband, inflamed from the strange insects' attacks, had looked at her reproachfully.

So, as mildly as she was able, she remarked that Prometheus was to blame. He should never have kept such things in a jar. She bent down and began to gather the broken pieces. Suddenly she came upon a curious stone. She picked it up. It was not a stone. She looked at it carefully. It seemed to be a chrysalis . . .

She shivered as she tried to throw it away before it hatched. But it stuck to her fingers.

At last she scraped it off on a fragment of the jar. She rubbed her hands to rid herself of the gumlike substance the chrysalis had left. Her eyes brightened in surprise. The pain of the bites and stings seemed soothed. Eagerly she told Epimetheus. The chrysalis was a balm—a wondrous healing balm.

Pandora was delighted. She smiled at her husband. Was it not a good thing after all that she'd opened the jar? As she'd always told him, everything turned out for the best.

A sudden movement aloft distracted her. She looked up. A bird had been perched in the polished rafters. It had been looking down with bright, inquisitive eyes. Now it flapped its wings and flew away. It had

---

23. *Atlas* (at'ləs), one of the Titans, whose punishment for revolt against Zeus was to support the weight of the heavens on his shoulders.

been a crane. She watched it through the casement. It flew with amazing speed toward the north. It pierced the colder air and crossed the mountains till at last it saw below it the pillar of Prometheus.

"What is there left to mankind now?" cried the despairing Titan as he saw the sideways-dropping god.

"Hope," answered great Hermes. "For better or worse—for who knows what color wings may unfold from a chrysalis?—hope was left behind."

COYOTE
AND THE ORIGIN
OF DEATH

George A. Dorsey

Coyote is the principal trickster (see note page 160) in the mythologies of the Indian peoples of the western United States. He is a confusing creature, sometimes looking and talking like a human being, sometimes behaving like an animal, sometimes aiding people, sometimes doing them injuries.

IN THE BEGINNING of this world there was no such thing as death. Everyone continued to live until there were so many people that there was no room for any more on the earth. The chiefs held a council to determine what to do. One man arose and said that he thought it would be a good plan to have the people die and be gone for a little while, and then return. As soon as he sat down Coyote jumped up and said that he thought that people ought to die forever, for this little world was not large enough to hold all of the people, and if the people who died came back to life, there would not be food enough for all. All of the other men objected, saying that they did not want their friends and relatives to die and be gone forever, for then people would grieve and worry and there would not be any happiness in the world. All except Coyote decided to have the people die and be gone for a little while, and then to come back to life again.

The medicine men built a large grass house facing the east, and when they had completed it they called the men of the tribe together and told them that they had decided to have the people who died come to the medicine house and there be restored to life. The chief medicine man said they would sing a song that would call the spirit of the dead to the grass house, and when the spirit came they would . . . restore it to life again. All of the people were glad, for they were anxious for the dead to be restored to life and come again and live with them.

"Coyote and the Origin of Death." THE TRADITIONS OF THE CADDO by George A. Dorsey. Washington: Carnegie Institution of Washington, 1905.

After a time—when the first man had died—the medicine men assembled in the grass house and sang. In about ten days a whirlwind blew from the west and circled about the grass house. Coyote saw it. And as the whirlwind was about to enter the house, he closed the door. The spirit in the whirlwind, finding the door closed, whirled on by. Death forever was then introduced, and people from that time on grieved about the dead and were unhappy.

Now whenever anyone meets a whirlwind or hears the wind whistle he says: "There is someone wandering about." Ever since Coyote closed the door, the spirits of the dead have wandered over the earth, trying to find some place to go, until at last they find the road to Spirit Land.

Coyote jumped up and ran away and never came back, for when he saw what he had done he was afraid. Ever after that he ran from one place to another, always looking back first over one shoulder and then over the other, to see if anyone was pursuing him, and ever since then he has been starving, for no one will give him anything to eat.

THOR'S VISIT
TO UTGARD

Roger Lancelyn Green

The Teutonic peoples of northern Europe called their gods the Aesir (ā'sir, ē'sir) (see note page 333). Chief among the Aesir was Odin (ōd'n), a god of wisdom and of war. He and his brothers killed the Giant Ymir (im'r) and fashioned Midgard (mid'gärd), the human world, from his body. Midgard is joined to Asgard (as'gärd, az'gärd), the home of the gods, by Bifrost (bēf'rōst), the rainbow bridge.

Thor (thôr), the god of thunder, is the son of Odin. He drives a brazen chariot drawn by two goats; the sound of thunder is the rumble of his chariot wheels. Thor's hammer Miolnir (myōl'nir) is the lightning that precedes the thunder. It was made for him by the Dwarfs and always returns to his hand after being thrown. In addition to this magical weapon Thor possesses an iron glove, with which he handles Miolnir, and a belt of strength. Thor is the champion of the Aesir against their enemies, the Giants, who live in Jotunheim (yô'tün hām), a cold world to the north. Loki (lō'kē) is a Giant who dwells with the Aesir (see selection page 154). He is full of malice and treachery. Thor is the only one among the Aesir with whom he is friendly and they are frequent companions in adventure.

AFTER THOR HAD RECOVERED his hammer Miolnir, killed Thrym the Giant with all his household, and returned safely to Asgard without having to give up Freya the Beautiful, the Giants begged for peace with the Aesir.[1] They even went so far as to promise Thor and Loki safe conduct if they would come on a visit to Utgard,[2] the Giant city in the heart of Jotunheim where Utgardhaloki[3] was king.

From MYTHS OF THE NORSEMEN by Roger Lancelyn Green. Copyright © 1960 by Roger Lancelyn Green. Published by Puffin Books, a Division of Penguin Books, Ltd., and reprinted by permission.
1. *Thrym the Giant . . . the Aesir.* Thrym (thrim) had stolen Thor's hammer. The Giant wanted Freya (frā'ə), the goddess of love and beauty, for its return. Thor traveled to Jotunheim disguised as Freya, astonished the Giants with "her" appetite at the wedding feast, and getting his hammer in his hands again, destroyed the Giant and his household. **2.** *Utgard,* (üt'gärd). **3.** *Utgardhaloki,* (üt'gärd hə lō'kē).

"No harm shall come to the Aesir, Thor and Loki, or to any attendants they may bring," vowed Utgardhaloki, "and I will send Skrymir[4] my messenger to lead them through Jotunheim. If he is not afraid, Thor will surely come."

A challenge like this was the sure way of bringing Thor, and he ordered out his chariot forthwith and harnessed his two goats, Gaptooth and Cracktooth.

"They do not ask us out of friendship," said cautious Loki. "Some guile is intended, you may be certain."

Nonetheless he stepped into the chariot beside Thor, and off they drove in a great thundercloud across Midgard, the lightning flashing and flickering from the wheels as they went.

In the evening they came to a farmhouse on the edge of the river Ifing,[5] the dark flood that never froze, which separated Midgard from Jotunheim. The good yeoman to whom it belonged welcomed his two strange guests, but confessed that he had very little food in the house, indeed scarcely enough for himself and his son and daughter, Thialfi and Roskva.[6]

"That is no matter!" cried Thor, and killing his two goats Gaptooth and Cracktooth, he helped to flay and joint them. Very soon they were simmering in the pot, and the dinner was ready.

"Whatever you do," Thor remarked, "let none of the bones of my goats be broken."

Then the meal began, and Thor showed his usual good appetite by eating one whole goat and a good deal of the other.

"What he said about the bones is only to keep the marrow for himself," whispered Loki the tempter to Thialfi, "for it has strange and wonderful powers, since these are no ordinary goats."

So Thialfi split one of the thigh bones when Thor was looking the other way, and scraped out some of the marrow with his knife. But he noticed that Loki was careful not to break any of the bones, so he contented himself with the one taste of marrow.

Thor and Loki slept that night in the farmhouse, and in the morning Thor flung all the bones into the goatskins, waved Miolnir over them, and at once Gaptooth and Cracktooth sprang up as full of life as ever.

But one of them limped a little in his hind leg, and seeing this Thor turned with a roar of fury and whirled his hammer above his head to slay the yeoman and his two children.

"One of you has broken the thigh bone!" he shouted, his eyes flashing fire and his knuckles growing white as he gripped Miolnir.

The yeoman cowered on the floor, realizing who his terrible guest was, and promised any recompense he chose to ask.

Seeing the man's fear, Thor's brow cleared and he said: "I will not smite. But your two children Thialfi and Roskva shall come with me,

4. *Skrymir*, (skrī′mir). 5. *Ifing*, (if′ing). 6. *Thialfi and Roskva*, (thyäl′fē *and* rosk′vä).

he to be my squire and she my handmaiden forevermore. See, it is an honour I do them and no evil. . . . Now look well to my goats so that the bone is set and whole before our return. Roskva shall remain with you until then, but Thialfi comes with us now."

So Thor and Loki continued their journey on foot, with Thialfi to attend on them. They went down beside the river Ifing until they reached the sea, and crossed where it was deepest in a boat that lay waiting for them. On the further shore they left the boat and advanced inland through a great forest. As evening approached they came out into open country among bare rocks and dark valleys; but nowhere could they find a house.

At last, just as darkness was beginning to fall, and they were feeling exceedingly tired and hungry, they came to a strange building. It was a great hall with an entrance so wide that it took up the whole end, but there was no one in it, no hearth nor fire, and no furniture.

It was better than nothing, however, in that freezing land, and the wayfarers made themselves as comfortable as possible in their strange lodging.

In the middle of the night they were wakened suddenly by a great earthquake, the ground shook all round them, and the hall trembled and swayed from side to side. Nothing else happened, but as he was exploring further Thor found a smaller room leading off the hall on the right-hand side, and into this his companions moved for greater warmth. Loki and the boy huddled together in the furthest corner, shaking with fear, but Thor gripped the handle of Miolnir firmly and stood on guard in the doorway. He could hear a roaring and a bellowing sound nearby, and from time to time a great crash: but he could see nothing.

At last the sky turned grey, and going out of the hall Thor saw in the first light of morning a Giant lying on the hillside a little distance away, snoring loudly. He was not a small Giant by any means—indeed he was the largest that Thor had ever seen.

Then Thor knew what the noises were that he had heard in the night, and in a fit of anger he girded himself with his belt of strength, and swung Miolnir in his hands, wondering where to strike.

At that moment the Giant woke, and Thor decided that it was safer not to use his hammer just then. Instead he asked:

"Who are you that have disturbed our slumbers with your snores?"

"I am Skrymir," answered the Giant in a voice that echoed among the mountains. "I have come to lead you to Utgard. I need not ask if you are Thor, for your hammer betrays you. But indeed you are rather smaller than I expected. . . . Hallo, what have you been doing with my glove?"

With that he picked up what Thor had taken for a hall, shook Loki and Thialfi out of it, and put it on, slipping his thumb into the room where they had passed the night.

Then he opened his bag and made a huge breakfast: leaving Thor and his companions to be content with what they could find.

"I'll carry your bag of provisions in my own," said Skrymir when he had finished his breakfast. "Then we can dine together tonight in a more friendly fashion."

Thor agreed readily, and Thialfi handed over the empty wallet, which Skrymir dropped into his own bag before lacing up the top and slinging it over his shoulder.

"Now follow me!" he boomed, and went striding away over the mountains while Thor and Loki did their best to keep up with him, and Thialfi followed painfully behind—though indeed he was the swiftest-footed of all men.

Late in the evening Skrymir found them shelter for the night under a mighty oak tree where they could get out of the bitter wind among its roots, and he lay on the hillside beyond its huge trunk.

"I am too tired to bother about supper," said the Giant as he stretched himself out. "But here is the food-bag: open it and help yourselves."

He flung down his sack, and a few moments later was snoring like a volcano on the other side of the tree.

Thor set himself to unlace the food-bag; but pull and lever as he might, not a single thong could he loosen. Nor could he cut through the stiff leather.

"This Giant is mocking us!" he exclaimed at last, and in a rage he rushed round the tree and hit Skrymir on the head with Miolnir.

The Giant stirred in his sleep, yawned, and muttered sleepily:

"That was a big leaf which dropped on my head! . . . What are you doing, Thor? You have finished supper, I suppose, and are ready for bed?"

"We're just thinking about going to sleep," growled Thor, and when Skrymir was snoring once more, he led Loki and Thialfi to another oak tree at a little distance where they settled down in hungry discomfort to get what rest they could.

Midnight came and Thor still could not sleep. Giant Skrymir had rolled on to his back and was snoring until the trees shook as if a great storm was raging.

"I'll silence that monster!" grumbled Thor. "If we cannot eat, we might at least get a little sleep!"

He strode round to where Skrymir lay, planted his feet firmly, whirled Miolnir round his head and struck him on the crown with all his strength so that the hammer-head sank almost out of sight.

"What's happening now?" asked the Giant sitting up. "Curse this oak tree! An acorn landed right on my head and woke me! . . . Or was it you, Thor, with news of some danger threatening us?"

"There's no danger that I know of," answered Thor. "It's now about midnight, and I had just woken and was stretching my legs for a few moments."

Skrymir grunted, and went to sleep again; but Thor, bristling with fury, sat with hammer in hand planning how he would strike one more blow which should make an end of the Giant.

"If I can strike a really good one," he thought to himself, "he shall never see the light of day again!"

When dawn was just beginning to break Thor decided that his time had come. Skrymir appeared to be sleeping soundly, lying in such a way that Thor could reach one of his temples quite easily. So he rushed upon him whirling Miolnir with all his strength, and delivered a crashing blow.

Skrymir sat up suddenly and rubbed his head.

"It's those birds up in the oak tree!" he exclaimed. "One of them dropped a twig on my forehead. . . . Ah, Thor! So you're awake already. A good thing, for we have a long journey before us if you are to reach Utgard before night."

They continued all day across the mountains, but as afternoon was advancing, Skrymir stopped and said to Thor:

"I must leave you here and go northwards. If you turn east you will reach Utgard before evening. But before we part, let me give you some advice. I heard you talking among yourselves and remarking that you had seen Giants smaller than I am. Let me warn you that in the castle of Utgard you will find several far taller than I. So when you get there be careful not to utter boastful words—for the followers of Utgardhaloki will not take them from such mere babes as you. . . . In fact, my advice would be to turn back while you have the chance, and get home as quickly as you can."

With that, Skrymir slung his bag over his shoulder and strode away towards the snow-covered mountains of the far north. And neither Thor nor Loki nor Thialfi was sorry to see him go.

They did not turn back, however, but went on towards the east, and as night was falling they came to a castle which was so high that it hurt the backs of their necks to look up to the top of it. There was an iron grating in the gateway, and this was closed. Thor strained his hardest to open it, but in vain: however they soon found that they were small enough to squeeze between the bars.

Inside they saw a mighty hall with wide-open doors, and on walking into it found many Giants sitting on benches along either side, while Utgardhaloki, the Giant King, sat at the high table on the dais at the end.

Thor and Loki saluted him politely, but at first he took no notice of them and went on picking his teeth. At length however, he smiled at them scornfully, and said:

"As you seem to have come on a long journey, I suppose you are the Aesir from Asgard, and this small boy here must be Thor himself. Perhaps, however, you are greater than you seem: so tell us if you pride yourselves on any special accomplishments. We are all skilled here in feats of strength and endurance, and in craft and cunning as well. Now which of you will challenge one of us to prove his worth?"

"That I will!" cried Loki. "There is one craft in which I excel, particularly at the moment, and that is eating. I'll have an eating match with any of you, and wager that no one can eat faster than I."

"Well, that is a good contest," said Utgardhaloki, "and we will put you to the test at once. Our champion eater is called Logi,[7] and he is ready to eat against you or anyone at any time."

Then a great wooden trough was placed in the middle of the floor and filled with meat, and Loki sat down at one end and Logi at the other. Each set to work as fast as he could, and they met exactly in the middle.

"But Logi has won," Utgardhaloki pointed out. "For while Loki ate only the flesh, leaving the bare bones on the dish, Logi ate bones and dish and all!"

Presently Utgardhaloki looked at Thialfi and said: "And this child? Is there anything he can do?"

"I'll run a race with any one of you who cares to try," answered Thialfi boldly.

"A good accomplishment is running," said Utgardhaloki, "but you must be very swift if you are to outdistance my champion."

Then he led the way out of the hall to a long strip of ground inside the castle walls. "We will put you to the test at once," he said, and called for Hugi,[8] a young Giant, and bade him race with Thialfi.

The course was set and the two runners sped away. But in the first heat Hugi was so much ahead that when he reached the winning-post he turned round and went back to meet Thialfi.

Then said Utgardhaloki: "You will need to exert yourself a bit more, Thialfi, if you are to beat Hugi—though no one who has come here has ever run faster than you have just done. Now try a second heat."

They set off again, but this time Hugi reached the end of the course so long before Thialfi that he had time to turn and meet him a quarter of the way back.

"Thialfi has run this heat well also," said Utgardhaloki, "but I do not think that he can beat Hugi. However, he may have one more chance, and that shall decide the match."

---

7. *Logi*, (lō′gē). 8. *Hugi*, (hü′gē).

They set off for the third time, but now Hugi ran so fast that he was able to reach the winning-post, turn round, and meet Thialfi halfway back along the course.

"So Hugi is a better runner than Thialfi," said Utgardhaloki as he led the way back into the hall. "But these were only small contests. Thor, I am certain, will wish to show his strength, for we have heard great tales of his mighty deeds—and indeed we know that he has won victories against a Giant or two before now."

"We came here in peace, and not to perform the deeds of war," said Thor warily. "But I am quite ready to contend with anyone in a drinking match."

"An excellent notion," cried Utgardhaloki, and he bade one of his servants bring in the sconce-horn which was handed round among his warriors when they boasted of their powers of drinking.

"If one of us drinks this horn full at a single draught," he said, "we think well of him. Many a Giant, however, needs to pull at it twice; but we think very little of anyone who needs to raise it to his lips a third time."

Thor took the horn, and it did not seem particularly big, except for its great length. He was very thirsty, and as he raised it to his lips he was confident that he would need to take no second draught to empty it. But when his breath failed and he raised his head from the horn and looked to see how much he had drunk, it seemed hardly any emptier than when he started.

"That was well drunk," exclaimed Utgardhaloki, "and yet it was not much. I would not have believed if I had not actually seen it that Thor of Asgard was so poor a drinker. Still, I feel sure you are only waiting to drain the horn at your next draught."

Thor answered nothing, but raised the horn to his lips again, thinking that he would drink deeply indeed this time, and he strained at it until his breath gave out. Yet as he took the horn from his lips he realized that the end had not tilted up as far as it should; and when he came to look inside, it seemed as if less had gone than before: but now he could at least see below the rim.

"How now, Thor!" cried Utgardhaloki. "You'll drink again, surely, even if the third draught is more than is good for you? The third will surely be the greatest—but even if you empty the horn this time, you are not so mighty a champion as you are said to be among the Aesir. Though what you may yet do in other contests remains to be seen."

At that Thor became angry. He raised the horn again and drank with all his might, straining until he could hold his breath no longer. He set down the horn and as he drew back gasping, he saw that at least the liquid in it had sunk quite a distance from the top. But he would not try again, and declared that he had drunk enough for one night.

"Now it is evident that you are not as mighty as we thought," remarked Utgardhaloki. "You cannot even swallow a little drink such as this. But will you try your hand at other games? You may do better in some feat of strength."

"We hardly call such drinks as that little ones in Asgard," grumbled Thor. "But what game do you suggest now to try my strength?"

"Young lads here," said Utgardhaloki, "begin by a small trial of strength which is to lift my cat off the ground. I would not suggest so easy a test to Thor of the Aesir, did I not realize how very much less powerful you are than I expected."

As he said this an enormous grey cat leapt into the middle of the floor and stood there spitting. Thor went forward and set his hands under its belly meaning to lift it by the middle. But the cat arched its back as Thor lifted, and though he strained upwards with all his strength he could only raise one paw off the ground.

"It is just as I expected," smiled Utgardhaloki. "But indeed my cat is a very large one, and our people are big and strong, not weak and puny like Thor the Thunderer."

"Small as I am," shouted Thor, "I'll wrestle with any of you. For now you have angered me, my strength grows double!"

"I see no Giant here who would not think it a disgrace to wrestle with such a midget," said Utgardhaloki looking round the hall. "But we must not be deceived by appearances. Summon my old nurse, Elli,[9] and let Thor wrestle with her. She has thrown men who seemed to me no less mighty than this great god of Asgard."

Straightway there came into the hall an old woman, bent and stricken with years. Thor flushed angrily when he saw her, but Utgardhaloki insisted on the match, and when at last Thor took hold of her and tried to throw her, he discovered that it was not as easily done as he expected. In fact, the harder he gripped her the firmer she stood; and when she caught hold of him in her turn, Thor felt himself tottering on his feet, and in spite of all he could do she brought him to his knees.

"Enough of this!" cried Utgardhaloki. "It is useless for Thor to try his strength with any of my warriors since he cannot even hold his own against this old woman. Sit down now, all three of you, and let us eat and drink. Only Loki has eaten and only Thor has drunk; but doubtless you can both take more of food and ale—for I would like you to see how well we in Utgard can entertain our guests."

So they made good cheer far into the night, and slept there in the hall. And in the morning, when they were dressed and ready, Utgardhaloki drank a parting cup with them, and led them out of Utgard and well on their way back towards Midgard.

When he turned to bid them farewell he said: "Now tell me, before we part, what you think of my castle of Utgard and the greatest of the

9. *Elli*, (el/lē).

Giant kind who live there? Do you admit that you have at last met Giants who are mightier than you?"

"I must confess," said Thor sadly, "that I have got little but shame from my dealings with you. When I am gone you will speak of me as a weakling, and I am ill content with that. It was with a very different purpose that I came to visit Utgard as the envoy of the Aesir."

"Now I will tell you the truth," said Utgardhaloki, "since you are well away from my castle—which, if it is in my power, you shall never enter again. Indeed had I known how mighty you were, you had never come here at all: for so great is your strength that you have put us and all the world in deadly peril.

"Know then that I have cheated you with false seemings and illusions of the eye.

"To go back to the beginning: it was I who met you on the way, calling myself Skrymir; and as for my provision-bag, it was tied with iron made by Trolls[10]—so that you could not possibly have untied it. Of the three blows you dealt me with your hammer Miolnir, the first was far the lightest, but it would have killed me if it had really landed on me. On your way home you will see a long mountain shaped like a saddle, with three deep gorges in it, one far deeper than the rest: those gorges you made with your hammer, for in each case I slipped aside so that the mountain received the blows and not I.

"In the same way I cheated you over your contests in my castle hall. The Giant against whom Loki ate so well was called Logi—and he was Fire itself which burned up the trough and bones as well as the meat. Thialfi ran against Hugi, who is Thought: and no man can run as swiftly as thought.

"When you drank from my horn, and the drink seemed to sink but slowly, you performed a wonder which I should not have believed possible. For the other end of the horn was joined to the sea, and it sank visibly throughout all the world when you drank. You caused the first ebb-tide: and the tides shall ebb and flow for ever more in memory of your deed.

"When you strove to lift my cat we were all in deadly terror. For he was the Midgard Serpent which stretches round the whole world—and when you raised it, the head and tail of Jormungand[11] scarcely touched the ground.

"Finally, your last feat was as remarkable as the rest. For Elli with whom you wrestled was Old Age—and yet she only brought you to your knees, though never a man lived, nor shall ever live, who will not at the last be vanquished by Old Age.

---

10. *Trolls* (trōlz), beings sometimes identified with the Giants, sometimes with the Dwarfs. The Trolls had certain supernatural powers and lived underground in caves. **11.** *the Midgard Serpent . . . Jormungand.* Jormungand (yŏr′mün gänd) was one of the three monstrous children of Loki. The other two were Fenris, the great wolf, and the goddess Hela, who ruled the dead in Helheim, the icy Underworld.

"Now we must part, and it will be best for both of us if you never come here to seek me again. Should you do so, I will defend my castle by wiles such as I have already used against you—or by others. But if you stay away from Jotunheim, there may be peace between the Aesir and the Giants."

Then a sudden gust of fury filled Thor, and he whirled up Miolnir to fling at Utgardhaloki, deeming that this time there should be no mistake.

But Utgardhaloki was gone; and suddenly the mist came down from the mountains so that when Thor turned back to destroy the castle of Utgard and crush it to pieces, there was no castle to be seen.

So Thor, Loki, and Thialfi turned and groped their way through the fog, back into the mountains, and they could scarcely see more than a few yards in front of them until they came to the great mountain with the three gorges which Thor had cleft with his hammer.

Beyond it the fog cleared, and they made their way easily enough until they came to the farmhouse where Thor had left his chariot.

The goat whose bone had been broken by Thialfi had now quite recovered, and the next day they set out for Asgard, taking Roskva with them.

When Thor told Odin and the other Aesir how Utgardhaloki had tricked him, and repeated what he had told him before they parted, Odin said:

"You have done well in the Land of the Giants, though at first it seemed but ill. For now they know our strength—and we know what they can do to outwit us. We may not be able to destroy them, but I do not think that they will come against Asgard, nor overrun Midgard. Yet they will come against us at Ragnarok, on the Day of the Last Great Battle."[12]

"Nevertheless I am determined to wipe out this insult to my prowess in Giant blood," growled Thor.

"You need not doubt that Giant blood will still be shed," answered Odin. "Though we are at peace with Utgardhaloki, there are Giants who will still try to harm us or to bring ruin to men in Midgard. I do not think the hammer Miolnir will ever grow rusty!"

"No!" muttered Thor. "And when I have conquered the Giants, I am determined to try my strength against the Midgard Serpent! Had I known that Utgardhaloki's cat was Jormungand, instead of trying to lift its paw from the ground I would have stroked its head with Miolnir."

---

12. *Ragnarok . . . the Last Great Battle.* Ragnarok (rag/nä rok), "the twilight of the gods," is the time of the final battle between the Aesir and their enemies, led by Loki, in which nearly all the gods are slain and the world is destroyed and renewed (see selection page 328).

URASHIMA TARO

Marjory Bruce

MANY HUNDREDS OF YEARS AGO, in a village on the craggy sea-coast of Japan, there dwelt a fisher-lad whose name was Urashima Taro.[1] Of all the fishermen in the village he was the most skillful with his line and net, and he was the kindest-hearted. If one of his comrades had bad luck when his own was good, he always shared his "catch" with him. And he could not bear to see any creature, however lowly, tormented or hurt.

One fine evening, when Urashima was on his way home to his father's little cottage, he came upon a group of mischievous boys teasing an unlucky tortoise. One boy cast pebbles at its shell, another rapped it with a stick, a third tried to poke twigs inside. The sight made Urashima very angry.

"You cruel children," he said, "what evil has the poor thing done? Do you know that unless you put it back into the sea it will die?"

"What then?" cried the bad boys. "It is only a silly old tortoise. It may die if it pleases. *We* do not care."

"Will you not give your tortoise to me?" asked Urashima.

"No, we will not," returned the bad boys. "It is *ours*. We want it."

Now Urashima had in his hand a small stock of money, slung on a string through the hole left for that purpose in the centre of each coin. It was his earnings for an entire week, hard-won with many hours of patient labour.

"Listen to me, boys," said Urashima, "if you will not *give* me your tortoise, perhaps you will *sell* it."

And he jingled the string of coins before their eyes.

The bad boys hesitated.

"Urashima Taro" from A TREASURY OF TALES FOR LITTLE FOLKS selected and edited by Marjory Bruce, published by Thomas Y. Crowell Co., Inc., 1927.
1. *Urashima Taro,* (ù rä shē mä tä rō).

"Think," urged Urashima, "what a lot of things you could buy with this money—much better playthings than a poor tortoise."

"There is some truth in what Urashima Taro says," remarked the ringleader. "Let us take the money and give him the tortoise."

So they took Urashima's little store of coin, and ran off, laughing and jumping, and the fisher-lad was left alone with his purchase.

"Poor old fellow," said Urashima, stroking the hard, tawny-coloured shell, "I wonder if it is true that you tortoises live for a thousand years. Perhaps you are still young, and may have nine hundred and ninety years of life before you still. Anyhow, I am going to put you back into the sea. And I advise you, as a friend, not to allow yourself to get caught again!"

Then Urashima lifted the tortoise in his arms, went down to the beach, and let it slide softly into the water.

Next day the lad was early astir. He knew that he would have to work extra hard in order to make up for the money he had given the bad boys; all his earnings for a whole week had gone. The sea was as smooth as glass, and reflected the lovely turquoise colour of the cloudless sky. Urashima's slender boat drifted along, and soon left the craft of the other fishermen far behind.

Presently he heard a soft voice calling him by name.

"Urashima Taro—Urashima!"

Urashima stood up in the boat and shaded his eyes with his hand, but there was no human creature in sight.

"Urashima!" called the voice again.

It came from the sea. Looking down, he saw a tortoise swimming alongside his boat, and he thought it seemed remarkably like the one which he had befriended the day before.

"Honourable Mr. Tortoise," said Urashima, politely, "was it you who called me just now?"

"Yes," replied the tortoise, "do you not remember me? I have come to thank you for your kindness to me yesterday."

"That is very good of you," said Urashima. "Would you care to come into my boat and bask in the sun for a while? I know that you tortoises love to do that."

"Many thanks," responded the tortoise, and Urashima helped it to climb aboard.

Presently his queer passenger began to talk again.

"Have you ever seen the Rin-Gin,[2] the palace of the Dragon-King, Urashima?"

Urashima shook his head. "All we fishermen have heard of that palace, but none of us has ever beheld it."

"If it would interest you to see it," said the tortoise, "I can show you the way thither."

2. *Rin-Gin*, (rin gin).

"It would interest me very much," answered Urashima, "but I am only a human being. I could not swim anything like as far as you could."

"*Swim?*" repeated the tortoise. "But why should you *swim?* I can carry you on my back with ease."

"Perhaps I am heavier than you think," hinted the fisher-lad, who was afraid that if he were to say "You are too small to carry me" he might hurt the feelings of his new friend.

"Not a bit of it," returned the tortoise, clambering over the edge of the boat and slipping down into the bright blue water.

"Try and see! Perhaps I am larger than *you* think, honourable Mr. Urashima!"

Urashima looked, and it certainly seemed that the tortoise had grown much bigger since it went back into the sea.

"Come on," urged the tortoise.

"All right!" said Urashima Taro.

He jumped upon the tortoise's back, and away the creature swam, carrying him as easily as if he had been a baby.

"Honourable Mr. Tortoise," said Urashima presently, "I hope you are not going to dive, for if you do, I shall be drowned."

"I *am* going to dive," returned the tortoise, "but you are *not* going to be drowned."

And down, down, down it went, through the clear blue water.

To his astonishment Urashima found that he could breathe quite as well under the sea as above it. Fishes, great and small, of a thousand gorgeous colours and quaint forms, swam over his head as birds fly on dry land, and lovely starry anemones, and delicately fringed seaweeds, grew like flowers on the bed of the sea.

Presently, far off, Urashima saw a great gateway, and beyond that the roofs of some magnificent buildings, all glittering with brilliant green and blue tiles.

"We shall soon be there," remarked the tortoise, swimming faster than ever.

A few moments later the creature halted outside the great gateway, and the porter, who was a large and splendid-looking fish, opened the gate.

"This is the honourable Mr. Urashima Taro, from the land of Japan," explained the tortoise. "He has come to visit the Rin-Gin, the palace of the Dragon-King of the Sea."

"He is very welcome," said the fish.

Urashima now descended from the tortoise's back, and the fish, floating slowly before him, led the way into the palace.

No words could possibly describe the beauty of that great palace in the depths of the sea. It was built of green and blue jewels, of coral and beryl, sapphire and pearl. Round it were wide gardens which reminded Urashima of the gardens of his own Japan, for maples and firs and plum and cherry-trees grew there, and wistaria climbed over arches, and little bridges of red lacquer spanned tiny torrents of foaming grey water.

In the eastern part of the garden it was always spring, and the fruit-trees were gay with unfading blossom. To the south was perpetual summer. To the west lay the autumn garden, where the maples were ruddy-golden and the chrysanthemums shone like fire. To the north was the realm of winter, and there the fir-trees were white with snow, and the torrents under the little bridges were frozen into long icicles as they fell.

All these marvels and glories took Urashima's breath away. But there remained one far beyond all the rest, and that was the lady Otohimé,[3] the daughter of the Dragon-King of the Sea. When she approached Urashima he fell upon his knees, and bowed his head upon the sand, for never had he dreamt that any being could be so beautiful. Her robes were of green silk shot through with threads of silver and gold, and her long, fine black hair hung like a great mantle upon her shoulders.

"Welcome and greeting, Urashima Taro," said the lady Otohimé.

"Most humbly do I thank your honourable ladyship," stammered Urashima, not daring to raise his head.

"It is *I* who must thank *you*, Urashima Taro," returned the lady Otohimé. "Listen, and you shall learn why. Once a year, as we immortals reckon years, it is the will of my father, the Dragon-King of the Sea, that I should assume the form of some sea-creature, and allow myself to be caught by some mortal's net or snare. If that mortal be merciful, great is his reward. But if he be cruel, his punishment also is great. Urashima Taro, arise. Fear nothing, my friend. I was that tortoise whom you delivered from the hands of the cruel children who would have made me suffer much pain."

So Urashima arose, and he and the lady Otohimé went forth into the garden where it was always spring. And fish-servants brought them rice, and sake[4] in cups of pearl, and fish-minstrels made music for them under the blossoming trees.

Urashima found favour in the eyes of the lady Otohimé. She sought leave of her father, the Dragon-King of the Sea, to take the fisher-lad for her husband. And so they were married, and even in the Rin-Gin, the sea-palace of many marvels, such rejoicings were never known as the rejoicings at the wedding of Urashima Taro and the beautiful daughter of the Dragon-King.

Urashima was very happy with his royal bride in the depths of the sea, and for a long time he forgot all about his father and mother, and his old home on the craggy coast of Japan. Then, one day, the lady Otohimé noticed that her husband was looking thoughtful and sad.

---

3. *Otohimé*, (ō tō hē mä). **4.** *sake* (sä kē), an alcoholic beverage made from rice.

"What ails you, Urashima Taro?" she asked.

"I have just remembered," said Urashima, "that far away, in the land of the mortals whence I come, I have a father and a mother. They are old. Unless I make haste, perchance I may never see them again. Surely they have wept for me, thinking that I had left them never to return."

"Alas, Urashima," cried the lady Otohimé, "have you ceased to love me? Are you no longer happy in the Rin-Gin?"

"No," said Urashima, sorrowfully, "I have not ceased to love your honourable ladyship. But I cannot be happy until I have beheld my father and mother again. I am ashamed that I should have forgotten them so long. Let me go to them, even if it be but for one day. Then I will return."

Then the lady Otohimé wept bitter tears.

"If you wish to depart," she told him, "I cannot keep you here. Go, then. But take with you this casket, lest I, too, should be forgotten."

With these words she placed in Urashima's hands a little box of golden lacquer tied tightly round with a cord and tassels of scarlet silk.

"This casket," said the lady Otohimé, "holds something very precious and very rare. Take it with you, my husband, wherever you go. But remember, you must not open it. For if you do, great evil will befall you."

Urashima Taro promised that nothing would ever persuade him to open the golden lacquer box. He bade farewell very sadly to the lady Otohimé, cast a last regretful glance at the gardens of the four seasons, and then went down to the great gateway at which he had arrived, and where he found a tortoise waiting to bear him whence he had come.

The tortoise swam steadily, on and on, till at last the blue peaks of Japan arose upon the horizon. Urashima's heart began to beat faster. He recognized the coastline, the fir-woods and the craggy shore. Soon he would see his old home again, and kneel down before his father and mother, imploring their forgiveness.

He jumped off the tortoise's back in his impatience, and waded ashore. Coming toward him was an aged man whom he took for his father. A moment later Urashima realized his mistake. Then he ran in the direction where his father's house had stood.

What a change! The little hut had vanished, and a much larger house, with purple iris-flowers growing between the roof-tiles, occupied its place.

"Surely my family has grown rich in my absence," thought Urashima.

A man came out of the house, and Urashima approached him politely.

"Honourable Sir, can you tell me whether the parents of Urashima Taro the fisherman still live in this house?"

The man stared at him in amazement.

"Who may *you* be, Mr. Stranger?" he asked.

"I am Urashima Taro."

The man burst out laughing at this. "You! Why, he has been dead for more than three hundred years, Urashima Taro!"

"Pardon me," said Urashima, "I am he. I have been absent for some time—I do not know exactly for how long—perhaps one year, perhaps two—but I have returned because I am anxious to see my aged parents again before they die."

"If you are really Urashima Taro you have arrived three hundred years too late," returned the man. "Why, the house where he lived was pulled down in my great-grandfather's time, and even *then* it was many years since that fisher-lad vanished one fine morning. Either you are joking, or you are a ghost."

"I am *not* a ghost," cried Urashima, stamping on the ground. "You know that ghosts have no feet! I am as much alive as you are—I am Urashima Taro!"

"Urashima Taro lived three hundred years ago," retorted the man. "It is all written in the village records which are kept in the temple. Why do you repeat such a foolish jest?"

Feeling sick with fear and disappointment, Urashima continued his walk along the seashore. At every step he saw changes which showed only too plainly that the man had spoken truly, and that not one year, or two, but three centuries had come and gone since he last beheld that place.

"Everyone whom I knew and loved in the land of the mortals has long been dead," thought Urashima, sadly. "Why should I tarry here? I must go back as quickly as I can to the beautiful land of the immortals, and to my wife, the lady Otohimé."

He walked down to the edge of the sea and gazed anxiously across the waves. The tortoise which had brought him from the Rin-Gin had vanished. How was he to find his way back to the realm of the Dragon-King again?

Urashima sat down on a rock and buried his head in his hands. What could he do? He was alone in a strange, unfriendly world, and his only possession was the golden lacquer casket which he had promised that he would not open. He took it on his knee, and looked wistfully at the scarlet cords which had been knotted by the hands of the lady Otohimé.

"Surely," he said to himself, "if I break my vow, she will forgive me. Surely if I untie these cords, and open the lid, I shall find something that will tell me how to win my way back to her again!"

So Urashima set the casket upon the ground, and untied the scarlet cords, and lifted the lid. The casket was empty! Only there seemed to waft from it a faint purple cloud, which hovered over his head for a moment and then rose into the air and floated away across the sea.

Till that moment Urashima Taro had looked just as he did when he left Japan three hundred years before, a strong, dark-haired, well-built lad of twenty-one. But as he stood watching the purple cloud fading and receding a great change came over him. His bright eyes grew dim, his black locks turned white, his sturdy limbs became suddenly withered and bent. Then, with a cry of despair, he fell upon his knees, with his face against the ground.

Next morning some fishermen going down to the sea with their nets found an aged man lying dead beside a casket of golden lacquer. They peeped into the casket, but there was nothing inside.

"Is this the same man who spoke to you yesterday?" one of the fishermen asked the other.

"Oh, no," answered his comrade, "he was a sturdy young fellow, he who tried to make me believe that he was Urashima Taro."

MORTE D'ARTHUR[1]

Alfred, Lord Tennyson

The tales of Arthur and his knights were the most popular stories of the Middle Ages. Arthur was presented as a king who ruled Britain, defeated a variety of opponents, established a knightly order, the Round Table, at his court at Camelot (kam′ə lot), and saw the order flourish and then dissolve in intrigue and civil war (see note page 56). "Morte D'Arthur" is an early poem by Alfred, Lord Tennyson (1809–1892) which he later incorporated in The Idylls of the King, *a series of twelve narrative poems which retell the Arthurian tales collected in the fifteenth century by Sir Thomas Malory. It tells of the aftermath of Arthur's last battle at Camlann (kam′lan) against an army of rebels led by his nephew, Modred (mō′dred).*

SO ALL DAY LONG the noise of battle roll'd
Among the mountains by the winter sea,
Until King Arthur's table, man by man,
Had fallen in Lyonness[2] about their lord,
5 King Arthur; then, because his wound was deep,
The bold Sir Bedivere[3] uplifted him,
Sir Bedivere, the last of all his knights,
And bore him to a chapel nigh the field,
A broken chancel[4] with a broken cross,
10 That stood on a dark strait of barren land.
On one side lay the ocean, and on one

"Morte D'Arthur." THE POETIC AND DRAMATIC WORKS OF ALFRED, LORD TENNYSON. Boston: Houghton, Mifflin and Company, 1898.
1. *Morte D'Arthur* (môrt där′tür′), "The Death of Arthur," the title which the printer William Caxton (1422?–1491) gave to his edition of the compilation of Arthurian romance in prose by Sir Thomas Malory. **2.** *Lyonness* (li′ō nes′), a legendary country supposed to have once been attached to the peninsula of Cornwall in southwestern England, but long since sunk under the sea. Lyonness is sometimes identified with Cornwall itself. **3.** *Bedivere,* (bed′ə vir′). **4.** *chancel* (chan′səl), the space around the altar of a church.

Lay a great water, and the moon was full.
　　Then spake King Arthur to Sir Bedivere:
"The sequel of to-day unsolders all
15 The goodliest fellowship of famous knights
Whereof this world holds record. Such a sleep
They sleep—the men I loved. I think that we
Shall never more, at any future time,
Delight our souls with talk of knightly deeds,
20 Walking about the gardens and the halls
Of Camelot, as in the days that were.
I perish by this people which I made—
Tho' Merlin[5] sware that I should come again
To rule once more—but let what will be be,
25 I am so deeply smitten thro' the helm
That without help I cannot last till morn.
Thou therefore take my brand Excalibur,[6]
Which was my pride; for thou rememberest how
In those old days, one summer noon, an arm
30 Rose up from out the bosom of the lake,
Clothed in white samite,[7] mystic, wonderful,
Holding the sword—and how I row'd across
And took it, and have worn it, like a king;
And, wheresoever I am sung or told
35 In aftertime, this also shall be known.
But now delay not; take Excalibur,
And fling him far into the middle mere;[8]
Watch what thou seest, and lightly bring me word."
　　To him replied the bold Sir Bedivere:
40 "It is not meet, Sir King, to leave thee thus,
Aidless, alone, and smitten thro' the helm.
A little thing may harm a wounded man.
Yet I thy hest will all perform at full,
Watch what I see, and lightly bring thee word."
45 　　So saying, from the ruin'd shrine he stept
And in the moon athwart the place of tombs,
Where lay the mighty bones of ancient men,
Old knights, and over them the sea-wind sang
Shrill, chill, with flakes of foam. He, stepping down
50 By zigzag paths and juts of pointed rock,
Came on the shining levels of the lake.
　　There drew he forth the brand Excalibur,
And o'er him, drawing it, the winter moon,
Brightening the skirts of a long cloud, ran forth

---

5. *Merlin* (mėr′lən), a magician and prophet who was Arthur's chief adviser. 6. *Excalibur* (ek skal′ə bər), the magic sword of Arthur. 7. *samite* (sam′it), a rich, heavy silk fabric. 8. *mere* (mir), a lake or pond.

55 And sparkled keen with frost against the hilt;
For all the haft twinkled with diamond sparks,
Myriads of topaz-lights, and jacinth-work
Of subtlest jewellery. He gazed so long
That both his eyes were dazzled, as he stood,
60 This way and that dividing the swift mind,
In act to throw; but at the last it seem'd
Better to leave Excalibur conceal'd
There in the many-knotted water-flags,
That whistled stiff and dry about the marge.
65 So strode he back slow to the wounded king.
Then spake King Arthur to Sir Bedivere:
"Hast thou perform'd my mission which I gave?
What is it thou hast seen, or what hast heard?"
And answer made the bold Sir Bedivere:
70 "I heard the ripple washing in the reeds,
And the wild water lapping on the crag."
To whom replied King Arthur, faint and pale:
"Thou hast betray'd thy nature and thy name,
Not rendering true answer, as beseem'd
75 Thy fealty, nor like a noble knight;
For surer sign had follow'd, either hand,
Or voice, or else a motion of the mere.
This is a shameful thing for men to lie.
Yet now, I charge thee, quickly go again
80 As thou art lief[9] and dear, and do the thing
I bade thee, watch, and lightly bring me word."
Then went Sir Bedivere the second time
Across the ridge, and paced beside the mere,
Counting the dewy pebbles, fix'd in thought;
85 But when he saw the wonder of the hilt,
How curiously and strangely chased,[10] he smote
His palms together, and he cried aloud:
"And if indeed I cast the brand away,
Surely a precious thing, one worthy note,
90 Should thus be lost forever from the earth,
Which might have pleased the eyes of many men.
What good should follow this, if this were done?
What harm, undone? deep harm to disobey,
Seeing obedience is the bond of rule.
95 Were it well to obey then, if a king demand
An act unprofitable, against himself?
The king is sick, and knows not what he does.
What record, or what relic of my lord

---

9. *lief* (lēf), beloved. **10.** *chased* (chās′d), carved or engraved.

Should be to aftertime, but empty breath
100 And rumors of a doubt? but were this kept,
Stored in some treasure-house of mighty kings,
Some one might show it at a joust of arms,
Saying, 'King Arthur's sword, Excalibur,
Wrought by the lonely maiden of the lake;
105 Nine years she wrought it, sitting in the deeps
Upon the hidden bases of the hills.'
So might some old man speak in the aftertime
To all the people, winning reverence;
But now much honor and much fame were lost."
110   So spake he, clouded with his own conceit,
And hid Excalibur the second time,
And so strode back slow to the wounded king.
    Then spoke King Arthur, breathing heavily:
"What is it thou hast seen, or what hast heard?"
115   And answer made the bold Sir Bedivere:
"I heard the water lapping on the crag,
And the long ripple washing in the reeds."
    To whom replied King Arthur, much in wrath:
"Ah, miserable and unkind, untrue,
120 Unknightly, traitor-hearted! Woe is me!
Authority forgets a dying king,
Laid widow'd of the power in his eye
That bow'd the will. I see thee what thou art,
For thou, the latest-left of all my knights,
125 In whom should meet the offices of all,
Thou wouldst betray me for the precious hilt;
Either from lust of gold, or like a girl
Valuing the giddy pleasure of the eyes.
Yet, for a man may fail in duty twice,
130 And the third time may prosper, get thee hence;
But, if thou spare to fling Excalibur,
I will arise and slay thee with my hands."
    Then quickly rose Sir Bedivere, and ran,
And, leaping down the ridges lightly, plunged
135 Among the bulrush-beds, and clutch'd the sword,
And strongly wheel'd and threw it. The great brand
Made lightnings in the splendor of the moon,
And flashing round and round, and whirl'd in an arch,
Shot like a streamer of the northern morn,
140 Seen where the moving isles of winter shock
By night, with noises of the northern sea.[11]

11. *shot like a streamer . . . the northern sea.* The poet compares the flight of the sword to the aurora borealis, bands of light appearing in the sky around the polar regions. The "moving isles of winter" are icebergs.

So flash'd and fell the brand Excalibur;
But ere he dipt the surface, rose an arm
Cloth'd in white samite, mystic, wonderful,
145 And caught him by the hilt, and brandish'd him
Three times, and drew him under in the mere.
And lightly went the other to the king.
    Then spoke King Arthur, drawing thicker breath:
"Now see I by thine eyes that this is done.
150 Speak out; what is it thou hast heard, or seen?"
    And answer made the bold Sir Bedivere:
"Sir King, I closed mine eyelids, lest the gems
Should blind my purpose, for I never saw,
Nor shall see, here or elsewhere, till I die,
155 Not tho' I live three lives of mortal men,
So great a miracle as yonder hilt.
Then with both hands I flung him, wheeling him;
But when I look'd again, behold an arm,
Clothed in white samite, mystic, wonderful,
160 That caught him by the hilt, and brandish'd him
Three times, and drew him under in the mere."
    And answer made King Arthur, breathing hard:
"My end draws nigh; 't is time that I were gone.
Make broad thy shoulders to receive my weight,
165 And bear me to the margin; yet I fear
My wound hath taken cold, and I shall die."
    So saying, from the pavement he half rose,
Slowly, with pain, reclining on his arm,
And looking wistfully with wide blue eyes
170 As in a picture. Him Sir Bedivere
Remorsefully regarded thro' his tears,
And would have spoken, but he found not words,
Then took with care, and kneeling on one knee,
O'er both his shoulders drew the languid hands,
175 And rising bore him thro' the place of tombs.
    But, as he walk'd, King Arthur panted hard,
Like one that feels a nightmare on his bed
When all the house is mute. So sigh'd the king,
Muttering and murmuring at his ear, "Quick, quick!
180 I fear it is too late, and I shall die."
But the other swiftly strode from ridge to ridge,
Clothed with his breath, and looking, as he walk'd,
Larger than human on the frozen hills.
He heard the deep behind him, and a cry
185 Before. His own thought drove him like a goad.
Dry clash'd his harness in the icy caves

And barren chasms, and all to left and right
The bare black cliff clang'd round him, as he based
His feet on juts of slippery-crag that rang
190 Sharp-smitten with the dint of armed heels—
And on a sudden, lo! the level lake,
And the long glories of the winter moon.

Then saw they how there hove a dusky barge,
Dark as a funeral scarf from stem to stern,
195 Beneath them; and descending they were ware
That all the decks were dense with stately forms
Black-stoled, black-hooded, like a dream—by these
Three queens with crowns of gold—and from them rose
A cry that shiver'd to the tingling stars,
200 And, as it were one voice, an agony
Of lamentation, like a wind that shrills
All night in a waste land, where no one comes,
Or hath come, since the making of the world.

Then murmur'd Arthur, "Place me in the barge,"
205 And to the barge they came. There those three queens
Put forth their hands, and took the king, and wept.
But she that rose the tallest of them all
And fairest laid his head upon her lap,
And loosed the shatter'd casque,[12] and chafed his hands,
210 And call'd him by his name, complaining loud,
And dropping bitter tears against his brow
Striped with dark blood; for all his face was white
And colorless, and like the wither'd moon
Smote by the fresh beam of the springing east;
215 And all his greaves and cuisses[13] dash'd with drops
Of onset; and the light and lustrous curls—
That made his forehead like a rising sun
High from the dais-throne—were parch'd with dust;
Or, clotted into points and hanging loose,
220 Mix'd with the knightly growth that fringed his lips.
So like a shatter'd column lay the king;
Not like that Arthur who, with lance in rest,
From spur to plume a star of tournament,
Shot thro' the lists at Camelot, and charged
225 Before the eyes of ladies and of kings.

Then loudly cried the bold Sir Bedivere:
"Ah! my Lord Arthur, whither shall I go?
Where shall I hide my forehead and my eyes?
For now I see the true old times are dead,
230 When every morning brought a noble chance,

---

12. *casque* (kask), a helmet. **13.** *greaves and cuisses* (grēvz *and* kwiz′ez), armor for the legs.

And every chance brought out a noble knight.
Such times have been not since the light that led
The holy Elders with the gift of myrrh.[14]
But now the whole ROUND TABLE is dissolved
235 Which was an image of the mighty world;
And I, the last, go forth companionless,
And the days darken round me, and the years,
Among new men, strange faces, other minds."
     And slowly answer'd Arthur from the barge:
240 "The old order changeth, yielding place to new,
And God fulfils himself in many ways,
Lest one good custom should corrupt the world.
Comfort thyself: what comfort is in me?
I have lived my life, and that which I have done
245 May He within himself make pure! but thou,
If thou shouldst never see my face again,
Pray for my soul. More things are wrought by prayer
Than this world dreams of. Wherefore, let thy voice
Rise like a fountain for me night and day.
250 For what are men better than sheep or goats
That nourish a blind life within the brain,
If, knowing God, they lift not hands of prayer
Both for themselves and those who call them friend?
For so the whole round earth is every way
255 Bound by gold chains about the feet of God.
But now farewell. I am going a long way
With these thou seest—if indeed I go—
For all my mind is clouded with a doubt—
To the island-valley of Avilion;[15]
260 Where falls not hail, or rain, or any snow,
Nor ever wind blows loudly, but it lies
Deep-meadow'd, happy, fair with orchard lawns
And bowery hollows crown'd with summer sea,
Where I will heal me of my grievous wound."
265   So said he, and the barge with oar and sail
Moved from the brink, like some full-breasted swan
That, fluting a wild carol ere her death,
Ruffles her pure cold plume, and takes the flood
With swarthy webs. Long stood Sir Bedivere
270 Revolving many memories, till the hull
Look'd one black dot against the verge of dawn,
And on the mere the wailing died away.

---

14. *the light . . . a gift of myrrh.* At the time of the birth of Christ, three kings were led by a star to his birthplace, each carrying a gift. One of the gifts was myrrh (mėr), a fragrant resin once used in preparing the dead for burial (Matthew, Chapter 2). **15.** *Avilion* (ə vil/ē ən).

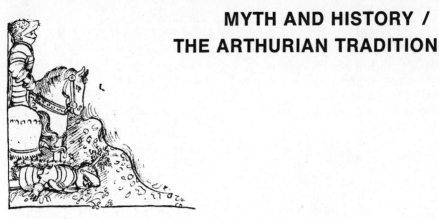

MYTH AND HISTORY /
THE ARTHURIAN TRADITION

During the Middle Ages an enormous body of literature developed around the figure of Arthur, in which he appears as the Christian king of a more or less fabulous "Britain" and the head of an order of chivalry, the Knights of the Round Table. The writers of these romances borrowed so freely from so many different sources that it is a very difficult task to isolate the various elements making up the Arthurian tradition and determine what is myth and what is history.

Fifty years ago a majority of scholars would probably have pronounced the whole Matter of Britain—the stories of Arthur and his knights—a myth, only differing as to what sort of god Arthur was. Since then, partly as a result of archaeological findings, critical opinion has shifted, and now there is fairly general agreement that at the back of the Arthurian tradition there exists the memory of a Dark Age war leader of the Britons, the Celtic inhabitants of the former Roman province of Britannia. Although very little historical evidence of this individual exists, there is enough to outline a career. One source lists a series of twelve successful battles against the Anglo-Saxon invaders of Britain, the last being so great a victory that there was peace in Britain for many years. Another source gives eloquent testimony to Arthur's ability as a warrior. In a Welsh poem lamenting the death of soldiers killed in the North of England fighting the invaders, one fighter is praised for having "glutted black ravens on the rampart of the fort"—fed many scavengers with the corpses of the men he killed—"although he was not Arthur." Another source tells of the final bitter fight at Camlann where Arthur fell.

The romancers fleshed out this faint outline with a variety of materials, drawing heavily upon the mythologies of the Celtic peoples of Brittany, Wales, and Ireland to furnish Arthur with knights and the knights with adventures. For example, the bitter experience of the Britons, driven westward by their Anglo-Saxon conquerors, bred the hope that Arthur had survived Camlann, and would one day return and set them free. There was a Welsh tradition of an orchard island in the west. The Breton bards, who were intermediaries between the Arthurian origins in British history and Celtic myth and the great writers of romance who came later, called the place *Avalon* (the Welsh word *afallen* means "apple trees"). Later romancers equated the Isle of Avalon with the equally mythical Isle of Glass (another Welsh tradition). In this way it became identified with Glastonbury, a town located on a series of small island-like hills projecting into the marshes of Somerset, an apple-growing region in southwestern England, on the Welsh border, site of the impressive ruins of the early medieval abbey of Glastonbury. In earlier days the place undoubtedly was surrounded by water and was perhaps sacred even in pre-Christian times. But the identification of Glastonbury with Avalon still left Arthur's whereabouts a mystery. The monks of the abbey solved the problem by producing his grave in 1191 A.D., and the tomb was to be seen until the dissolution of the monasteries in the sixteenth century.

Archaeological research now tends to disprove the monks' claim, but this mixture of a pinch of fact in a brew of legend was so successful that the Matter of Britain remained the favorite reading of Europe until the Renaissance.

2

IN
THE
BEGINNING

from **THE METAMORPHOSES OF OVID**

Rolfe Humphries

The Romans were an essentially practical people, and their religion was utilitarian rather than imaginative. Although the gods have their Roman names (see note page 70), the mythology of the Metamorphoses *of the Roman poet Ovid (43 B.C.–17 or 18 A.D.) is Greek, though much of his statement of the myths is probably of his own invention.*

Before the ocean was, or earth, or heaven,
Nature was all alike, a shapelessness,
Chaos, so-called, all rude and lumpy matter,
Nothing but bulk, inert, in whose confusion
5 Discordant atoms warred: there was no sun
To light the universe; there was no moon
With slender silver crescents filling slowly;
No earth hung balanced in surrounding air;
No sea reached far along the fringe of shore.
10 Land, to be sure, there was, and air, and ocean,
But land on which no man could stand, and water
No man could swim in, air no man could breathe,
Air without light, substance forever changing,
Forever at war: within a single body
15 Heat fought with cold, wet fought with dry, the hard
Fought with the soft, things having weight contended
With weightless things.
          Till God, or kindlier Nature,
Settled all argument, and separated
Heaven from earth, water from land, our air
20 From the high stratosphere, a liberation
So things evolved, and out of blind confusion
Found each its place, bound in eternal order.

The force of fire, that weightless element,
Leaped up and claimed the highest place in Heaven;
25 Below it, air; and under them the earth
Sank with its grosser portions; and the water,
Lowest of all, held up, held in, the land.

Whatever god it was, who out of chaos
Brought order to the universe, and gave it
30 Division, subdivision, he molded earth,
In the beginning, into a great globe,
Even on every side, and bade the waters
To spread and rise, under the rushing winds,
Surrounding earth; he added ponds and marshes,
35 He banked the river-channels, and the waters
Feed earth or run to sea, and that great flood
Washes on shores, not banks. He made the plains
Spread wide, the valleys settle, and the forest
Be dressed in leaves; he made the rocky mountains
40 Rise to full height, and as the vault of Heaven
Has two zones, left and right, and one between them
Hotter than these, the Lord of all Creation
Marked on the earth the same design and pattern.
The torrid zone too hot for men to live in,
45 The north and south too cold, but in the middle
Varying climate, temperature and season.
Above all things the air, lighter than earth,
Lighter than water, heavier than fire,
Towers and spreads; there mist and cloud assemble,
50 And fearful thunder and lightning and cold winds,
But these, by the Creator's order, held
No general dominion; even as it is,
These brothers brawl and quarrel; though each one
Has his own quarter, still, they come near tearing
55 The universe apart. Eurus[1] is monarch
Of the lands of dawn, the realms of Araby,
The Persian ridges under the rays of morning.
Zephyrus[2] holds the west that glows at sunset,
Boreas,[3] who makes men shiver, holds the north,
60 Warm Auster[4] governs in the misty southland,
And over them all presides the weightless ether,
Pure without taint of earth.
                              These boundaries given,
Behold, the stars, long hidden under darkness,

---

1. *Eurus* (yür/əs), the east wind. 2. *Zephyrus*, (zef/ər əs). 3. *Boreas*, (bôr/ē əs, bōr/ē əs). 4. *Auster*, (ô/stèr).

Broke through and shone, all over the spangled heaven,
65 Their home forever, and the gods lived there,
And shining fish were given the waves for dwelling
And beasts the earth, and birds the moving air.

But something else was needed, a finer being,
More capable of mind, a sage, a ruler,
70 So Man was born, it may be, in God's image,
Or Earth, perhaps, so newly separated
From the old fire of Heaven, still retained
Some seed of the celestial force which fashioned
Gods out of living clay and running water.
75 All other animals look downward; Man,
Alone, erect, can raise his face toward Heaven.

The Golden Age was first, a time that cherished
Of its own will, justice and right; no law,
No punishment, was called for; fearfulness
80 Was quite unknown, and the bronze tablets held
No legal threatening; no suppliant throng
Studied a judge's face; there were no judges,
There did not need to be. Trees had not yet
Been cut and hollowed, to visit other shores.
85 Men were content at home, and had no towns
With moats and walls around them; and no trumpets
Blared out alarums; things like swords and helmets
Had not been heard of. No one needed soldiers.
People were unaggressive, and unanxious;
90 The years went by in peace. And Earth, untroubled,
Unharried by hoe or plowshare, brought forth all
That men had need for, and those men were happy,
Gathering berries from the mountain sides,
Cherries, or blackcaps, and the edible acorns.
95 Spring was forever, with a west wind blowing
Softly across the flowers no man had planted,
And Earth, unplowed, brought forth rich grain; the field,
Unfallowed, whitened with wheat, and there were rivers
Of milk, and rivers of honey, and golden nectar
100 Dripped from the dark-green oak-trees.
                                          After Saturn
Was driven to the shadowy land of death,
And the world was under Jove,[5] the Age of Silver

---

5. *Saturn . . . Jove.* The Romans identified their gods Saturn (sat′ərn) and Jupiter (jü′pə tər), or Jove (jōv), with the Greek gods Cronus (krō′nəs) and Zeus (züs), respectively. See note page 11.

Came in, lower than gold, better than bronze.
Jove made the springtime shorter, added winter,
105 Summer, and autumn, the seasons as we know them.
That was the first time when the burnt air glowed
White-hot, or icicles hung down in winter.
And men built houses for themselves; the caverns,
The woodland thickets, and the bark-bound shelters
110 No longer served; and the seeds of grain were planted
In the long furrows, and the oxen struggled
Groaning and laboring under the heavy yoke.

Then came the Age of Bronze, and dispositions
Took on aggressive instincts, quick to arm,
115 Yet not entirely evil. And last of all
The Iron Age succeeded, whose base vein
Let loose all evil: modesty and truth
And righteousness fled earth, and in their place
Came trickery and slyness, plotting, swindling,
120 Violence and the damned desire of having.
Men spread their sails to winds unknown to sailors,
The pines came down their mountain-sides, to revel
And leap in the deep waters, and the ground,
Free, once, to everyone, like air and sunshine,
125 Was stepped off by surveyors. The rich earth,
Good giver of all the bounty of the harvest,
Was asked for more; they dug into her vitals,
Pried out the wealth a kinder lord had hidden
In Stygian[6] shadow, all that precious metal,
130 The root of evil. They found the guilt of iron,
And gold, more guilty still. And War came forth
That uses both to fight with; bloody hands
Brandished the clashing weapons. Men lived on plunder.
Guest was not safe from host, nor brother from brother,
135 A man would kill his wife, a wife her husband,
Stepmothers, dire and dreadful, stirred their brews
With poisonous aconite, and sons would hustle
Fathers to death, and Piety lay vanquished,
And the maiden Justice, last of all immortals,
140 Fled from the bloody earth.
                                     Heaven was no safer.
Giants attacked the very throne of Heaven,
Piled Pelion on Ossa,[7] mountain on mountain

---

6. *Stygian* (stij′ē ən). The Styx (stiks) was a river in the Underworld. **7.** *Giants . . . Pelion on Ossa.* Two giants, Otus and Ephialtes, were killed while trying to attack Mount Olympus, the home of the gods, by piling the mountains Pelion (pē′lē on) and Ossa (os′ə) on one another.

Up to the very stars. Jove struck them down
With thunderbolts, and the bulk of those huge bodies
145 Lay on the earth, and bled, and Mother Earth,
Made pregnant by that blood, brought forth new bodies,
And gave them, to recall her older offspring,
The forms of men. And this new stock was also
Contemptuous of gods, and murder-hungry
150 And violent. You would know they were sons of blood.

And Jove was witness from his lofty throne
Of all this evil, and groaned as he remembered
The wicked revels of Lycaon's[8] table,
The latest guilt, a story still unknown
155 To the high gods. In awful indignation
He summoned them to council. No one dawdled.
Easily seen when the night skies are clear,
The Milky Way shines white. Along this road
The gods move toward the palace of the Thunderer,[9]
160 His royal halls, and, right and left, the dwellings
Of other gods are open, and guests come thronging.
The lesser gods live in a meaner section,
An area not reserved, as this one is,
For the illustrious Great Wheels of Heaven.
165 (Their Palatine Hill,[10] if I might call it so.)

They took their places in the marble chamber
Where high above them all their king was seated,
Holding his ivory sceptre, shaking out
Thrice, and again, his awful locks, the sign
170 That made the earth and stars and ocean tremble,
And then he spoke, in outrage: "I was troubled
Less for the sovereignty of all the world
In that old time when the snake-footed giants
Laid each his hundred hands on captive Heaven.[11]
175 Monstrous they were, and hostile, but their warfare
Sprung from one source, one body. Now, wherever
The sea-gods roar around the earth, a race
Must be destroyed, the race of men. I swear it!
I swear by all the Stygian rivers gliding
180 Under the world, I have tried all other measures.
The knife must cut the cancer out, infection
Averted while it can be, from our numbers.

---

8. *Lycaon's*, (lī cā/onz). **9.** *the Thunderer*, the god Jupiter, whose weapon was the thunderbolt. **10.** *Palatine Hill.* On the Palatine (pal/ə tīn) Hill in Rome was the palace of the Emperor. **11.** *that old time . . . captive Heaven.* The first children of Uranus, the sky, and Gaea, the earth, were hundred-handed giants. These monsters later attacked the gods and nearly overcame them.

Those demigods, those rustic presences,
Nymphs, fauns, and satyrs,[12] wood and mountain dwellers,
185 We have not yet honored with a place in Heaven,
But they should have some decent place to dwell in,
In peace and safety. Safety? Do you reckon
They will be safe, when I, who wield the thunder,
Who rule you all as subjects, am subjected
190 To the plottings of the barbarous Lycaon?"

They burned, they trembled. Who was this Lycaon,
Guilty of such rank infamy? They shuddered
In horror, with a fear of sudden ruin,
As the whole world did later, when assassins
195 Struck Julius Caesar down, and Prince Augustus
Found satisfaction in the great devotion
That cried for vengeance,[13] even as Jove took pleasure,
Then, in the gods' response. By word and gesture
He calmed them down, awed them again to silence,
200 And spoke once more:
                            "He has indeed been punished.
On that score have no worry. But what he did,
And how he paid, are things that I must tell you.
I had heard the age was desperately wicked,
I had heard, or so I hoped, a lie, a falsehood,
205 So I came down, as man, from high Olympus,[14]
Wandered about the world. It would take too long
To tell you how widespread was all that evil.
All I had heard was grievous understatement!
I had crossed Maenala,[15] a country bristling
210 With dens of animals, and crossed Cyllene,
And cold Lycaeus' pine woods.[16] Then I came
At evening, with the shadows growing longer,
To an Arcadian[17] palace, where the tyrant
Was anything but royal in his welcome.
215 I gave a sign that a god had come, and people
Began to worship, and Lycaon mocked them,
Laughed at their prayers, and said: 'Watch me find out
Whether this fellow is a god or mortal,
I can tell quickly, and no doubt about it.'

---

12. *nymphs, fauns, and satyrs.* Nymphs (nimfs), fauns (fônz), and satyrs (sā′tərz, sat′ərz) were minor
gods and goddesses of the wild places. 13. *assassins . . . vengeance.* The Roman general and statesman
Julius Caesar (102?–44 B.C.) was assassinated by political opponents, who were in turn defeated
militarily by his nephew and adopted son Octavian, the emperor Augustus (63 B.C.–14 A.D.). 14.
Olympus, (ō lim′pəs). 15. *Maenala,* (mē nä′lä). 16. *Cyllene . . . Lycaesus' pine woods.* Cyllene (si lē′
nē) and Lycaeus (lī sē′əs) are mountains. 17. *Arcadian,* (är kā′dē ən). Arcadia was a district in the
central Peloponnesus, the peninsula which forms the southern part of Greece.

220 He planned, that night, to kill me while I slumbered;
That was his way to test the truth. Moreover,
And not content with that, he took a hostage,
One sent by the Molossians,[18] cut his throat,
Boiled pieces of his flesh, still warm with life,
225 Broiled others, and set them before me on the table.
That was enough. I struck, and the bolt of lightning
Blasted the household of that guilty monarch.
He fled in terror, reached the silent fields,
And howled, and tried to speak. No use at all!
230 Foam dripped from his mouth; bloodthirsty still, he turned
Against the sheep, delighting still in slaughter,
And his arms were legs, and his robes were shaggy hair,
Yet he is still Lycaon, the same grayness,
The same fierce face, the same red eyes, a picture
235 Of bestial savagery. One house has fallen,
But more than one deserves to. Fury reigns
Over all the fields of Earth. They are sworn to evil,
Believe it. Let them pay for it, and quickly!
So stands my purpose."
                              Part of them approved
240 With words and added fuel to his anger,
And part approved with silence, and yet all
Were grieving at the loss of humankind,
Were asking what the world would be, bereft
Of mortals: who would bring their altars incense?
245 Would earth be given the beasts, to spoil and ravage?
Jove told them not to worry; he would give them
Another race, unlike the first, created
Out of a miracle; he would see to it.

He was about to hurl his thunderbolts
250 At the whole world, but halted, fearing Heaven
Would burn from fire so vast, and pole to pole
Break out in flame and smoke, and he remembered
The fates had said that some day land and ocean,
The vault of Heaven, the whole world's mighty fortress,
255 Besieged by fire, would perish. He put aside
The bolts made in Cyclopean[19] workshops; better,
He thought, to drown the world by flooding water.
So, in the cave of Aeolus,[20] he prisoned

---

18. *Molossians* (mō losh′ənz), the people of an area in northwestern Greece. **19.** *Cyclopean,* (si′klə-
pē′ən). The Cyclopes were a race of one-eyed giants, descendants of the monstrous children of Uranus
and Gaea. They forged the thunderbolts of Jupiter in the forge of the fire-god Vulcan under Mt. Etna, a
volcano in Sicily. **20.** *Aeolus,* (ē′ə ləs).

The North-wind, and the West-wind, and such others
260 As ever banish cloud, and he turned loose
The South-wind, and the South-wind came out streaming
With dripping wings, and pitch-black darkness veiling
His terrible countenance. His beard is heavy
With rain-cloud, and his hoary locks a torrent,
265 Mists are his chaplet, and his wings and garments
Run with the rain. His broad hands squeeze together
Low-hanging clouds, and crash and rumble follow
Before the cloudburst, and the rainbow, Iris,
Draws water from the teeming earth, and feeds it
270 Into the clouds again. The crops are ruined,
The farmers' prayers all wasted, all the labor
Of a long year, comes to nothing.
       And Jove's anger,
Unbounded by his own domain, was given
Help by his dark-blue brother. Neptune[21] called
275 His rivers all, and told them, very briefly,
To loose their violence, open their houses,
Pour over embankments, let the river horses
Run wild as ever they would. And they obeyed him.
His trident struck the shuddering earth; it opened
280 Way for the rush of waters. The leaping rivers
Flood over the great plains. Not only orchards
Are swept away, not only grain and cattle,
Not only men and houses, but altars, temples,
And shrines with holy fires. If any building
285 Stands firm, the waves keep rising over its roof-top,
Its towers are under water, and land and ocean
Are all alike, and everything is ocean,
An ocean with no shore-line.
        Some poor fellow
Seizes a hill-top; another, in a dinghy,
290 Rows where he used to plough, and one goes sailing
Over his fields of grain or over the chimney
Of what was once his cottage. Someone catches
Fish in the top of an elm-tree, or an anchor
Drags in green meadow-land, or the curved keel brushes
295 Grape-arbors under water. Ugly sea-cows
Float where the slender she-goats used to nibble
The tender grass, and the Nereids[22] come swimming
With curious wonder, looking, under water,
At houses, cities, parks, and groves. The dolphins

---

21. *Neptune* (nep′tün), god of the sea. 22. *Nereids* (nir′ē idz), the fifty daughters of the sea-god
Nereus.

300 Invade the woods and brush against the oak-trees;
The wolf swims with the lamb; lion and tiger
Are borne along together; the wild boar
Finds all his strength is useless, and the deer
Cannot outspeed that torrent; wandering birds
305 Look long, in vain, for landing-place, and tumble,
Exhausted, into the sea. The deep's great license
Has buried all the hills, and new waves thunder
Against the mountain-tops. The flood has taken
All things, or nearly all, and those whom water,
310 By chance, has spared, starvation slowly conquers.

Phocis, a fertile land, while there was land,
Marked off Oetean from Boeotian fields.[23]
It was ocean now, a plain of sudden waters.
There Mount Parnassus[24] lifts its twin peaks skyward,
315 High, steep, cloud-piercing. And Deucalion[25] came there
Rowing his wife. There was no other land,
The sea had drowned it all. And here they worshipped
First the Corycian[26] nymphs and native powers,
Then Themis,[27] oracle and fate-revealer.
320 There was no better man than this Deucalion,
No one more fond of right; there was no woman
More scrupulously reverent than Pyrrha.[28]
So, when Jove saw the world was one great ocean,
Only one woman left of all those thousands,
325 And only one man left of all those thousands,
Both innocent and worshipful, he parted
The clouds, turned loose the North-wind, swept them off,
Showed earth to heaven again, and sky to land,
And the sea's anger dwindled, and King Neptune
330 Put down his trident, calmed the waves, and Triton,[29]
Summoned from far down under, with his shoulders
Barnacle-strewn, loomed up above the waters,
The blue-green sea-god, whose resounding horn
Is heard from shore to shore. Wet-bearded, Triton
335 Set lip to that great shell, as Neptune ordered,
Sounding retreat, and all the lands and waters
Heard and obeyed. The sea has shores; the rivers,
Still running high, have channels; the floods dwindle,

---

23. *Phocis . . . Boeotian fields.* Phocis (fōk′əs) was a country in central Greece. Mt. Oeta (ē′tä) is northwest of Phocis, the district of Boeotia (bē ō′shə) southeast. **24.** *Parnassus* (pär nas′əs), a mountain in central Greece. **25.** *Deucalion,* (dü cā′lē ən). **26.** *Corycian,* (kō rish′ən). The Corycian cave on Mt. Parnassus was sacred to the woodland god Pan and the nymphs. **27.** *Themis* (thē′mis), a goddess who personified the order of nature. **28.** *Pyrrha,* (pir′ə). **29.** *Triton* (trit′n), a sea-god.

Hill-tops are seen again; the trees, long buried,
340 Rise with their leaves still muddy. The world returns.

Deucalion saw that world, all desolation,
All emptiness, all silence, and his tears
Rose as he spoke to Pyrrha: "O my wife,
The only woman, now, on all this earth,
345 My consort and my cousin and my partner
In these immediate dangers, look! Of all the lands
To East or West, we two, we two alone,
Are all the population. Ocean holds
Everything else; our foothold, our assurance,
350 Are small as they can be, the clouds still frightful.
Poor woman—well, we are not all alone—
Suppose you had been, how would you bear your fear?
Who would console your grief? My wife, believe me,
Had the sea taken you, I would have followed.
355 If only I had the power, I would restore
The nations as my father[30] did, bring clay
To life with breathing. As it is, we two
Are all the human race, so Heaven has willed it,
Samples of men, mere specimens."
                                        They wept,
360 And prayed together, and having wept and prayed,
Resolved to make petition to the goddess
To seek her aid through oracles. Together
They went to the river-water, the stream Cephisus,[31]
Still far from clear, but flowing down its channel,
365 And they took river-water, sprinkled foreheads,
Sprinkled their garments, and they turned their steps
To the temple of the goddess, where the altars
Stood with the fires gone dead, and ugly moss
Stained pediment and column. At the stairs
370 They both fell prone, kissed the chill stone in prayer:
"If the gods' anger ever listens
To righteous prayers, O Themis, we implore you,
Tell us by what device our wreck and ruin
May be repaired. Bring aid, most gentle goddess,
375 To sunken circumstance."
                              And Themis heard them,
And gave this oracle: "Go from the temple,
Cover your heads, loosen your robes, and throw
Your mother's bones behind you!" Dumb, they stood

---

30. *my father,* the Titan Prometheus, who one tradition credited with the creation of humankind. See selection page 11. 31. *Cephisus,* (sē fī′səs).

In blank amazement, a long silence, broken
380 By Pyrrha, finally: she would not do it!
With trembling lips she prays whatever pardon
Her disobedience might merit, but this outrage
She dare not risk, insult her mother's spirit
By throwing her bones around. In utter darkness
385 They voice the cryptic saying over and over,
What can it mean? They wonder. At last Deucalion
Finds the way out: "I might be wrong, but surely
The holy oracles would never counsel
A guilty act. The earth is our great mother,
390 And I suppose those bones the goddess mentions
Are the stones of earth; the order means to throw them,
The stones, behind us."
                                        She was still uncertain,
And he by no means sure, and both distrustful
Of that command from Heaven; but what damage,
395 What harm, would there be in trying? They descended,
Covered their heads, loosened their garments, threw
The stones behind them as the goddess ordered.
The stones—who would believe it, had we not
The unimpeachable witness of Tradition?—
400 Began to lose their hardness, to soften, slowly,
To take on form, to grow in size, a little,
Become less rough, to look like human beings,
Or anyway as much like human beings
As statues do, when the sculptor is only starting,
405 Images half blocked out. The earthy portion,
Damp with some moisture, turned to flesh, the solid
Was bone, the veins were as they always had been.
The stones the man had thrown turned into men,
The stones the woman threw turned into women,
410 Such being the will of God. Hence we derive
The hardness that we have, and our endurance
Gives proof of what we have come from.

CLASSICAL MYTHOLOGY / THE OLYMPIANS

The gods of ancient Greece lived on top of Olympus (ō lim′pəs), a high mountain in the north. The major gods and goddesses formed a court around Zeus (züs), god of the sky, and Hera (hir′ə), his queen. After the Romans conquered Greece, they borrowed heavily from the mythology of the Greeks and adjusted their own pantheon to the older model. The following is a list of the principal Olympians, their concerns, and their Roman names:

Greek		Roman
Aphrodite (af′rə dī′te)	goddess of love and beauty	Venus (vē′nəs)
Apollo (ə pol′ō)	god of the sun, music, poetry, prophecy, and healing	Apollo (ə pol′ō)
Ares (er′ēz)	god of war	Mars (märz)
Artemis (är′tə mis)	goddess of the hunt, the forests, wild animals, and the moon	Diana (dī ä′nə)
Athene (ə thē′nē)	goddess of wisdom, warfare, the arts, and industry	Minerva (mə nėr′və)
Demeter (di mē′tər)	goddess of agriculture	Ceres (sir′ēz)
Dionysus (dī′ə nī′səs)	god of wine	Bacchus (bäk′əs)

Hades* (hā′dēz)	god of the Underworld, ruler of the dead	Pluto (plü′tō), Dis (dis)
Hephaestus (hə fes′təs)	god of fire and metalworking	Vulcan (vul′kən)
Hera (hir′ə)	queen of the gods	Juno (jü′nō)
Hermes (hėr′mēz)	messenger of Zeus, god of merchants, gamblers, and thieves	Mercury (mėr′kyər ē)
Hestia (hes′tē ə)	goddess of the hearth	Vesta (ves′tə)
Persephone* (pər sef′ə nē)	goddess of the Underworld, ruler of the dead	Proserpina (prō sėr′pə nə)
Poseidon (pə sīd′n)	god of the sea	Neptune (nep′tün)
Zeus (züs)	god of the sky, king of the gods	Jupiter (jü′pə tər), Jove (jōv)

---

*Hades and Persephone are not properly Olympian, but rather Chthonian (thō′nē ən), or Underworld, gods.

THE WAR
OF THE GODS

Theodor H. Gaster

ONCE UPON A TIME there was no heaven and no earth. There was nothing in the world but water and the two great beings who ruled it. The fresh water belonged to Apsu, and the salt water to his wife, Tiamat.[1] But at that time the two mixed and mingled together, for there were as yet neither rivers nor seas.

Out of their marriage there sprang at length two colossal creatures, Lahmu and his mate, Lahamu; and from them, in turn, rose a second pair, Anshar and his mate, Kishar. Anshar was the spirit of all above, and Kishar the spirit of all below; and from them came Anu, or Heaven.

The son of Anu was Ea,[2] wise as he was strong, far superior to his parents and to any that had been before him.

After the birth of Ea, the family of the gods grew apace, and a loud and noisy crew they were! Up and down they raced, bawling and screaming at the tops of their voices, until poor Grandma Tiamat was nothing but a bundle of nerves. Nevertheless she suffered in silence and made no complaint. "Children are children," thought she, "and what cannot be cured must be endured." But Grandpa Apsu was of another mind, and one day he could stand the din no longer. So he sent for Mummu, the dwarf whom he kept in his house to counsel and amuse him.

From THE OLDEST STORIES IN THE WORLD by Theodor Gaster. Copyright 1952 by Theodor H. Gaster. Reprinted by permission of The Viking Press, Inc.
1. *Apsu . . . Tiamat*, (äp′sü, tyä′mat). 2. *Ea*, (ä′ä).

"Come," said he, "let us go together to Tiamat and talk to her about it." And off they went to Tiamat to discuss what to do about the children.

But Apsu was in no mood for quiet discussion. "Listen," he cried, "I can stand it no more—not a moment's rest by day, and not a wink of sleep at night. We must have our peace and quiet, and I am going to get rid of them all!"

When she heard these words, Tiamat, pale with anger, turned to Apsu. "What do you mean?" she thundered. "Are we now to destroy what we ourselves created? Of course they set us on edge, as all children do older people, but we should take it in our stride!"

But her words had no effect. As soon as she had spoken them Mummu sidled up to his master and whispered in his ear. "Sir," said he, "take no notice. If you want your peace and quiet, go ahead and destroy them!"

The advice delighted Apsu. Lifting the dwarf upon his knees, he threw his arms around his neck and kissed him. Then they set off together to tell the gods what they had decided.

When the gods heard the decision they were seized with panic and started rushing to and fro across the vault of heaven, wringing their hands in wild dismay. Then they sat down in a gloomy, mournful silence, brooding on the fate that hung over their heads.

All except Ea, the wisest and shrewdest and most subtle of all the hosts of heaven, to whom there is nothing unforeseen, and nothing which he cannot forestall. While all his brothers and sisters huddled together in helpless despair, Ea was busy forming a plan. Suddenly, without a word, he rose from his seat, took a pitcher and filled it with water, and recited over it a high and holy spell. Then he brought it to Apsu and Mummu and bade them drink.

Within a few moments Apsu was fast asleep, and Mummu was nodding his head, drowsy and scarcely able to keep awake. Ea lost no time. Quick as a flash, he ripped off Apsu's loincloth and crown and removed his halo and put them on himself. Then he bound Apsu in fetters and slew him and seized his dwelling. As for the wicked counselor Mummu, he trussed him up, passed a ring through his nose, and dragged him away to a dungeon.

When he had conquered his enemies and set up a pillar to record his triumph, he made a gay and beautiful bower, and when he had finished it he took Damkina, his bride. And there, in that holy and blessed abode, there was born to them the mightiest and strongest of gods, the prince of princes, the king of kings, Lord Marduk[3] himself. At the breasts of goddesses was he suckled, and along with their milk he drank majesty and power. Lithe was his figure, lustrous his eyes, lordly his gait; and he was fully mature from the day of his birth. No

3. *Marduk*, (mär'dük).

sooner did his father behold Marduk than he was filled with joy and his face shone, and he set on him the stamp of approval and decided then and there to confer on him a double meed of godhead. So Ea gave him a form so stately and grand that human mind cannot conceive it nor human tongue express it. Four eyes Marduk had, and four ears, and whenever his lips moved fire blazed forth from them. His stature was huge, and his limbs were immense, and he was clothed in the radiance of ten gods.

But high adventure was in his blood, and as he grew he began to develop a taste for mischievous escapades, which became wilder and wilder. Once, for a prank, he tied the winds on a leash, so that they could blow only where he chose. Another time he calmly muzzled the dragon which guarded the heavenly abodes.

At last the gods could stand it no longer, and off to Tiamat they went to complain.

"Can't you see how Marduk is turning things upside down?" they cried. "His antics are making us dizzy. But you sit idly by. It's the same story all over again. When Apsu and Mummu complained you refused to do anything. You had in your hands a mighty saw, which Apsu himself had fashioned, but even when he was in the deadliest peril you simply refused to use it! And look what has happened to you—you are left a widow. Even if you did not care for your husband, at least you might care for your children! Get up and give him a trouncing!"

Thus importuned, Tiamat could not but consent. "Very well," she replied. "We will go out together and fight him. But I warn you, he is a match for us all, and we can't do it without reinforcements. So first we shall do a little creating."

Thereupon the gods gathered together around Tiamat, and a council of war was held. Day and night they plotted and schemed and drew up plans for the battle, while Tiamat fashioned terrible beasts, sharp of tooth and unsparing of fang, and into their veins she poured venom instead of blood. Raging monsters they were, wreathed in fire and flame, and all about them was a sheen so bright that whoever beheld them must needs turn tail. Viper there was, and Dragon; Mammoth and Great Lion; Mad Dog and Scorpion-Man; furious demons of the storm, Dragon-Fly and Centaur—eleven horrible beings, fearless in combat, whose onslaught none could withstand.

Then she appointed, as commander of the host, a god named Kingu. "Kingu," she said, "you shall raise the standard and lead the charge and guard the spoil. Your word shall be supreme, for, behold, I have raised you to high estate, and you shall be as my consort!" And therewith she bestowed upon him the symbols of power and fastened on his breast the great Tablets of Decision. And when he had been invested, Tiamat and Kingu together turned to the gods and cried:

The fire may rage, the flame may burn;
   Your breath shall put it out!
The mightiest to a weakling turn,
   The proud be put to rout!

And with these words ringing in their ears the army set forth.

Meanwhile, Marduk himself knew nothing of what was afoot. But as soon as Ea learned that his beloved son was threatened he was filled with such anger and indignation that he could not think clearly, but only sit and brood in silence. At length, however, his hot-headedness gave way to cool deliberation, and a plan came to his mind. At once he rose up and went to Anshar. Shrewd and wise and subtle, he knew full well how best to arouse that ancient god.

"Tiamat," said he, "is planning a rebellion against the court of heaven." Then he told Anshar how Tiamat had massed all the gods and created terrible monsters and was already going forth to battle.

When Anshar heard these words he smote his thigh in anger and bit his lip, and his heart was filled with foreboding. "Ea," cried he, "you have already shown your mettle by besting Apsu and Mummu. Now go forth again and slay Kingu and Tiamat!"

So Ea went forth to do battle against the advancing host, but when he saw the monsters marching in the van and the terrible sheen that enwrapped them, he was stricken with terror, turned tail, and fled.

When Anshar heard that Ea had been routed he was filled with dismay and summoned before him his son Anu.

"Anu," said he, "you are my firstborn, a hero whom none can withstand. Go now and confront Tiamat. Try first to soothe and appease her, but, if she will not listen, tell her that you come in my name and demand her obedience!"

Thereupon Anu departed and made straight for Tiamat. But when he beheld her furious mien and the terrible look upon her face, he too was stricken with terror and, like Ea, ran away.

Back he came to Anshar and reported what had happened. When Anu had finished speaking, Anshar turned to Ea and shook his head in despair; and all the hosts of heaven huddled together, muttering one to another, "Behold, there is none that can confront Tiamat and come back alive!"

There they sat, cowed, craven, and disconsolate, until at length Anshar rose from his throne and faced them in all his glory and might. "There is but one," he said, "who could ever be our champion—the stalwart warrior, the soldier intrepid, the valiant, impetuous Marduk himself!"

When Ea heard these words he summoned Marduk into an inner chamber so that he might speak privily with him. And he told him all about the plot of Tiamat. But he did not tell him that the plot was aimed against Marduk himself. "It is," he said, as he had told Anshar, "a rebellion against the court of heaven."

Then an earnest look stole across his face. "Marduk," he said slowly, "I am speaking to you now as your father, so listen carefully and obey. I want you to pay a visit to your great-grandfather Anshar. Though your brothers and sisters may complain about you, Anshar has always been partial to you, and he has a warm spot for you in his heart. When you come before him, strut around boldly, and wear your best soldierly expression, for that will especially amuse him."

So Marduk did as his father bade him, and paid a visit to Anshar and strutted before him like a man who is very sure of himself. And when Anshar saw his soldierly gait and bearing his heart was indeed cheered, and he kissed Marduk tenderly on the lips.

Marduk was deeply moved. "Anshar," he said softly, "you know that I have always loved you and that there is nothing which I would not do for your sake. My father has told me what is afoot, and how Tiamat is plotting a rebellion against the court of heaven. Who's afraid of that? Tiamat is only a woman, and I am ready to go out and fight her. In no time you will be trampling on her neck!"

"Very well," replied Anshar. "Go forth and confront her. See first if you can quiet her with words or some holy spell. But if she will not listen, mount the chariot of the whirlwind and fight!"

Marduk, however, was his father's son, and if he was strong and intrepid, he was also shrewd and ambitious. "This," thought he, "is my golden chance. Why should I brave the monsters and save the honor of heaven for nought?" So he squared his massive shoulders and looked his great-grandfather boldly in the face.

"Anshar," he said, "I am ready to go forth. But if I am to be your champion and conquer Tiamat and save your life, then you must make me chief of the gods. Go, call the assembly together and issue the decree! From now on, I alone shall make the decisions, and whatever I say shall be law!"

When he heard these words Anshar sent at once for his trusted messenger Gaga.

"Go," said he, "to my aged parents Lahmu and Lahamu, whom you will find in the depths of the sea. Tell them that Tiamat is raising a rebellion against the court of heaven and that Marduk has offered to fight her on condition that he becomes chief of the gods. Explain to them that this is a decision which I cannot make alone, for it affects the hosts below no less than those above. So bid them gather together all the gods in their realm, and let them come hither that we may take counsel together!"

So Gaga went and delivered the message to Lahmu and Lahamu and told them all that had passed; and Lahmu and Lahamu in turn sent word to all the gods in their realm and bade them repair to the courts of heaven.

When the gods received the summons they could scarcely believe their ears. "Something unusual must have happened," they murmured, "for Tiamat to behave like this. We had better go and find out."

Presently the courts of heaven were thronged with gods and goddesses coming from all directions. As they met one another they would pause and embrace and exchange words of greeting. Then, when all were assembled, food and drink was set before them, and they sat down to a hearty banquet.

By the time the meeting came to order, all were in a happy and carefree mood, and as soon as the resolution was laid before them, no one bothered to challenge or contest it. A dais was hastily constructed, and Marduk was seated in triumph upon it, while the company showered upon him lavish expressions of praise and approval.

"Marduk for chieftain!" they cried. "Whatever he says shall be law! His to exalt, and his to abase! All the powers of Anu shall be conferred upon him! Marduk for king of the world, and may none of his arrows miss!"

Then someone brought forward a garment. "Marduk," they cried, "that you may show what power you have, say but the word and this garment shall be destroyed. Say but the word again, and it shall be whole!"

So Marduk uttered the word, and, behold, the garment was destroyed. And again he uttered the word, and, behold, it was whole.

Then all the gods believed in Marduk, for they saw that his power was indeed supreme, and they bowed themselves low before him and cried out, "Marduk is king, Marduk is king!" And they handed him the scepter and set him upon the throne and placed in his hand the emblems of kingship, and they gave him a mighty sword and they said, "Go, cut the throat of Tiamat, and let the winds bear her blood away!"

As soon as the gods had returned to their homes, Marduk at once set about to prepare weapons for the combat. He took a bow in his hand and set an arrow within it, and before him he carried the flail of the lightning; and his whole body shone in the gleam. Then he made a net to imprison his foes, and he created great stormwinds to march by his side.

When all was ready he grasped in his hand the great bludgeon of the thunder and mounted the chariot of the whirlwind. Four monsters were they that drew it: Rager, Ruthless, Stormer, and Fleet—each of them filled with venom, dauntless and sharp of tooth. Over his lips he smeared red ocher to protect him against the powers of evil; and in his hand was a fragrant herb to drown the stench of Tiamat and her beasts. Then he rode forth.

When Kingu and the vanguard saw him approaching they were filled with terror, for this they had not foreseen, and now all their plans were upset. But Tiamat herself neither wavered nor flinched. Boldly she strode forward, and the words of her war-song rent the air:

So you are the chief, you boast,
　And all must yield you place!
Well, here come gods in a host,
　To challenge you face to face!

No sooner, however, did the words reach his ears than Marduk raised his club and brandished it in her face and hurled back his retort:

Yours was the power and might,
　You were the queen of all;
But nought to your heart was right
　Save quarrel and strife and brawl!

You, whom we hailed as our mother,
　Have nought in your soul but spite;
Brother must strive with brother,
　And son against father must fight!

Brutal and base and black-hearted,
　Faithless to living and dead,
No sooner was Apsu departed
　Then Kingu you took in his stead!

What courage is this or defiance
　To challenge the ancient and old,
On monsters to place your reliance,
　To come forth with thousands untold?

Come forth by yourself, I say,
　Let your minions be banished from sight!
Come forth of yourself to the fray,
　And hand to hand let us fight!

At these words Tiamat was stung to frenzy and, without looking to left or to right, she lunged blindly at her taunter, jaws agape to swallow him up; and even as she advanced, screaming insult and defiance, the gods who rode at her side furbished their weapons for combat.

But Marduk was too quick. No sooner did he see her bearing down upon him than, quick as a flash, he spread his net in her path and enmeshed her, and in less time than it takes to tell she was struggling furiously within it. Then he called to the stormwind, who had been marching in the rear of his host, and bade him advance. And the stormwind charged forward and rushed into the gaping jaws of Tiamat, so that she could not close her lips. Instantly Marduk drew his bow and shot his dart into the wide-open mouth, and the dart went down into Tiamat's maw and rent her veins and pierced her heart. Then, as her great body sagged and fell, he bound her and extinguished her life; and upon her prostrate corpse he planted his heel.

When the hosts of Tiamat saw that their leader had been slain, they broke ranks and attempted to flee, but at once the forces of Marduk closed in upon them and bound them in fetters and broke their weapons. And Marduk took them and placed them in a net and hurled them down into the caverns of the earth, to remain there as prisoners forever. The eleven monsters also he tied with ropes and trampled underfoot, so that all their might departed and all their pride was brought low, and they became as tame beasts upon a leash. As for Kingu, a special judgment was pronounced upon him: no more was he to be reckoned among the immortals.

Having thus disposed of her allies, Marduk turned again to the fallen Tiamat. Raising aloft his mighty club, he brought it down with full force upon her skull, and the wind bore away the blood from her severed veins.

When Anshar and Ea and all their companions saw what Marduk had done, they were overwhelmed with joy and relief, and at once they hastened toward him, bearing gifts and tribute. But Marduk would not stay to receive them, for already he was busy with other tasks; to him the end of Tiamat was but the beginning of his own new order. Taking the carcass of his prostrate foe, he split it in two like an oyster, and one half of it he raised aloft to form the firmament of heaven. Then he paced out the length of the waters which lay beneath that firmament, and he measured their width, and of the other half of Tiamat's body he made a kind of covering for them; and that covering was the foundation of the earth. And he set Anu in the realm that was above the firmament, and Enlil[4] in the realm that was between the firmament and the earth, and Ea in the waters that were below the earth. So Anu became the god of the sky, and Enlil the god of the air, and Ea the god of the deep.

Then Marduk assigned places to all the other gods, and he created luminaries to shine in the heavens—even the sun and the moon and the stars—and he arranged the times and seasons of their movements. And he made courses for the stars, and he determined the lengths of the months; and he opened a gate in the east whence the sun might come forth at dawn, and a gate in the west whither it might repair at dusk.

---

4. *Enlil* (en′lil′), the god later called Bel, or Baal, "the lord."

But, behold, when all was set in order the gods came clustering around him, making bitter complaint. "Lord Marduk," they cried, "you have given us places and stations and assigned to each of us a task. But none have you appointed to serve us and sustain us while we perform them. Who is to tend our homes and give us our food?"

When Marduk heard these words he fell into deep thought. Then suddenly his face lit up. "I know what I will do," said he to himself. "I will take blood and bone and fashion a little puppet. Its name shall be Man. Man shall serve the gods and tend their needs while they perform their tasks!"

But when he imparted this plan to Ea, that wise and shrewd old god was able at once to improve upon it. "Why make new blood and bone?" he asked. "Let one of the rebels supply them!"

So Marduk ordered the bound rebels to be brought before him, and he questioned them closely and bade them declare in truth who was the prime offender of them all, that he might be put to death.

Now, the rebels had been simple soldiers in the host of Tiamat, and they saw no reason why any of them should bear the guilt of the war. "The prime offender," they replied with one accord, "was Kingu. He was our leader and commander, who both planned the attack and led it!"

Thereupon Kingu was led forth from his dungeon and delivered into the hands of Ea. And Ea cut off his head and slit open his veins, and out of the bone and blood he fashioned a puppet called Man, to serve the gods and tend their needs.

Then the gods gathered around Marduk in great joy. "Lord Marduk," they cried, "you have eased our burden and lightened our labors, and we would show you our thanks by building you a shrine on earth where you too may rest awhile from your toils. Year by year we will come to that shrine and pay you homage and sing your praise."

So for two whole years they worked and slaved with brick and mortar, and in the third year the city of Babylon[5] was upreared, and towering above it was the palace of Esagila, the shrine of Marduk.

When the building was completed all the gods gathered together and held a feast within it, and Marduk sat among them and received their homage and declared the laws and the fates and the destinies of the whole world. And he took the great bow wherewith he had vanquished his foe, and he hung it in the heavens for all to see.

And so it remains unto this day. Man is the servant of the gods; and each New Year's Day the gods repair to the shrine of Marduk in Babylon to pay homage to him; and he declares to them the fates and destinies of the whole world. And the Bow hangs in heaven, for all to see.

---

5. *Babylon* (bab/ə lən, bab/ə lon), a great city in ancient times, located on the Euphrates River in southwest Asia.

from
BOOK OF
THE HOPI

Frank Waters

THE FIRST WORLD was Tokpela.[1]

But first, they say, there was only the Creator, Taiowa.[2] All else was endless space. There was no beginning and no end, no time, no shape, no life. Just an immeasurable void that had its beginning and end, time, shape, and life in the mind of Taiowa the Creator.

Then he, the infinite, conceived the finite. First he created Sótuknang[3] to make it manifest, saying to him, "I have created you, the first power and instrument as a person, to carry out my plan for life in endless space. I am your Uncle. You are my Nephew. Go now and lay out these universes in proper order so they may work harmoniously with one another according to my plan."

Sótuknang did as he was commanded. From endless space he gathered that which was to be manifest as solid substance, molded it into forms, and arranged them into nine universal kingdoms: one for Taiowa the Creator, one for himself, and seven universes for the life to come. Finishing this, Sótuknang went to Taiowa and asked, "Is this according to your plan?"

"It is very good," said Taiowa. "Now I want you to do the same thing with the waters. Place them on the surfaces of these universes so they will be divided equally among all and each."

So Sótuknang gathered from endless space that which was to be manifest as the waters and placed them on the universes so that each would be half solid and half water. Going now to Taiowa, he said, "I want you to see the work I have done and if it pleases you."

"It is very good," said Taiowa. "The next thing now is to put the forces of air into peaceful movement about all."

1. *Tokpela* (tōk pe lä), "Endless Space." 2. *Taiowa*, (ti ō wä). 3. *Sótuknang*, (sho tùk näng).

This Sótuknang did. From endless space he gathered that which was to be manifest as the airs, made them into great forces, and arranged them into gentle ordered movements around each universe.

Taiowa was pleased. "You have done a great work according to my plan, Nephew. You have created the universes and made them manifest in solids, waters, and winds, and put them in their proper places. But your work is not yet finished. Now you must create life and its movement to complete the four parts, Túwaquachi,[4] of my universal plan."

Sótuknang went to the universe wherein was that to be Tokpela, the First World, and out of it he created her who was to remain on that earth and be his helper. Her name was Kókyangwúti,[5] Spider Woman.

When she awoke to life and received her name, she asked, "Why am I here?"

"Look about you," answered Sótuknang. "Here is this earth we have created. It has shape and substance, direction and time, a beginning and an end. But there is no life upon it. We see no joyful movement. We hear no joyful sound. What is life without sound and movement? So you have been given the power to help us create this life. You have been given the knowledge, wisdom, and love to bless all the beings you create. That is why you are here."

Following his instructions, Spider Woman took some earth, mixed with it some *túchvala*[6], and molded it into two beings. Then she covered them with a cape made of white substance which was the creative wisdom itself, and sang the Creation Song over them. When she uncovered them the two beings, twins, sat up and asked, "Who are we? Why are we here?"

To the one on the right Spider Woman said, "You are Pöqánghoya[7] and you are to help keep this world in order when life is put upon it. Go now around all the world and put your hands upon the earth so that it will become fully solidified. This is your duty."

Spider Woman then said to the twin on the left, "You are Palöngawhoya[8] and you are to help keep this world in order when life is put upon it. This is your duty now: go about all the world and send out sound so that it may be heard throughout all the land. When this is heard you will also be known as 'Echo,' for all sound echoes the Creator."

Pöqánghoya, traveling throughout the earth, solidified the higher reaches into great mountains. The lower reaches he made firm but still pliable enough to be used by those beings to be placed upon it and who would call it their mother.

---

4. *Túwaquachi,* (tù wä kù ä chē). 5. *Kókyangwúti,* (kok yäng wü tē). 6. *túchvala* (tùch vä lä), saliva. 7. *Pöqánghoya,* (pèr käng hō yä). 8. *Palöngawhoya,* (pä lèrng ow hō yä).

Palöngawhoya, traveling throughout the earth, sounded out his call as he was bidden. All the vibratory centers along the earth's axis from pole to pole resounded his call; the whole earth trembled; the universe quivered in tune. Thus he made the whole world an instrument of sound, and sound an instrument for carrying messages, resounding praise to the Creator of all.

"This is your voice, Uncle," Sótuknang said to Taiowa. "Everything is tuned to your sound."

"It is very good," said Taiowa.

When they had accomplished their duties, Pöqánghoya was sent to the north pole of the world axis and Palöngawhoya to the south pole, where they were jointly commanded to keep the world properly rotating. Pöqánghoya was also given the power to keep the earth in a stable form of solidness. Palöngawhoya was given the power to keep the air in gentle ordered movement, and instructed to send out his call for good or for warning through the vibratory centers of the earth.

"These will be your duties in time to come," said Spider Woman.

She then created from the earth trees, bushes, plants, flowers, all kinds of seed-bearers and nut-bearers to clothe the earth, giving to each a life and name. In the same manner she created all kinds of birds and animals—molding them out of earth, covering them with her white-substance cape, and singing over them. Some she placed to her right, some to her left, others before and behind her, indicating how they should spread to all four corners of the earth to live.

Sótuknang was happy, seeing how beautiful it all was—the land, the plants, the birds and animals, and the power working through them all. Joyfully he said to Taiowa, "Come see what our world looks like now!"

"It is very good," said Taiowa. "It is ready now for human life, the final touch to complete my plan."

So Spider Woman gathered earth, this time of four colors, yellow, red, white, and black; mixed with *túchvala,* the liquid of her mouth; molded them; and covered them with her white-substance cape which was the creative wisdom itself. As before, she sang over them the Creation Song, and when she uncovered them these forms were human beings in the image of Sótuknang. Then she created four other beings after her own form. They were *wúti,*[9] female partners, for the first four male beings.

When Spider Woman uncovered them the forms came to life. This was at the time of the dark purple light, Qoyangnuptu,[10] the first phase of the dawn of Creation, which first reveals the mystery of man's creation.

They soon awakened and began to move, but there was still a

9. *wúti,* (wù tē). 10. *Qoyangnuptu,* (kō yäng nùp tù).

dampness on their foreheads and a soft spot on their heads. This was at the time of the yellow light, Síkangñuqua,[11] the second phase of the dawn of Creation, when the breath of life entered man.

In a short time the sun appeared above the horizon, drying the dampness on their foreheads and hardening the soft spot on their heads. This was the time of the red light, Tálawva,[12] the third phase of the dawn of Creation, when man, fully formed and firmed, proudly faced his Creator.

"That is the Sun," said Spider Woman. "You are meeting your Father the Creator for the first time. You must always remember and observe these three phases of your Creation. The time of the three lights, the dark purple, the yellow, and the red reveal in turn the mystery, the breath of life, and warmth of love. These comprise the Creator's plan of life for you as sung over you in the Song of Creation:

SONG OF CREATION

The dark purple light rises in the north,
A yellow light rises in the east.
Then we of the flowers of the earth come forth
To receive a long life of joy.
We call ourselves the Butterfly Maidens.

Both male and female make their prayers to the east,
Make the respectful sign to the Sun our Creator.
The sounds of bells ring through the air,
Making a joyful sound throughout the land,
Their joyful echo resounding everywhere.

Humbly I ask my Father,
The perfect one, Taiowa, our Father,
The perfect one creating the beautiful life
Shown to us by the yellow light,
To give us perfect light at the time of the red light.

The perfect one laid out the perfect plan
And gave to us a long span of life,
Creating song to implant joy in life.
On this path of happiness, we the Butterfly Maidens
Carry out his wishes by greeting our Father Sun.

The song resounds back from our Creator with joy,
And we of the earth repeat it to our Creator.
At the appearing of the yellow light,

---

11. *Síkangnuqua*, (shē käng nù kù ä). 12. *Tálawva*, (tä low vä).

Repeats and repeats again the joyful echo,
Sounds and resounds for times to come.

The First People of the First World did not answer her; they could not speak. Something had to be done. Since Spider Woman received her power from Sótuknang, she had to call him and ask him what to do. So she called Palöngawhoya and said, "Call your Uncle. We need him at once."

Palöngawhoya, the echo twin, sent out his call along the world axis to the vibratory centers of the earth, which resounded his message throughout the universe. "Sótuknang, our Uncle, come at once! We need you!"

All at once, with the sound as of a mighty wind, Sótuknang appeared in front of them. "I am here. Why do you need me so urgently?"

Spider Woman explained. "As you commanded me, I have created these First People. They are fully and firmly formed; they are properly colored; they have life; they have movement. But they cannot talk. That is the proper thing they lack. So I want you to give them speech. Also the wisdom and the power to reproduce, so that they may enjoy their life and give thanks to the Creator."

So Sótuknang gave them speech, a different language to each color, with respect for each other's difference. He gave them the wisdom and the power to reproduce and multiply.

Then he said to them, "With all these I have given you this world to live on and to be happy. There is only one thing I ask of you. To respect the Creator at all times. Wisdom, harmony, and respect for the love of the Creator who made you. May it grow and never be forgotten among you as long as you live."

So the First People went their directions, were happy, and began to multiply.

So the First People kept multiplying and spreading over the face of the land and were happy. Although they were of different colors and spoke different languages, they felt as one and understood one another without talking. It was the same with the birds and animals. They all suckled at the breast of their Mother Earth, who gave them her milk of grass, seeds, fruit, and corn, and they all felt as one, people and animals.

But gradually there were those who forgot the commands of Sótuknang and the Spider Woman to respect their Creator. More and more they used the vibratory centers of their bodies solely for earthly purposes, forgetting that their primary purpose was to carry out the plan of Creation.

There then came among them Lavaíhoya,[13] the Talker. He came in

---

13. *Lavaíhoya*, (lä vi hō yä).

the form of a bird called Mochni,[14] and the more he kept talking the more he convinced them of the differences between them: the difference between people and animals, and the differences between the people themselves by reason of the colors of their skins, their speech, and belief in the plan of the Creator.

It was then that animals drew away from people. The guardian spirit of animals laid his hands on their hind legs just below the tail, making them become wild and scatter from the people in fear. You can see this slightly oily spot today on deer and antelope—on the sides of their back legs as they throw up their tails to run away.

In the same way, people began to divide and draw away from one another—those of different races and languages, then those who remembered the plan of Creation and those who did not.

There came among them a handsome one, Káto'ya,[15] in the form of a snake with a big head. He led the people still farther away from one another and their pristine wisdom. They became suspicious of one another and accused one another wrongfully until they became fierce and warlike and began to fight one another.

All the time Mochni kept talking and Káto'ya became more beguiling. There was no rest, no peace.

But among all the people of different races and languages there were a few in every group who still lived by the laws of Creation. To them came Sótuknang. He came with the sound as of a mighty wind and suddenly appeared before them. He said, "I have observed this state of affairs. It is not good. It is so bad I talked to my Uncle, Taiowa, about it. We have decided this world must be destroyed and another one created so you people can start over again. You are the ones we have chosen."

They listened carefully to their instructions.

Said Sótuknang, "You will go to a certain place. Your *kópavi*,[16] the vibratory center on top of the head, will lead you. This inner wisdom will give you the sight to see a certain cloud, which you will follow by day, and a certain star, which you will follow by night. Take nothing with you. Your journey will not end until the cloud stops and the star stops."

So all over the world these chosen people suddenly disappeared from their homes and people and began following the cloud by day and the star by night. Many other people asked them where they were going and, when they were told, laughed at them. "We don't see any cloud or any star either!" they said. This was because they had lost the inner vision of the *kópavi* on the crown of their heads; the door was closed to them. Still there were a very few who went along anyway because they believed the people who did see the cloud and the star. This was all right.

---

14. *Mochni* (mōch nē), a bird like the mockingbird. **15.** *Káto'ya,* (kä tō yä). **16.** *kópavi,* (kō pä vē).

After many days and nights the first people arrived at the certain place. Soon others came and asked, "What are you doing here?" And they said, "We were told by Sótuknang to come here." The other people said, "We too were led here by the vapor and the star!" They were all happy together because they were of the same mind and understanding even though they were of different races and languages.

When the last ones arrived Sótuknang appeared. "Well, you are all here, you people I have chosen to save from the destruction of this world. Now come with me."

He led them to a big mound where the Ant People lived, stamped on the roof, and commanded the Ant People to open up their home. When an opening was made on top of the anthill, Sótuknang said to the people, "Now you will enter this Ant kiva,[17] where you will be safe when I destroy the world. While you are here I want you to learn a lesson from these Ant People. They are industrious. They gather food in the summer for the winter. They keep cool when it is hot and warm when it is cool. They live peacefully with one another. They obey the plan of Creation."

So the people went down to live with the Ant People. When they were all safe and settled Taiowa commanded Sótuknang to destroy the world. Sótuknang destroyed it by fire because the Fire Clan had been its leaders. He rained fire upon it. He opened up the volcanoes. Fire came from above and below and all around until the earth, the waters, the air, all was one element, fire, and there was nothing left except the people safe inside the womb of the earth.

This was the end of Tokpela, the First World.

While this was going on the people lived happily underground with the Ant People. Their homes were just like the people's homes on the earth-surface being destroyed. There were rooms to live in and rooms where they stored their food. There was light to see by, too. The tiny bits of crystal in the sand of the anthill had absorbed the light of the sun, and by using the inner vision of the center behind their eyes they could see by its reflection very well.

Only one thing troubled them. The food began to run short. It had not taken Sótuknang long to destroy the world, nor would it take him long to create another one. But it was taking a long time for the First World to cool off before the Second World could be created. That was why the food was running short.

"Do not give us so much of the food you have worked so hard to gather and store," the people said.

"Yes, you are our guests," the Ant People told them. "What we have is yours also." So the Ant People continued to deprive themselves of food in order to supply their guests. Every day they tied their belts

17. *kiva* (kē və), a ceremonial room or building, traditionally round, and usually underground.

tighter and tighter. That is why ants today are so small around the waist.

Finally that which had been the First World cooled off. Sótuknang purified it. Then he began to create the Second World. He changed its form completely, putting land where the water was and water where the land had been, so the people upon their Emergence would have nothing to remind them of the previous wicked world.

When all was ready he came to the roof of the Ant kiva, stamped on it, and gave his call. Immediately the Chief of the Ant People went up to the opening and rolled back the *núta*.[18] "*Yung-ai!* Come in! You are welcome!" he called.

Sótuknang spoke first to the Ant People. "I am thanking you for doing your part in helping to save these people. It will always be remembered, this you have done. The time will come when another world will be destroyed; and when wicked people know their last day on earth has come, they will sit by an anthill and cry for the ants to save them. Now, having fulfilled your duty, you may go forth to this Second World I have created and take your place as ants."

Then Sótuknang said to the people, "Make your Emergence now to this Second World I have created. It is not quite so beautiful as the First World, but it is beautiful just the same. You will like it. So multiply and be happy. But remember your Creator and the laws he gave you. When I hear you singing joyful praises to him I will know you are my children, and you will be close to me in your hearts."

So the people emerged to the Second World. Its name was Tokpa.[19] Its direction was south, its color blue, its mineral *qöchásiva*, silver. Chiefs upon it were *salavi*, the spruce; *kwáhu*, the eagle; and *kolíchiyaw*, the skunk.

It was a big land, and the people multiplied rapidly, spreading over it to all directions, even to the other side of the world. This did not matter, for they were so close together in spirit they could see and talk to each other from the center on top of the head. Because this door was still open, they felt close to Sótuknang and they sang joyful praises to the Creator, Taiowa.

They did not have the privilege of living with the animals, though, for the animals were wild and kept apart. Being separated from the animals, the people tended to their own affairs. They built homes, then villages and trails between them. They made things with their hands and stored food like the Ant People. Then they began to trade and barter with one another.

This was when the trouble started. Everything they needed was on this Second World, but they began to want more. More and more they traded for things they didn't need, and the more goods they got, the

---

18. *núta* (nù tä), a straw thatch over the opening of a kiva. **19.** *Tokpa* (tōk pä), "Dark Midnight."

more they wanted. This was very serious. For they did not realize they were drawing away, step by step, from the good life given them. They just forgot to sing joyful praises to the Creator and soon began to sing praises for the goods they bartered and stored. Before long it happened as it had to happen. The people began to quarrel and fight, and then wars between villages began.

Still there were a few people in every village who sang the song of their Creation. But the wicked people laughed at them until they could sing it only in their hearts. Even so, Sótuknang heard it through their centers and the centers of the earth. Suddenly one day he appeared before them.

"Spider Woman tells me your thread is running out on this world," he said. "That is too bad. The Spider Clan was your leader, and you were making good progress until this state of affairs began. Now my Uncle, Taiowa, and I have decided we must do something about it. We are going to destroy this Second World just as soon as we put you people who still have the song in your hearts in a safe place."

So again, as on the First World, Sótuknang called on the Ant People to open up their underground world for the chosen people. When they were safely underground, Sótuknang commanded the twins, Pöqánghoya and Palöngawhoya, to leave their posts at the north and south ends of the world's axis, where they were stationed to keep the earth properly rotating.

The twins had hardly abandoned their stations when the world, with no one to control it, teetered off balance, spun around crazily, then rolled over twice. Mountains plunged into seas with a great splash, seas and lakes sloshed over the land; and as the world spun through cold and lifeless space it froze into solid ice.

This was the end of Tokpa, the Second World.

For many years all the elements that had comprised the Second World were frozen into a motionless and lifeless lump of ice. But the people were happy and warm with the Ant People in their underground world. They watched their food carefully, although the ants' waists became still smaller. They wove sashes and blankets together and told stories.

Eventually Sótuknang ordered Pöqánghoya and Palöngawhoya back to their stations at the poles of the world axis. With a great shudder and a splintering of ice the planet began rotating again. When it was revolving smoothly about its own axis and stately moving in its universal orbit, the ice began to melt and the world began to warm to life. Sótuknang set about creating the Third World: arranging earths and seas, planting mountains and plains with their proper coverings, and creating all forms of life.

When the earth was ready for occupancy, he came to the Ant kiva with the proper approach as before and said, "Open the door. It is time for you to come out."

Once again when the *núta* was rolled back he gave the people their instructions. "I have saved you so you can be planted again on this new Third World. But you must always remember the two things I am saying to you now. First, respect me and one another. And second, sing in harmony from the tops of the hills. When I do not hear you singing praises to your Creator I will know you have gone back to evil again."

So the people climbed up the ladder from the Ant kiva, making their Emergence to the Third World.

Its name was Kuskurza,[20] its direction east, its color red. Chiefs upon it were the mineral *palásiva,* copper; the plant *píva,* tobacco; the bird *angwusi,* crow; and the animal *chöövio,* antelope.

Upon it once more the people spread out, multiplied, and continued their progress on the Road of Life. In the First World they had lived simply with the animals. In the Second World they had developed handicrafts, homes, and villages. Now in the Third World they multiplied in such numbers and advanced so rapidly that they created big cities, countries, a whole civilization. This made it difficult for them to conform to the plan of Creation and to sing praises to Taiowa and Sótuknang. More and more of them became wholly occupied with their own earthly plans.

Some of them, of course, retained the wisdom granted them upon their Emergence. With this wisdom they understood that the farther they proceeded on the Road of Life and the more they developed, the harder it was. That was why their world was destroyed every so often to give them a fresh start. They were especially concerned because so many people were using their reproductive power in wicked ways. There was one woman who was becoming known throughout the world for her wickedness in corrupting so many people. She even boasted that so many men were giving her turquoise necklaces for her favors she could wind them around a ladder that reached to the end of the world's axis. So the people with wisdom sang louder and longer their praises to the Creator from the tops of their hills.

The other people hardly heard them. Under the leadership of the Bow Clan they began to use their creative power in another evil and destructive way. Perhaps this was caused by that wicked woman. But some of them made a *pátuwvota*[21] and with their creative power made it fly through the air. On this many of the people flew to a big city, attacked it, and returned so fast no one knew where they came from. Soon the people of many cities and countries were making *pátuwvotas* and flying on them to attack one another. So corruption and war came to the Third World as it had to the others.

---

20. *Kuskurza,* (kùs kùr zä). 21. *pátuwvota,* (pä tùw vō tä), a shield made of hide.

This time Sótuknang came to Spider Woman and said, "There is no use waiting until the thread runs out this time. Something has to be done lest the people with the song in their hearts are corrupted and killed off too. It will be difficult, with all this destruction going on, for them to gather at the far end of the world I have designated. But I will help them. Then you will save them when I destroy this world with water."

"How shall I save them?" asked Spider Woman.

"When you get there look about you," commanded Sótuknang. "You will see these tall plants with hollow stems. Cut them down and put the people inside. Then I will tell you what to do next."

Spider Woman did as he instructed her. She cut down the hollow reeds; and as the people came to her, she put them inside with a little water and *hurúsuki*,[22] white cornmeal dough, for food, and sealed them up. When all the people were thus taken care of, Sótuknang appeared.

"Now you get in to take care of them, and I will seal you up," he said. "Then I will destroy the world."

So he loosed the waters upon the earth. Waves higher than mountains rolled in upon the land. Continents broke asunder and sank beneath the seas. And still the rains fell, the waves rolled in.

The people sealed up in their hollow reeds heard the mighty rushing of the waters. They felt themselves tossed high in the air and dropping back to the water. Then all was quiet, and they knew they were floating. For a long, long time—so long a time that it seemed it would never end—they kept floating.

Finally their movement ceased. The Spider Woman unsealed their hollow reeds, took them by the tops of their heads, and pulled them out. "Bring out all the food that is left over," she commanded.

The people brought out their *hurúsuki;* it was still the same size, although they had been eating it all this time. Looking about them, they saw they were on a little piece of land that had been the top of one of their highest mountains. All else, as far as they could see, was water. This was all that remained of the Third World.

"There must be some dry land somewhere we can go to," they said. "Where is the new Fourth World that Sótuknang has created for us?" They sent many kinds of birds, one after another, to fly over the waters and find it. But they all came back tired out without having seen any sign of land. Next they planted a reed that grew high into the sky. Up it they climbed and stared over the surface of the waters. But they saw no sign of land.

Then Sótuknang appeared to Spider Woman and said, "You must continue traveling on. Your inner wisdom will guide you. The door at the top of your head is open."

---

22. *hurúsuki,* (hù rù sù kē).

So Spider Woman directed the people to make round, flat boats of the hollow reeds they had come in and to crawl inside. Again they entrusted themselves to the water and the inner wisdom to guide them. For a long time they drifted with the wind and the movement of the waters and came to another rocky island.

"It is bigger than the other one, but it is not big enough," they said, looking around them and thinking they heard a low rumbling noise.

"No. It is not big enough," said Spider Woman.

So the people kept traveling toward the rising sun in their reed boats. After awhile they said, "There is that low rumbling noise we heard. We must be coming to land again."

So it was. A big land, it seemed, with grass and trees and flowers beautiful to their weary eyes. On it they rested a long time. Some of the people wanted to stay, but Spider Woman said, "No. It is not the place. You must continue on."

Leaving their boats, they traveled by foot eastward across the island to the water's edge. Here they found growing some more of the hollow plants like reeds or bamboo, which they cut down. Directed by Spider Woman, they laid some of these in a row with another row on top of them in the opposite direction and tied them all together with vines and leaves. This made a raft big enough for one family or more. When enough rafts were made for all, Spider Woman directed them to make paddles.

"You will be going uphill from now on and you will have to make your own way. So Sótuknang told you: The farther you go, the harder it gets."

After long and weary traveling, still east and a little north, the people began to hear the low rumbling noise and saw land. One family and clan after another landed with joy. The land was long, wide, and beautiful. The earth was rich and flat, covered with trees and plants, seed-bearers and nut-bearers, providing lots of food. The people were happy and kept staying there year after year.

"No. This is not the Fourth World," Spider Woman kept telling them. "It is too easy and pleasant for you to live on, and you would soon fall into evil ways again. You must go on. Have we not told you the way becomes harder and longer?"

Reluctantly the people traveled eastward by foot across the island to the far shore. Again they made rafts and paddles. When they were ready to set forth Spider Woman said, "Now I have done all I am commanded to do for you. You must go on alone and find your own place of Emergence. Just keep your doors open, and your spirits will guide you."

"Thank you, Spider Woman, for all you have done for us," they said sadly. "We will remember what you have said."

Alone they set out, traveling east and a little north, paddling hard day and night for many days as if they were paddling uphill.

At last they saw land. It rose high above the waters, stretching from north to south as far as they could see. A great land, a mighty land, their inner wisdom told them. "The Fourth World!" they cried to each other.

As they got closer, its shores rose higher and higher into a steep wall of mountains. There seemed no place to land. "Let us go north. There we will find our Place of Emergence," said some. So they went north, but the mountains rose higher and steeper.

"No! Let us go south! There we will find our Place of Emergence!" cried others. So they turned south and traveled many days more. But here too the mountain wall reared higher.

Not knowing what to do, the people stopped paddling, opened the doors on top of their heads, and let themselves be guided. Almost immediately the water smoothed out, and they felt their rafts caught up in a gentle current. Before long they landed and joyfully jumped out upon a sandy shore. "The Fourth World!" they cried. "We have reached our Place of Emergence at last!"

Soon all the others arrived and when they were gathered together Sótuknang appeared before them. "Well, I see you are all here. That is good. This is the place I have prepared for you. Look now at the way you have come."

Looking to the west and the south, the people could see sticking out of the water the islands upon which they had rested.

"They are the footprints of your journey," continued Sótuknang, "the tops of the high mountains of the Third World, which I destroyed. Now watch."

As the people watched them, the closest one sank under the water, then the next, until all were gone, and they could see only water.

"See," said Sótuknang, "I have washed away even the footprints of your Emergence; the stepping-stones which I left for you. Down on the bottom of the seas lie all the proud cities, the flying *pátuwvotas*, and the worldly treasures corrupted with evil, and those people who found no time to sing praises to the Creator from the tops of their hills. But the day will come, if you preserve the memory and the meaning of your Emergence, when these stepping-stones will emerge again to prove the truth you speak."

This at last was the end of the Third World, Kuskurza, an ancient name for which there is no modern meaning.

"I have something more to say before I leave you," Sótuknang told the people as they stood at their Place of Emergence on the shore of the present Fourth World. This is what he said:

"The name of this Fourth World is Túwaqachi, World Complete. You will find out why. It is not all beautiful and easy like the previous ones. It has height and depth, heat and cold, beauty and barrenness; it has everything for you to choose from. What you choose will determine if this time you can carry out the plan of Creation on it or whether it must in time be destroyed too. Now you will separate and go different ways to claim all the earth for the Creator. Each group of you will follow your own star until it stops. There you will settle. Now I must go. But you will have help from the proper deities, from your good spirits. Just keep your own doors open and always remember what I have told you. This is what I say."

Then he disappeared.

The people began to move slowly off the shore and into the land, when they heard the low rumbling noise again. Looking around, they saw a handsome man and asked, "Are you the one who has been making these noises we have heard?"

"Yes. I made them to help you find the way here. Do you not recognize me? My name is Másaw.[23] I am the caretaker, the guardian and protector of this land."

The people recognized Másaw. He had been appointed head caretaker of the Third World, but, becoming a little self-important, he had lost his humility before the Creator. Being a spirit, he could not die, so Taiowa took his appointment away from him and made him the deity of death and the underworld. This job Below was not as pleasant as the one Above. Then when the Third World was destroyed, Taiowa decided to give him another chance, as he had the people, and appointed him to guard and protect this Fourth World as its caretaker.

He was the first being the people had met here, and they were very respectful to him. "Will you give us your permission to live on this land?" they asked.

"Yes, I will give you my permission as owner of the land."

"Will you be our leader?" the people then asked.

"No," replied Másaw. "A greater one than I has given you a plan to fulfill first. When the previous parts of the world were pushed underneath the water, this new land was pushed up in the middle to become the backbone of the earth. You are now standing on its *átvila*.[24] But you have not yet made your migrations. You have not yet followed your stars to the place where you will meet and settle. This you must do before I can become your leader. But if you go back to evil ways again I will take over the earth from you, for I am its caretaker, guardian, and protector. To the north you will find cold and ice. That is the Back Door to this land, and those who may come through this Back Door will enter without my consent. So go now and claim the land with my permission."

When Másaw disappeared, the people divided into groups and clans to begin their migrations.

---

23. *Másaw*, (mä sow). 24. *átvila* (ät vē lä), westward slope.

"May we meet again!" they all called back to one another.

This is how it all began on this, our present Fourth World. As we know, its name is Túwaqachi, World Complete, its direction north, its color *sikyangpu,* yellowish white. Chiefs upon it are the tree *kneumapee,* juniper; the bird *mongwau,* the owl; the animal *tohopko,* the mountain lion; and the mixed mineral *sikyápala.*

Where all the people went on their migrations to the ends of the earth and back, and what they have done to carry out the plan of Creation from this Place of Beginning to the present time, is to be told next by all the clans as they come in.

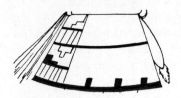

THE GREAT EXPLOSION

Robinson Jeffers

The universe expands and contracts like a great heart.
It is expanding, the farthest nebulae
Rush with the speed of light into empty space.
It will contract, the immense navies of stars and galaxies,
    dust-clouds and nebulae
5 Are recalled home, they crush against each other in one harbor, they
    stick in one lump
And then explode it, nothing can hold them down; there is no way
    to express that explosion; all that exists
Roars into flame, the tortured fragments rush away from each other
    into all the sky, new universes
Jewel the black breast of night; and far off the outer nebulae like
    charging spearmen again
Invade emptiness.
                No wonder we are so fascinated with fire-works
10 And our huge bombs: it is a kind of homesickness perhaps for the
    howling fire-blast that we were born from.

But the whole sum of the energies
That made and contained the giant atom survives. It will gather
    again and pile up, the power and the glory—
And no doubt it will burst again: diastole and systole:[1] the whole
    universe beats like a heart.
Peace in our time was never one of God's promises; but back and
    forth, die and live, burn and be damned,
15 The great heart beating, pumping into our arteries His
    terrible life.

1. *diastole and systole* (di as⁄tl ē and sis⁄tl ē), the rhythmic expansion and contraction of the chambers of the heart.

He is beautiful beyond belief.
And we, God's apes—or tragic children—share in the beauty. We see
    it above our torment, that's what life's for.
He is no God of love, no justice of a little city like Dante's
    Florence,[2] no anthropoid God
Making commandments: this is the God who does not care and will
    never cease. Look at the seas there
Flashing against this rock in the darkness—look at the tide-stream
    stars—and the fall of nations—and dawn
20 Wandering with wet white feet down the Carmel Valley[3] to meet the
    sea. These are real and we see their beauty.
The great explosion is probably only a metaphor—I know not—of
    faceless violence, the root of all things.

---

2. *Dante's Florence.* Dante Alighieri (dän′tä ä′lē gyer′ē) (1265–1321) was an Italian poet who wrote the *Divina Commedia,* an epic poem describing a journey through Hell, Purgatory, and Paradise. He was a native of Florence. **3.** *Carmel Valley,* the area in northern California where Jeffers lived.

HOW FLOWERS CHANGED THE WORLD

Loren Eiseley

IF IT HAD BEEN POSSIBLE to observe the Earth from the far side of the solar system over the long course of geological epochs, the watchers might have been able to discern a subtle change in the light emanating from our planet. That world of long ago would, like the red deserts of Mars, have reflected light from vast drifts of stone and gravel, the sands of wandering wastes, the blackness of naked basalt, the yellow dust of endlessly moving storms. Only the ceaseless marching of the clouds and the intermittent flashes from the restless surface of the sea would have told a different story, but still essentially a barren one. Then, as the millennia rolled away and age followed age, a new and greener light would, by degrees, have come to twinkle across those endless miles.

This is the only difference those far watchers, by the use of subtle instruments, might have perceived in the whole history of the planet Earth. Yet that slowly growing green twinkle would have contained the epic march of life from the tidal oozes upward across the raw and unclothed continents. Out of the vast chemical bath of the sea—not from the deeps, but from the element-rich, light-exposed platforms of the continental shelves[1]—wandering fingers of green had crept upward along the meanderings of river systems and fringed the gravels of forgotten lakes.

In those first ages plants clung of necessity to swamps and water-courses. Their reproductive processes demanded direct access to water. Beyond the primitive ferns and mosses that enclosed the

1. *continental shelves*, shallow portions of the sea bed that slope gradually out from the continents to a depth of about six hundred feet and end in an abrupt descent to deeper water.

borders of swamps and streams the rocks still lay vast and bare, the winds still swirled the dust of a naked planet. The grass cover that holds our world secure in place was still millions of years in the future. The green marchers had gained a soggy foothold upon the land, but that was all. They did not reproduce by seeds but by microscopic swimming sperm that had to wriggle their way through water to fertilize the female cell. Such plants in their higher forms had clever adaptations for the use of rain water in their sexual phases, and survived with increasing success in a wet land environment. They now seem part of man's normal environment. The truth is, however, that there is nothing very "normal" about nature. Once upon a time there were no flowers at all.

A little while ago—about one hundred million years, as the geologist estimates time in the history of our four-billion-year-old planet— flowers were not to be found anywhere on the five continents. Wherever one might have looked, from the poles to the equator, one would have seen only the cold dark monotonous green of a world whose plant life possessed no other color.

Somewhere, just a short time before the close of the Age of Reptiles, there occurred a soundless, violent explosion. It lasted millions of years, but it was an explosion, nevertheless. It marked the emergence of the angiosperms—the flowering plants. Even the great evolutionist, Charles Darwin,[2] called them "an abominable mystery," because they appeared so suddenly and spread so fast.

Flowers changed the face of the planet. Without them, the world we know—even man himself—would never have existed. Francis Thompson, the English poet, once wrote that one could not pluck a flower without troubling a star. Intuitively he had sensed like a naturalist the enormous interlinked complexity of life. Today we know that the appearance of the flowers contained also the equally mystifying emergence of man.

If we were to go back into the Age of Reptiles, its drowned swamps and birdless forests would reveal to us a warmer but, on the whole, a sleepier world than that of today. Here and there, it is true, the serpent heads of bottom-feeding dinosaurs might be upreared in suspicion of their huge flesh-eating compatriots. Tyrannosaurs, enormous bipedal caricatures of men, would stalk mindlessly across the sites of future cities and go their slow way down into the dark of geologic time.

In all that world of living things nothing saw save with the intense concentration of the hunt, nothing moved except with the grave sleepwalking intentness of the instinct-driven brain. Judged by modern standards, it was a world in slow motion, a cold-blooded world whose occupants were most active at noonday but torpid on chill

---

2. *Charles Darwin* (1809–1882), the English naturalist who formulated the theory of evolution through natural selection.

nights, their brains damped by a slower metabolism[3] than any known to even the most primitive of warm-blooded animals today.

A high metabolic rate and the maintenance of a constant body temperature are supreme achievements in the evolution of life. They enable an animal to escape, within broad limits, from the overheating or the chilling of its immediate surroundings, and at the same time to maintain a peak mental efficiency. Creatures without a high metabolic rate are slaves to weather. Insects in the first frosts of autumn all run down like little clocks. Yet if you pick one up and breathe warmly upon it, it will begin to move about once more.

In a sheltered spot such creatures may sleep away the winter, but they are hopelessly immobilized. Though a few warm-blooded mammals, such as the woodchuck of our day, have evolved a way of reducing their metabolic rate in order to undergo winter hibernation, it is a survival mechanism with drawbacks, for it leaves the animal helplessly exposed if enemies discover him during his period of suspended animation. Thus bear or woodchuck, big animal or small, must seek, in this time of descending sleep, a safe refuge in some hidden den or burrow. Hibernation is, therefore, primarily a winter refuge of small, easily concealed animals rather than of large ones.

A high metabolic rate, however, means a heavy intake of energy in order to sustain body warmth and efficiency. It is for this reason that even some of these later warm-blooded mammals existing in our day have learned to descend into a slower, unconscious rate of living during the winter months when food may be difficult to obtain. On a slightly higher plane they are following the procedure of the cold-blooded frog sleeping in the mud at the bottom of a frozen pond.

The agile brain of the warm-blooded birds and mammals demands a high oxygen consumption and food in concentrated forms, or the creatures cannot long sustain themselves. It was the rise of the flowering plants that provided that energy and changed the nature of the living world. Their appearance parallels in a quite surprising manner the rise of the birds and mammals.

Slowly, toward the dawn of the Age of Reptiles, something over two hundred and fifty million years ago, the little naked sperm cells wriggling their way through dew and raindrops had given way to a kind of pollen carried by the wind. Our present-day pine forests represent plants of a pollen-disseminating variety. Once fertilization was no longer dependent on exterior water, the march over drier regions could be extended. Instead of spores simple primitive seeds carrying some nourishment for the young plant had developed, but true flowers were still scores of millions of years away. After a long period of hesitant evolutionary groping, they exploded upon the world with truly revolutionary violence.

---

3. *metabolism* (mə tab′ə liz′əm), the physiological processes by which an organism maintains life.

The event occurred in Cretaceous[4] times in the close of the Age of Reptiles. Before the coming of the flowering plants our own ancestral stock, the warm-blooded mammals, consisted of a few mousy little creatures hidden in trees and underbrush. A few lizard-like birds with carnivorous teeth flapped awkwardly on ill-aimed flights among archaic shrubbery. None of these insignificant creatures gave evidence of any remarkable talents. The mammals in particular had been around for some millions of years, but had remained well lost in the shadow of the mighty reptiles. Truth to tell, man was still, like the genie in the bottle, encased in the body of a creature about the size of a rat.

As for the birds, their reptilian cousins the Pterodactyls,[5] flew farther and better. There was just one thing about the birds that paralleled the physiology of the mammals. They, too, had evolved warm blood and its accompanying temperature control. Nevertheless, if one had been seen stripped of his feathers, he would still have seemed a slightly uncanny and unsightly lizard.

Neither the birds nor the mammals, however, were quite what they seemed. They were waiting for the Age of Flowers. They were waiting for what flowers, and with them the true encased seed, would bring. Fish-eating, gigantic leather-winged reptiles, twenty-eight feet from wing tip to wing tip, hovered over the coasts that one day would be swarming with gulls.

Inland the montonous green of the pine and spruce forests with their primitive wooden cone flowers stretched everywhere. No grass hindered the fall of the naked seeds to earth. Great sequoias towered to the skies. The world of that time has a certain appeal but it is a giant's world, a world moving slowly like the reptiles who stalked magnificently among the boles of its trees.

The trees themselves are ancient, slow-growing and immense, like the redwood groves that have survived to our day on the California coast. All is stiff, formal, upright and green, monotonously green. There is no grass as yet; there are no wide plains rolling in the sun, no tiny daisies dotting the meadows underfoot. There is little versatility about this scene; it is, in truth, a giant's world.

A few nights ago it was brought home vividly to me that the world has changed since that far epoch. I was awakened out of sleep by an unknown sound in my living room. Not a small sound—not a creaking timber or a mouse's scurry—but a sharp, rending explosion as though an unwary foot had been put down upon a wine glass. I had come instantly out of sleep and lay tense, unbreathing. I listened for another step. There was none.

Unable to stand the suspense any longer, I turned on the light and passed from room to room glancing uneasily behind chairs and into closets. Nothing seemed disturbed, and I stood puzzled in the center of

4. *Cretaceous*, (kri tā/shəs). 5. *Pterodactyls*, (ter/ə dak/təlz).

the living room floor. Then a small button-shaped object upon the rug caught my eye. It was hard and polished and glistening. Scattered over the length of the room were several more shining up at me like wary little eyes. A pine cone that had been lying in a dish had been blown the length of the coffee table. The dish itself could hardly have been the source of the explosion. Beside it I found two ribbon-like strips of a velvety-green. I tried to place the two strips together to make a pod. They twisted resolutely away from each other and would no longer fit.

I relaxed in a chair, then, for I had reached a solution of the midnight disturbance. The twisted strips were wistaria pods that I had brought in a day or two previously and placed in the dish. They had chosen midnight to explode and distribute their multiplying fund of life down the length of the room. A plant, a fixed, rooted thing, immobilized in a single spot, had devised a way of propelling its offspring across open space. Immediately there passed before my eyes the million airy troopers of the milkweed pod and the clutching hooks of the sandburs. Seeds on the coyote's tail, seeds on the hunter's coat, thistledown mounting on the winds—all were somehow triumphing over life's limitations. Yet the ability to do this had not been with them at the beginning. It was the product of endless effort and experiment.

The seeds on my carpet were not going to lie stiffly where they had dropped like their antiquated cousins, the naked seeds on the pine-cone scales. They were travelers. Struck by the thought, I went out next day and collected several other varieties. I line them up now in a row on my desk—so many little capsules of life, winged, hooked or spiked. Every one is an angiosperm, a product of the true flowering plants. Contained in these little boxes is the secret of that far-off Cretaceous explosion of a hundred million years ago that changed the face of the planet. And somewhere in here, I think, as I poke seriously at one particularly resistant seedcase of a wild grass, was once man himself.

When the first simple flower bloomed on some raw upland late in the Dinosaur Age, it was wind pollinated, just like its early pine-cone relatives. It was a very inconspicuous flower because it had not yet evolved the idea of using the surer attraction of birds and insects to achieve the transportation of pollen. It sowed its own pollen and received the pollen of other flowers by the simple vagaries of the wind. Many plants in regions where insect life is scant still follow this principle today. Nevertheless, the true flower—and the seed that it produced—was a profound innovation in the world of life.

In a way, this event parallels, in the plant world, what happened among animals. Consider the relative chance for survival of the exteriorly deposited egg of a fish in contrast with the fertilized egg of a mammal, carefully retained for months in the mother's body until the young animal (or human being) is developed to a point where it may survive. The biological wastage is less—and so it is with the flowering plants. The primitive spore, a single cell fertilized in the beginning by a swimming sperm, did not promote rapid distribution, and the young plant, moreover, had to struggle up from nothing. No one had left it any food except what it could get by its own unaided efforts.

By contrast, the true flowering plants (angiosperm itself means "encased seed") grew a seed in the heart of a flower, a seed whose development was initiated by a fertilizing pollen grain independent of outside moisture. But the seed, unlike the developing spore, is already a fully equipped *embryonic plant* packed in a little enclosed box stuffed full of nutritious food. Moreover, by featherdown attachments, as in dandelion or milkweed seed, it can be wafted upward on gusts and ride the wind for miles; or with hooks it can cling to a bear's or a rabbit's hide; or like some of the berries, it can be covered with a juicy, attractive fruit to lure birds, pass undigested through their intestinal tracts and be voided miles away.

The ramifications of this biological invention were endless. Plants traveled as they had never traveled before. They got into strange environments heretofore never entered by the old spore plants or stiff pine-cone-seed plants. The well-fed, carefully cherished little embryos raised their heads everywhere. Many of the older plants with more primitive reproductive mechanisms began to fade away under this unequal contest. They contracted their range into secluded environments. Some, like the giant redwoods, lingered on as relics; many vanished entirely.

The world of the giants was a dying world. These fantastic little seeds skipping and hopping and flying about the woods and valleys brought with them an amazing adaptability. If our whole lives had not been spent in the midst of it, it would astound us. The old, stiff, sky-reaching wooden world had changed into something that glowed here and there with strange colors, put out queer, unheard-of fruits and little intricately carved seed cases, and, most important of all, produced concentrated foods in a way that the land had never seen before, or dreamed of back in the fish-eating, leaf-crunching days of the dinosaurs.

That food came from three sources, all produced by the reproductive system of the flowering plants. There were the tantalizing nectars and pollens intended to draw insects for pollenizing purposes, and which are responsible also for that wonderful jeweled creation, the humming-bird. There were the juicy and enticing fruits to attract larger animals, and in which tough-coated seeds were concealed, as in the tomato, for example. Then, as if this were not enough, there was the food in the actual seed itself, the food intended to nourish the embryo. All over the world, like hot corn in a popper, these incredible elaborations of the flowering plants kept exploding. In a movement that was almost instantaneous, geologically speaking, the angiosperms had taken over the world. Grass was beginning to cover the bare earth until, today, there are over six thousand species. All kinds of vines and bushes squirmed and writhed under new trees with flying seeds.

The explosion was having its effect on animal life also. Specialized groups of insects were arising to feed on the new sources of food and, incidentally and unknowingly, to pollinate the plant. The flowers bloomed and bloomed in ever larger and more spectacular varieties. Some were pale unearthly night flowers intended to lure moths in the evening twilight, some among the orchids even took the shape of female spiders in order to attract wandering males, some flamed redly in the light of noon or twinkled modestly in the meadow grasses. Intricate mechanisms splashed pollen on the breasts of hummingbirds, or stamped it on the bellies of black, grumbling bees droning assiduously from blossom to blossom. Honey ran, insects multiplied, and even the descendants of that toothed and ancient lizard-bird had become strangely altered. Equipped with prodding beaks instead of biting teeth they pecked the seeds and gobbled the insects that were really converted nectar.

Across the planet grasslands were now spreading. A slow continental upthrust which had been a part of the early Age of Flowers had cooled the world's climates. The stalking reptiles and the leather-winged black imps of the seashore cliffs had vanished. Only birds roamed the air now, hot-blooded and high-speed metabolic machines.

The mammals, too, had survived and were venturing into new domains, staring about perhaps a bit bewildered at their sudden eminence now that the thunder lizards were gone. Many of them, beginning as small browsers upon leaves in the forest, began to venture out upon this new sunlit world of the grass. Grass has a high silica content and demands a new type of very tough and resistant tooth enamel, but the seeds taken incidentally in the cropping of the grass are highly nutritious. A new world had opened out for the warm-blooded mammals. Great herbivores like the mammoths, horses and bisons appeared. Skulking about them had arisen savage flesh-feeding carnivores like the now extinct dire wolves and the saber-toothed tiger.

Flesh eaters though these creatures were, they were being sustained on nutritious grasses one step removed. Their fierce energy was being maintained on a high, effective level, through hot days and frosty nights, by the concentrated energy of the angiosperms. That energy, thirty per cent or more of the weight of the entire plant among some of the cereal grasses, was being accumulated and concentrated in the rich proteins and fats of the enormous game herds of the grasslands.

On the edge of the forest, a strange, old-fashioned animal still hesitated. His body was the body of a tree dweller, and though tough and knotty by human standards, he was, in terms of that world into which he gazed, a weakling. His teeth, though strong for chewing on the tough fruits of the forest, or for crunching an occasional unwary bird caught with his prehensile hands, were not the tearing sabers of the great cats. He had a passion for lifting himself up to see about, in his restless, roving curiosity. He would run a little stiffly and uncertainly, perhaps, on his hind legs, but only in those rare moments when he ventured out upon the ground. All this was the legacy of his climbing days; he had a hand with flexible fingers and no fine specialized hoofs upon which to gallop like the wind.

If he had any idea of competing in that new world, he had better forget it; teeth or hooves, he was much too late for either. He was a ne'er-do-well, an in-betweener. Nature had not done well by him. It was as if she had hesitated and never quite made up her mind. Perhaps as a consequence he had a malicious gleam in his eye, the gleam of an outcast who has been left nothing and knows he is going to have to take what he gets. One day a little band of these odd apes—for apes they were—shambled out upon the grass; the human story had begun.

Apes were to become men, in the inscrutable wisdom of nature, because flowers had produced seeds and fruits in such tremendous quantities that a new and totally different store of energy had become available in concentrated form. Impressive as the slow-moving, dim-brained dinosaurs had been, it is doubtful if their age had supported anything like the diversity of life that now rioted across the planet or flashed in and out among the trees. Down on the grass by a streamside, one of those apes with inquisitive fingers turned over a stone and hefted it vaguely. The group clucked together in a throaty tongue and moved off through the tall grass foraging for seeds and insects. The one still held, sniffed, and hefted the stone he had found. He liked the feel of it in his fingers. The attack on the animal world was about to begin.

If one could run the story of that first human group like a speeded-up motion picture through a million years of time, one might see the stone in the hand change to the flint ax and the torch. All that swarming grassland world with its giant bison and trumpeting mammoths would go down in ruin to feed the insatiable and growing numbers of a carnivore who, like the great cats before him, was taking his energy indirectly from the grass. Later he found fire and it altered the tough meats and drained their energy even faster into a stomach ill adapted for the ferocious turn man's habits had taken.

His limbs grew longer, he strode more purposefully over the grass. The stolen energy that would take man across the continents would fail him at last. The great Ice Age herds were destined to vanish. When they did so, another hand like the hand that grasped the stone by the river long ago would pluck a handful of grass seed and hold it contemplatively.

In that moment, the golden towers of man, his swarming millions, his turning wheels, the vast learning of his packed libraries, would glimmer dimly there in the ancestor of wheat, a few seeds held in a muddy hand. Without the gift of flowers and the infinite diversity of their fruits, man and bird, if they had continued to exist at all, would be today unrecognizable. Archaeopteryx,[6] the lizard-bird, might still be snapping at beetles on a sequoia limb; man might still be a nocturnal insectivore gnawing a roach in the dark. The weight of a petal has changed the face of the world and made it ours.

---

6. *Archaeopteryx,* (är⁄kē op⁄ter iks).

ENCOUNTER
AT DAWN

Arthur C. Clarke

Iᴛ ᴡᴀꜱ ɪɴ ᴛʜᴇ ʟᴀꜱᴛ ᴅᴀʏꜱ of the Empire. The tiny ship was far from home, and almost a hundred light-years from the great parent vessel searching through the loosely packed stars at the rim of the Milky Way. But even here it could not escape from the shadow that lay across civilization: beneath that shadow, pausing ever and again in their work to wonder how their distant homes were faring, the scientists of the Galactic Survey still labored at their never-ending task.

The ship held only three occupants, but between them they carried knowledge of many sciences, and the experience of half a lifetime in space. After the long interstellar night, the star ahead was warming their spirits as they dropped down toward its fires. A little more golden, a trifle more brilliant than the sun that now seemed a legend of their childhood. They knew from past experience that the chance of locating planets here was more than ninety percent, and for the moment they forgot all else in the excitement of discovery.

They found the first planet within minutes of coming to rest. It was a giant, of a familiar type, too cold for protoplasmic life and probably possessing no stable surface. So they turned their search sunward, and presently were rewarded.

It was a world that made their hearts ache for home, a world where everything was hauntingly familiar, yet never quite the same. Two great land masses floated in blue-green seas, capped by ice at either pole. There were some desert regions, but the larger part of the planet was obviously fertile. Even from this distance, the signs of vegetation were unmistakably clear. They gazed hungrily at the expanding landscape as they fell down into the atmosphere, heading toward noon in the subtropics. The ship plummeted through cloudless skies toward a great river, checked its fall with a surge of soundless power, and came to rest among the long grasses by the water's edge.

No one moved: there was nothing to be done until the automatic instruments had finished their work. Then a bell tinkled softly and the lights on the control board flashed in a pattern of meaningful chaos. Captain Altman rose to his feet with a sigh of relief.

"We're in luck," he said. "We can go outside without protection, if the pathogenic tests are satisfactory. What did you make of the place as we came in, Bertrond?"

"Geologically stable—no active volcanoes, at least. I didn't see any trace of cities, but that proves nothing. If there's a civilization here, it may have passed that stage."

"Or not reached it yet?"

Bertrond shrugged. "Either's just as likely. It may take us some time to find out on a planet this size."

"More time than we've got," said Clindar, glancing at the communications panel that linked them to the mother ship and thence to the Galaxy's threatened heart. For a moment there was a gloomy silence. Then Clindar walked to the control board and pressed a pattern of keys with automatic skill.

With a slight jar, a section of the hull slid aside and the fourth member of the crew stepped out onto the new planet, flexing metal limbs and adjusting servo motors to the unaccustomed gravity. Inside the ship, a television screen glimmered into life, revealing a long vista of waving grasses, some trees in the middle distance, and a glimpse of the great river. Clindar punched a button, and the picture flowed steadily across the screen as the robot turned its head.

"Which way shall we go?" Clindar asked.

"Let's have a look at those trees," Altman replied. "If there's any animal life we'll find it there."

"Look!" cried Bertrond. "A bird!"

Clindar's fingers flew over the keyboard: the picture centered on the tiny speck that had suddenly appeared on the left of the screen, and expanded rapidly as the robot's telephoto lens came into action.

"You're right," he said. "Feathers—beak—well up the evolutionary ladder. This place looks promising. I'll start the camera."

The swaying motion of the picture as the robot walked forward did not distract them: they had grown accustomed to it long ago. But they had never become reconciled to this exploration by proxy when all their impulses cried out to them to leave the ship, to run through the grass, and to feel the wind blowing against their faces. Yet it was too great a risk to take, even on a world that seemed as fair as this. There was always a skull hidden behind Nature's most smiling face. Wild beasts, poisonous reptiles, quagmires—death could come to the unwary explorer in a thousand disguises. And worst of all were the invisible enemies, the bacteria and viruses against which the only defense might often be a thousand light-years away.

A robot could laugh at all these dangers and even if, as sometimes happened, it encountered a beast powerful enough to destroy it—well, machines could always be replaced.

They met nothing on the walk across the grasslands. If any small animals were disturbed by the robot's passage, they kept outside its field of vision. Clindar slowed the machine as it approached the trees, and the watchers in the spaceship flinched involuntarily at the branches that appeared to slash across their eyes. The picture dimmed for a moment before the controls readjusted themselves to the weaker illumination; then it came back to normal. The forest was full of life. It lurked in the undergrowth, clambered among the branches, flew through the air. It fled chattering and gibbering through the trees as the robot advanced. And all the while the automatic cameras were recording the pictures that formed on the screen, gathering material for the biologists to analyze when the ship returned to base.

Clindar breathed a sigh of relief when the trees suddenly thinned. It was exhausting work, keeping the robot from smashing into obstacles as it moved through the forest, but on open ground it could take care of itself. Then the picture trembled as if beneath a hammer blow, there was a grinding metallic thud, and the whole scene swept vertiginously upward as the robot toppled and fell.

"What's that?" cried Altman. "Did you trip?"

"No," said Clindar grimly, his fingers flying over the keyboard. "Something attacked from the rear. I hope . . . ah . . . I've still got control."

He brought the robot to a sitting position and swiveled its head. It did not take long to find the cause of the trouble. Standing a few feet away, and lashing its tail angrily, was a large quadruped with a most ferocious set of teeth. At the moment it was, fairly obviously, trying to decide whether to attack again. Slowly, the robot rose to its feet, and as it did so the great beast crouched to spring. A smile flitted across Clindar's face: he knew how to deal with this situation. His thumb felt for the seldom-used key labeled "Siren." The forest echoed with a hideous undulating scream from the robot's concealed speaker, and the machine advanced to meet its adversary, arms flailing in front of it. The startled beast almost fell over backward in its effort to turn, and in seconds he was gone from sight.

"Now I suppose we'll have to wait a couple of hours until everything comes out of hiding again," said Bertrond ruefully.

"I don't know much about animal psychology," interjected Altman, "but is it usual for them to attack something completely unfamiliar?"

"Some will attack anything that moves, but that's unusual. Normally they attack only for food, or if they've already been threatened. What are you driving at? Do you suggest that there are other robots on this planet?"

"Certainly not. But our carnivorous friend may have mistaken our machine for a more edible biped. Don't you think that this opening in the jungle is rather unnatural? It could easily be a path."

"In that case," said Clindar promptly, "we'll follow it and find out. I'm tired of dodging trees, but I hope nothing jumps on us again: it's bad for my nerves."

"You were right, Altman," said Bertrond a little later. "It's certainly a path. But that doesn't mean intelligence. After all, animals—"

He stopped in midsentence, and at the same instant Clindar brought the advancing robot to a halt. The path had suddenly opened out into a wide clearing, almost completely occupied by a village of flimsy huts. It was ringed by a wooden palisade, obviously defense against an enemy who at the moment presented no threat. For the gates were wide open, and beyond them the inhabitants were going peacefully about their ways. For many minutes the three explorers stared in silence at the screen. Then Clindar shivered a little and remarked: "It's uncanny. It might be our own planet, a hundred thousand years ago. I feel as if I've gone back in time."

"There's nothing weird about it," said the practical Altman. "After all, we've discovered nearly a hundred planets with our type of life on them."

"Yes," retorted Clindar. "A hundred in the whole Galaxy! I still think it's strange it had to happen to us."

"Well, it had to happen to *somebody,*" said Bertrond philosophically. "Meanwhile, we must work out our contact procedure. If we send the robot into the village it will start a panic."

"That," said Altman, "is a masterly understatement. What we'll have to do is catch a native by himself and prove that we're friendly. Hide the robot, Clindar. Somewhere in the woods where it can watch the village without being spotted. We've a week's practical anthropology ahead of us!"

It was three days before the biological tests showed that it would be safe to leave the ship. Even then Bertrond insisted on going alone— alone, that is, if one ignored the substantial company of the robot. With such an ally he was not afraid of this planet's larger beasts, and his body's natural defenses could take care of the microorganisms. So, at least, the analyzers had assured him; and considering the complexity of the problem, they made remarkably few mistakes . . . .

He stayed outside for an hour, enjoying himself cautiously, while his companions watched with envy. It would be another three days before they could be quite certain that it was safe to follow Bertrond's example. Meanwhile, they kept busy enough watching the village through the lenses of the robot, and recording everything they could with the cameras. They had moved the spaceship at night so that it was hidden in the depths of the forest, for they did not wish to be discovered until they were ready.

And all the while the news from home grew worse. Though their remoteness here at the edge of the Universe deadened its impact, it lay heavily on their minds and sometimes overwhelmed them with a sense of futility. At any moment, they knew, the signal for recall might come as the Empire summoned up its last resources in its extremity. But until then they would continue their work as though pure knowledge were the only thing that mattered.

Seven days after landing, they were ready to make the experiment. They knew now what paths the villagers used when going hunting, and Bertrond chose one of the less frequented ways. Then he placed a chair firmly in the middle of the path and settled down to read a book.

It was not, of course, quite as simple as that: Bertrond had taken all imaginable precautions. Hidden in the undergrowth fifty yards away, the robot was watching through its telescopic lenses, and in its hand it held a small but deadly weapon. Controlling it from the spaceship, his fingers poised over the keyboard, Clindar waited to do what might be necessary. That was the negative side of the plan: The positive side was more obvious. Lying at Bertrond's feet was the carcass of a small, horned animal which he hoped would be an acceptable gift to any hunter passing this way.

Two hours later the radio in his suit harness whispered a warning. Quite calmly, though the blood was pounding in his veins, Bertrond laid aside his book and looked down the trail. The savage was walking forward confidently enough, swinging a spear in his right hand. He paused for a moment when he saw Bertrond, then advanced more cautiously. He could tell that there was nothing to fear, for the stranger was slightly built and obviously unarmed. When only twenty feet separated them, Bertrond gave a reassuring smile and rose slowly to his feet. He bent down, picked up the carcass, and carried it forward as an offering. The gesture would have been understood by any creature on any world, and it was understood here. The savage reached forward, took the animal, and threw it effortlessly over his shoulder. For an instant he stared into Bertrond's eyes with a fathomless expression; then he turned and walked back toward the village. Three times he glanced round to see if Bertrond was following, and each time Bertrond smiled and waved reassurance. The whole episode lasted little more than a minute. As the first contact between two races it was completely without drama, though not without dignity. Bertrond did not move until the other had vanished from sight. Then he relaxed and spoke into his suit microphone.

"That was a pretty good beginning," he said jubilantly. "He wasn't in the least frightened, or even suspicious. I think he'll be back."

"It still seems too good to be true," said Altman's voice in his ear. "I should have thought he'd have been either scared or hostile. Would *you* have accepted a lavish gift from a peculiar stranger with such little fuss?"

Bertrond was slowly walking back to the ship. The robot had now come out of cover and was keeping guard a few paces behind him.

"*I* wouldn't," he replied, "but I belong to a civilized community. Complete savages may react to strangers in many different ways, according to their past experience. Suppose this tribe has never had any enemies. That's quite possible on a large but sparsely populated planet. Then we may expect curiosity, but no fear at all."

"If these people have no enemies," put in Clindar, no longer fully occupied in controlling the robot, "why have they got a stockade round the village?"

"I meant no *human* enemies," replied Bertrond. "If that's true, it simplifies our task immensely."

"Do you think he'll come back?"

"Of course. If he's as human as I think, curiosity and greed will make him return. In a couple of days we'll be bosom friends."

Looked at dispassionately, it became a fantastic routine. Every morning the robot would go hunting under Clindar's direction, until it was now the deadliest killer in the jungle. Then Bertrond would wait until Yaan—which was the nearest they could get to his name—came striding confidently along the path. He came at the same time every day, and he always came alone. They wondered about this: did he wish to keep his great discovery to himself and thus get all the credit for his hunting prowess? If so, it showed unexpected foresight and cunning.

At first Yaan had departed at once with his prize, as if afraid that the donor of such a generous gift might change his mind. Soon, however, as Bertrond had hoped, he could be induced to stay for a while by simple conjuring tricks and a display of brightly colored fabrics and crystals, in which he took a childlike delight. At last Bertrond was able to engage him in lengthy conversations, all of which were recorded as well as being filmed through the eyes of the hidden robot.

One day the philologists might be able to analyze this material; the best that Bertrond could do was to discover the meanings of a few simple verbs and nouns. This was made more difficult by the fact that Yaan not only used different words for the same thing, but sometimes the same word for different things.

Between these daily interviews, the ship traveled far, surveying the planet from the air and sometimes landing for more detailed examinations. Although several other human settlements were observed, Bertrond made no attempt to get in touch with them, for it was easy to see that they were all at much the same cultural level as Yaan's people.

It was, Bertrond often thought, a particularly bad joke on the part of Fate that one of the Galaxy's very few truly human races should have been discovered at this moment of time. Not long ago this would have been an event of supreme importance; now civilization was too hard-pressed to concern itself with these savage cousins waiting at the dawn of history. Not until Bertrond was sure he had become part of Yaan's everyday life did he introduce him to the robot. He was showing Yaan the patterns in a kaleidoscope when Clindar brought the machine striding through the grass with its latest victim dangling across one metal arm. For the first time Yaan showed something akin to fear; but he relaxed at Bertrond's soothing words, though he continued to watch the advancing monster. It halted some distance away, and Bertrond walked forward to meet it. As he did so, the robot raised its arms and handed him the dead beast. He took it solemnly and carried it back to Yaan, staggering a little under the unaccustomed load.

Bertrond would have given a great deal to know just what Yaan was thinking as he accepted the gift. Was he trying to decide whether the robot was master or slave? Perhaps such conceptions as this were beyond his grasp: to him the robot might be merely another man, a hunter who was a friend of Bertrond. Clindar's voice, slightly larger than life, came from the robot's speaker.

"It's astonishing how calmly he accepts us. Won't anything scare him?"

"You will keep judging him by your own standards," replied Bertrond. "Remember, his psychology is completely different, and much simpler. Now that he has confidence in me, anything that I accept won't worry him."

"I wonder if that will be true of all his race?" queried Altman. "It's hardly safe to judge by a single specimen. I want to see what happens when we send the robot into the village."

"Hello!" exclaimed Bertrond. "*That* surprised him. He's never met a person who could speak with two voices before."

"Do you think he'll guess the truth when he meets us?" said Clindar.

"No. The robot will be pure magic to him—but it won't be any more wonderful than fire and lightning and all the other forces he must already take for granted."

"Well, what's the next move?" asked Altman, a little impatiently. "Are you going to bring him to the ship, or will you go into the village first?"

Bertrond hesitated. "I'm anxious not to do too much too quickly. You know the accidents that have happened with strange races when that's been tried. I'll let him think this over, and when we get back tomorrow I'll try to persuade him to take the robot back to the village."

In the hidden ship, Clindar reactivated the robot and started it moving again. Like Altman, he was growing a little impatient of this excessive caution, but on all matters relating to alien life forms Bertrond was the expert, and they had to obey his orders.

There were times now when he almost wished he were a robot himself, devoid of feelings or emotions, able to watch the fall of a leaf or the death agonies of a world with equal detachment. . . .

The sun was low when Yaan heard the great voice crying from the jungle. He recognized it at once, despite its inhuman volume: it was the voice of his friend, and it was calling him.

In the echoing silence, the life of the village came to a stop. Even the children ceased their play: the only sound was the thin cry of a baby frightened by the sudden silence. All eyes were upon Yaan as he walked swiftly to his hut and grasped the spear that lay beside the entrance. The stockade would soon be closed against the prowlers of the night, but he did not hesitate as he stepped out into the lengthening shadows. He was passing through the gates when once again that mighty voice summoned him, and now it held a note of urgency that came clearly across all the barriers of language and culture. The shining giant who spoke with many voices met him a little way from the village and beckoned him to follow. There was no sign of Bertrond. They walked for almost a mile before they saw him in the distance, standing not far from the river's edge and staring out across the dark, slowly moving waters. He turned as Yaan approached, yet for a moment seemed unaware of his presence. Then he gave a gesture of dismissal to the shining one, who withdrew into the distance.

Yaan waited. He was patient and, though he could never have expressed it in words, contented. When he was with Bertrond he felt the first intimations of that selfless, utterly irrational devotion his race would not fully achieve for many ages.

It was a strange tableau. Here at the river's brink two men were standing. One was dressed in a closely-fitting uniform equipped with tiny, intricate mechanisms. The other was wearing the skin of an animal and was carrying a flint-tipped spear. Ten thousand generations lay between them, ten thousand generations and an immeasurable gulf of space. Yet they were both human. As she must do often in eternity, Nature had repeated one of her basic patterns.

Presently Bertrond began to speak, walking to and fro in short, quick steps as he did, and in his voice there was a trace of madness.

"It's all over, Yaan. I'd hoped that with our knowledge we could have brought you out of barbarism in a dozen generations, but now you will have to fight your way up from the jungle alone, and it may take you a million years to do so. I'm sorry—there's so much we could have done. Even now I wanted to stay here, but Altman and Clindar talk of duty, and I suppose that they are right. There is little enough that we can do, but our world is calling and we must not forsake it.

"I wish you could understand me, Yaan. I wish you knew what I was saying. I'm leaving you these tools: some of them you will discover how to use, though as likely as not in a generation they'll be lost or forgotten. See how this blade cuts: it will be ages before your world can make its like. And guard this well: when you press the button— look! If you use it sparingly, it will give you light for years, though sooner or later it will die. As for these other things—find what use for them you can.

"Here come the first stars, up there in the east. Do you ever look at the stars, Yaan? I wonder how long it will be before you have discovered what they are, and I wonder what will have happened to us by then. Those stars are our homes, Yaan, and we cannot save them. Many have died already, in explosions so vast that I can imagine them no more than you. In a hundred thousand of your years, the light of those funeral pyres will reach your world and set its peoples wondering. By then, perhaps, your race will be reaching for the stars. I wish I could warn you against the mistakes we made, and which now will cost us all that we have won.

"It is well for your people, Yaan, that your world is here at the frontier of the Universe. You may escape the doom that waits for us. One day, perhaps, your ships will go searching among the stars as we have done, and they may come upon the ruins of our worlds and wonder who we were. But they will never know that we met here by this river when your race was young.

"Here come my friends; they would give me no more time. Good-by, Yaan—use well the things I have left you. They are your world's greatest treasures."

Something huge, something that glittered in the starlight, was sliding down from the sky. It did not reach the ground, but came to rest a little way above the surface, and in utter silence a rectangle of light opened in its side. The shining giant appeared out of the night and stepped through the golden door. Bertrond followed, pausing for a moment at the threshold to wave back at Yaan. Then the darkness closed behind him. No more swiftly than smoke drifts upward from a fire, the ship lifted away. When it was so small that Yaan felt he could hold it in his hands, it seemed to blur into a long line of light slanting upward into the stars. From the empty sky a peal of thunder echoed over the sleeping land; and Yaan knew at last that the gods were gone and would never come again.

For a long time he stood by the gently moving waters, and into his soul there came a sense of loss he was never to forget and never to understand. Then, carefully and reverently, he collected together the gifts that Bertrond had left.

Under the stars, the lonely figure walked homeward across a nameless land. Behind him the river flowed softly to the sea, winding through the fertile plains on which, more than a thousand centuries ahead, Yaan's descendants would build the great city they were to call Babylon.[1]

---

1. *Babylon* (bab′ə lən), an ancient city located on the Euphrates River in southwestern Asia.

3

MISCHIEF
AND
INVENTION

ESHU

Judith Gleason

Eshu (e′shü) is one of the Orisha (ō rē′shä), the gods of the Yoruba people of western Nigeria. Eshu is a trickster (see note page 160) and possesses the peculiar double nature common to such figures, being looked upon both as a protective, benevolent spirit, as well as a mischievous, malicious one, with a propensity to do evil that may hopefully be directed against enemies.

THERE WERE TWO FRIENDS who loved each other like yam porridge and pepper soup. Whenever they went out, they wore identical cloths. Their farm plots, thanks to the chief's respect for their friendship, were adjoining. The path to and from the village was all that divided them as they worked, and all day long they called across courteous greetings:

"Good-day my very special friend, I hope the sun is not beating too hard upon your shoulders."

"Not at all, my dear age-mate; I salute you for working so steadily in the heat."

"May your soil yield even finer crops than mine."

"My compliments upon your new wife; may she bring forth sons to commend your industry."

"Salutations on the coming cool of the evening."

"May the sun not deceive you into lingering too late in the field."

And so on, as weaver bird converses with weaver bird, these friends continued to embroider their amity.

Until one day an old man walked down the path between them. It was Eshu. He was wearing a pointed cap, black on one side and red on the other. He held his pipe to the nape of his neck and slung his stick over his shoulder so that it dangled down his back instead of over his chest as he usually carried it. The two friends answered his greeting, then went on with their work and thought no more about him until, late in the afternoon as they prepared to go home, one of them said, "I wonder what business that old man had in our village?"

"Whatever it was, he must have completed it quickly," said the other.

"How do you know?"

"Because he left before noon, don't you remember? Long before our wives brought out our dinners."

"True, he passed by midmorning," said the other, "but he was heading into the village, not out of it."

"Nonsense," said his friend, "he was going in the opposite direction, up country, not towards the village as you said. Perhaps you've confused him with another. This traveler was an old, old man with a stick slung over his shoulder. You know, the one who used to wear a black cap."

"Don't take that tone with me. I know precisely who he is, and today he looked exactly the same and, as always, his face was following his pipe bowl into our village."

"You looked at his pipe, but I saw his feet. For all we know, he may have been puffing through a hole in the back of his neck; but this much is clear: That old man in his brand new red hat was leaving our village farther and farther behind him."

"How absurd to talk about backwards pipe-smoking. You're just trying to throw me off the track."

"Not at all. There are infinite possibilities in this world, which only a clod like you would fail to consider. For example, it's perfectly possible, although unlikely, that the sun won't set this evening. What I saw I saw, without error, and you, too stubborn to admit your lack of observation, your lack of imagination, retaliate by accusing me of playing with the facts just to get a wedge under your bulk. Why shouldn't a man buy a hat of a different color? And why shouldn't he invent a new way of smoking? I've half a mind to cut a hole in the back of my neck just to show you it can be done."

"And stop the sun, I suppose. I've always thought you a little mad, and now I'm convinced of it. Some witch is eating you. You ought to go to a doctor—"

"So that's it! I don't care what you think. You're impossible. I can't imagine why I ever found you good company. Your stupid face revolts me. I can't stop myself," he said, hitting his friend over the head with his hoe.

"So you admit you're mad, mad enough to pick a fight with me. Well I accept the challenge. Crazy or not, there's but one way to deal with unreasonable aggressors." And with that he threw his one-time friend flat on his back.

"Crude, evil-tempered man," said the other, "flat-footed rhinoceros, illegitimate offspring of a mortar and pestle. Begone. I don't care how late it is. I wouldn't walk home at midnight with you. Our friendship is finished. Dead. No words will ever pass between us again."

When the chief heard of the astonishing quarrel between these two whose loyalty he had always supposed more durable than that of other men, he sighed deeply and went off to perform a sacrifice to Eshu. The next time village council met, he reallocated the land so that henceforth the former friends would work at opposite corners of the communal tract. Then, holding up an old hoe for all to see, he said, mysteriously, "The sacrifice that iron refused to make is what's eating him."

HOW KWAKU ANANSE WON A KINGDOM WITH A GRAIN OF CORN

Peggy Appiah

Ananse the Spider is the hero of countless tales among the peoples of West Africa. It is the Ashanti people of Ghana who call him Kwaku Ananse (kwä′ kü än än′ sē). He is Gizo to the Hausa people of Nigeria. The slave trade brought West Africans to the New World and the Anansesem, the "spider stories," came with them (see selection page 225), Ananse becoming Aunt Nancy in the Gullah dialect of English spoken in the Sea Islands of Georgia and South Carolina.

NYAME[1] THE SKY GOD, tired of watching the stupidity of his creatures, decided one day to find out which was the wisest amongst them. Sending out his messengers he issued a challenge to all the creatures of the world, saying that he would give more wisdom and honor to the one who proved himself the wisest.

The people heard the messengers in silence for they were afraid to make such a bold claim, afraid of the wrath of God should they try and fail.

"How can we accept such a challenge from the Great God?" they said.

"Surely the task would be too hard. Surely if we fail we will be punished. Better far to keep silent and let others claim the reward."

Thus it was that instead of a crowd of different creatures claiming Nyame's reward, only Kwaku Ananse the spider came to answer his challenge.

From ANANSE THE SPIDER: TALES FROM AN ASHANTI VILLAGE, by Peggy Appiah. Copyright © 1966 by Peggy Appiah. Reprinted by permission of Pantheon Books, a Division of Random House, Inc. and David Higham Associates, Ltd.
1. *Nyame,* (ən yä′mē).

"O Great God of the skies!" said Ananse, "I come to accept your challenge. For long I have been accepted by the animals as the cleverest of them all. Now I would like to prove it to you, too."

The Great God, looking down at Ananse, wondered that such a small creature should accept his challenge. Calling together his messengers and before the assembled people of his Kingdom, he declared: "Ananse the spider has accepted my challenge. But let me warn you, Kwaku Ananse, before all these witnesses, that if indeed you accept my challenge, accept also my warning. If you fail in your task such calamities will fall upon you and your family that you will wish a hundred times you had never made so bold a claim."

Ananse, unafraid, bowed low. "I accept the challenge, O Nyame, and will take the consequences."

So Nyame the Sky God gave to Kwaku Ananse the spider one grain of corn, saying to him: "With this one grain of corn you are to bring before me all the people—men, women and children—of the Kingdom beyond the Great River."

Taking the corn, Ananse bowed again before his God, and returned to his family. His family had heard of his bold claim and of the warning of Nyame and were weeping bitterly at his foolishness. His wife and children chided him for accepting a task that would surely bring nothing but suffering upon them.

The behavior of his family annoyed Ananse, so sure was he of his success. He went whistling around the house as he hurriedly collected the necessities for his journey. Then he waved goodbye to family and friends and set out on his journey to the Kingdom Beyond the River.

As the evening of the first day drew to a close and the fireflies began to flutter around him in the forest, Kwaku Ananse drew near to a big village. From inside the compounds smells of cooking came to him on the evening breeze.

Stopping a group of children at play in the street, Ananse, drawing himself up, said to them: "Do you know who I am? I am the great Kwaku Ananse, messenger of God. I am going on a journey to beyond the Great River to do God's business. Show me the house of the Chief as I would stay with him this night."

So the children took Ananse to the house of the Chief and reported what he had said. The Chief welcomed him warmly, for he was honored by a visit from God's messenger.

"Quick," he called to his wives. "Get together the best food in the palace and cook a meal fit for God's messenger." And the wives hurried to do his bidding.

"Quick," he called to his servants. "Prepare the best room and get water for the bath for we have an honored guest." And the servants hurried to do his bidding.

When Ananse had bathed and eaten he joined the Chief and his elders in the courtyard. They talked long into the night and Kwaku Ananse, being a wonderful storyteller, charmed them all by his tales and his talk.

At last yawning, Ananse turned to the Chief.

"Nana,"[2] he said, "the time is late and I have a long journey tomorrow. I beg you to let me go and sleep."

"Of course, of course," said the Chief, who rose to accompany Ananse to his room.

When they reached his room, Kwaku Ananse went in and soon returned holding something in his hand.

"Oh, by the way, Nana, God has entrusted me with this very special grain of corn, so special that he has asked me to guard it with my life; but this corn is peculiar, it will not sleep with man, it will not sleep in a granary, nor will it sleep in a room by itself. It must sleep with chickens. I suppose, Nana, that you have chickens?"

"Of course I have chickens," said the Chief. "Give me, I pray you, the grain of corn and I will take it myself and put it with the chickens for the night, and you shall have it in the morning."

So the Chief took the grain of corn and put it carefully into the hut with his chickens, and they all settled for the night.

In the morning, Ananse got up early, bathed, and ate an excellent breakfast. Then he went over to greet the Chief and thanked him for his hospitality. "Nana, I must be on my way, on God's journey, but before I go give me the grain of corn, I beg you."

So the Chief went to the chickens' house to look for the grain of corn; but alas he found it not. The chickens, waking early, had gobbled it up. He searched and searched in vain and at last, grey in the face and tearing his hair, he came to Ananse.

"Ananse, Kwaku Ananse, you must help me. What shall I do? Alas and alack, my chickens have eaten up God's grain of corn. I will give you anything you want, only protect me from the wrath of God. Take my chickens, take money, only help me, I pray you."

Ananse looked very serious and shook his head.

"This is indeed a disaster. I am afraid that God will be very angry. But I will do my best to help you since you have been so kind to me. Which of your chickens swallowed the grain of corn?"

"How can I tell?" replied the Chief.

Ananse went to the chickens' house and seeing one very fat hen he pointed her out to the Chief.

"I am sure, Nana, that it was that fat hen. Look how greedy she is. I know that it was she. Give her to me and as I go I will remove the grain of corn from her with my magic."

"Take them all," said the Chief.

"No," replied Ananse. "I will take just this one."

---

2. *Nana* (nä′nä), a term of respect.

So Ananse went on his way with the blessings of Chief and villagers, and with the fat hen tucked under his arm. All day Ananse walked, resting only for a few minutes so that the hen could peck around and drink from a forest stream. It was already dark when he heard the noise of drumming, and following the sound came to another large village. He stopped on the edge of a crowd and addressed an old woman: "Grandmother," he said. "Do you know me? I am the famous Kwaku Ananse, the messenger of God. Take me, I pray you, to your Chief, for I am tired and would rest the night in your village."

The old lady had indeed heard of Kwaku Ananse, and elbowing her way excitedly through the crowd told the Chief that the messenger of God was there.

Immediately the Chief left the drumming and dancing, and taking Ananse to his palace begged him to stay with him and do him the honor of attending the celebrations. He called in his wives to prepare a meal and shouted to his servants to get ready the bath and room; then he waited patiently till Kwaku Ananse had bathed and eaten, and took him out to watch the dancing. The drums played a special tune in his honor, and the assembled people cheered him.

It was a pleasant evening, and as the moon was high they sat late. At last Ananse, tired from his long walk, begged the Chief to let him go to rest. The Chief immediately stopped the drumming and accompanied him to his room to say good night.

Kwaku Ananse went into his room and came out again with his fat hen.

"Nana," he said. "Here is God's own chicken, who is traveling with me. She is a very friendly hen but has one peculiarity; she will not sleep with other hens. Indeed, she will not sleep with men. She will sleep only in one place and that is with sheep. I imagine that you, Nana, have many sheep, and I beg you to let her sleep with them."

The Chief willingly took the hen and put her gently down with his sheep for the night. Kwaku Ananse slept soundly.

In the morning, when he had bathed and eaten a good meal, Kwaku Ananse stood for a minute at the door of his room and breathed deeply of the early morning air; then humming a little tune as he went, he wandered over to greet the Chief.

"Good morning," he said. "Nana, this is indeed a beautiful village and I have enjoyed my stay. However, since I am on God's business, I must hurry on my way. Give me, I pray, God's chicken so that we can go."

The Chief went to the place where his sheep had spent the night and looked for the chicken. Alas and alack, in the night she had been trampled on by the sheep and lay dead on the ground. The Chief was terrified, and wringing his hands and crying out he ran to Kwaku Ananse.

"Kwaku Ananse, Kwaku Ananse, messenger of God! A terrible calamity has befallen us, come and look; my sheep have trodden on God's chicken and killed her. What are we to do, what are we to do? Protect me, I pray you, from the wrath of God and I will do anything you demand. Take my sheep, take money, only protect me."

Ananse looked very stern. "If you had not been so kind," he said, "I would do nothing for you. But you have entertained me royally and I must do something in return. Which of your sheep trod on God's chicken, do you think?"

"How can I tell?" said the Chief.

"I am sure it was that fat one with three black legs," said Kwaku Ananse, "Give it to me and I will persuade God to take it instead of the chicken."

"Take them all," said the Chief, "only protect me from the wrath of God."

But Ananse took just the one sheep, protesting that he did not want to rob the Chief. So he went on his way with the blessings of the Chief and people, leading the sheep through the forest.

The way seemed long that day, for the sheep often stopped to graze by the path and they were both troubled by flies. At dusk, however, they came to a banana plantation, and making their way through it and under some orange trees they came to a village on the banks of the Great River.

Stopping three fishermen he saw on their way home, Ananse asked: "Which is the house of the Chief? I am the great Kwaku Ananse, God's messenger, and this is God's favorite sheep. I have come to spend a night in your village that we may bless it with our presence."

One of the fishermen hurriedly dropped his fish, and running to the Chief's house told him of the arrival of Kwaku Ananse. Now the Chief was having a bath, but he called to his favorite nephew and sent him out to welcome Ananse and bring him to the palace. He dried himself quickly and was ready to greet Ananse when he arrived.

"Kwaku Ananse, messenger of God," he said warmly. "Long have I heard of your wisdom and courage, and I am indeed honored to have you as my guest. I welcome, too, God's favorite sheep and whilst he is here we will do all that we can to protect and care for him."

He called to his wives to hurry with the food.

He called to his servants to put fresh water on for the bath.

He called to his maidservants to prepare the room, and lastly he sent his daughters out to cut food for the sheep.

After they had eaten, the Chief took Ananse to the river bank, and because the moon was high and it was a beautiful night, they went out in the royal canoe and paddled gently down the river, listening to the sounds of the forest and hearing the animals come down to drink.

When they returned they drank together, and then Ananse yawned and the Chief said: "I fear that you are tired after your journey, Kwaku Ananse. Let me take you to your room that you may sleep and rest." So together they went to Ananse's room.

The sheep was standing outside and Ananse turned to the Chief: "This is a strange sheep, Nana. It is God's own favorite sheep. In every way it is like other sheep except that it cannot sleep with other sheep, it cannot sleep with goats, nor can it sleep with men, but only with cows. I hope that you have some cows, Nana, or I am afraid that we shall get no sleep tonight."

"Of course I have cows," said the Chief. "It is near here that the cattle cross on their way to the Kingdom beyond the Great River, and of each herd I am given one cow. I have some of the finest cattle in the country. Give me God's sheep, I pray, and I will put it in with my cattle for the night, then we can all sleep in peace." Kwaku Ananse slept soundly.

In the morning the fishermen, on their way to work, woke Ananse early, and he bathed and ate his breakfast. There was still a slight mist rising from the river as he went to greet the Chief. The Chief was not yet ready, so Ananse drew his cloth around him and watched the river flow by. At last the Chief joined him and after greeting one another they discussed how Ananse should cross the river and how long it would take to reach the capital of the Kingdom on the other side. Then at last Ananse asked the Chief for the sheep, and together they went to fetch it from amongst the cows.

Alas, in the night, frightened by noises from the forest, the cows had trampled on the sheep and it was dead. The Chief trembled with fear. Weeping, and on his knees, he begged Ananse to forgive him. Ananse feigned anger: "What have you done, O Chief? This was God's favorite sheep, and I trusted you with it. You have let your cows trample on it. How could you be so careless? Why did you not set someone to watch during the night? I fear that God will be so angry he will make the waters of the river flow over your village so that even the graves of your ancestors will be washed away."

"Help me, help me, I beg you, O great Kwaku Ananse. O messenger of God, come to my aid. It was an accident. Take all my cattle, take my wives and my children, only spare my people, I pray you."

Ananse pretended to be mollified and asked the Chief which of his cows had killed the sheep.

"How can I tell?" said the Chief.

"I am sure it was that fat one over there, the one with the great wide horns. She is stamping her feet and, see, there is wool on them. Give her to me and I will persuade God to take her instead of the sheep."

In vain the Chief begged Kwaku Ananse to take all the cows. Ananse took just the one. He went on his way with the blessings of Chief and people, who accompanied him to the river bank. There he embarked in a canoe, and with the cow swimming behind, a rope on her horns, he crossed to the other side.

Once on the further bank Kwaku Ananse waved to the Chief and villagers, and taking a stick he drove the cow before him along the path from the river.

Ananse had not gone very far when he heard before him the sound of wailing and crying. He came upon a funeral procession on its way to a graveyard.

"Who is it that has died?" he asked.

"A child," the people said. "A young boy, who was drowned in the river. He was an only child. There are his parents, see how they weep."

Kwaku Ananse pushed his way through the procession and addressed the weeping parents gently: "Good people, do not weep so bitterly, I pray. I am God's messenger, and I will take the boy and carry him to God's Kingdom. Then you can be sure of his happiness. Do not bury him in the graveyard, for God has sent me to look for just such a child. See this fat cow? I will give it to you so that you can feast in God's honor. Only give me the body of the child that I may take it to God."

The parents listened, amazed. Soon everyone was discussing the offer. They saw how fat the cow was, and they were poor people. They thought of the certainty that the child would be taken to God. They accepted the offer.

So Ananse tied the child on his back in the manner that women carry their babies. He took a cloth from one of the women to make sure the child was covered.

"Go quickly," cried the people. "Take the child quickly to God's Kingdom, that he may reach there in time." Kwaku Ananse hurried on his way. The people took the cow back to their village, and were soon feasting on it.

Ananse walked slowly with the burden on his back. It was hot and he did not want to reach the capital of the Kingdom before nightfall.

He approached the town as the women were returning from their farms with headloads of plantain, cassava,[3] and firewood for the evening meal. He stopped one young woman and asked her to take him to the great Chief: "For I am God's messenger, and I have come a great distance to visit him. See, I am bringing God's favorite son to stay with him for the night. The child sleeps, and I need a room for him."

The woman called to the others, and dropping their headloads they ran ahead into the town calling to the people that God's messenger had arrived with God's favorite son. Soon a large crowd collected and they

---

3. *plantain, cassava.* Plantain (plan′tən) is a tropical fruit of the same family as the banana. Its starchy fruit is cooked and eaten. Cassava (kə sä′və) is a tropical plant from whose root a nutritious starch is made.

accompanied Kwaku Ananse to the palace, keeping at a safe distance lest they disturb God's son.

The Chief and his elders, as soon as they received the news, hurried out to greet Kwaku Ananse personally. They all feared Nyame the Sky God, and felt it a great honor that he should send his messenger and his son to stay with them.

Hurriedly, the best guest rooms were swept. Fresh mats were put on the ground, and the Chief ordered that one of the best of his cloths should be put down for the sleeping child to lay upon.

Ananse laid the child carefully on the cloth, his face to the wall, and asked all the people to leave the room. "The child is tired," he said, "and must have absolute quiet."

Addressing the Chief he said sternly, "It is forbidden, Your Majesty, for people to disturb God's son. Tell all your people to keep away, and put a guard at the door so that no one shall enter. Let us leave him to sleep, and when I have bathed I will tell you of my journey."

"Will he not eat?" said the Chief.

"Not until morning," replied Kwaku Ananse solemnly.

Bathed, and refreshed by an excellent meal, Kwaku Ananse was led before the Chief and elders. He told them of his journey, of dangers he had encountered, and of his own bravery. So well did he talk that they never thought to question him, but only to ask more and more about his adventures on the way. Many were the tales he told, so it was late before they thought of sleep.

At last Kwaku Ananse finished his tales. "God," he told them, "wishes his son to see something of the world so he has asked me to take him around. Having heard much of the famed Kingdom beyond the Great River, O Chief, I have brought him to visit you. Tomorrow when he wakes you shall greet him as befits the son of Nyame the Sky God. It is late now, and in God's Kingdom he is used to sleeping with other children. On no account must he awake in the presence of adults. The children of God are many, and it is their custom to sleep together. Let me, therefore, see where your children sleep, O Chief, that I may see if it is suitable for him."

The Chief led Kwaku Ananse to a big hut. There, stretched out on many mats, lay his children. All but the oldest were asleep. Seeing an empty mat in the middle, Kwaku Ananse went to fetch God's son, making sure that the child was well covered in his cloth. He laid him gently on the mat, and he and the Chief crept out. Soon everyone in the palace slept. Only Kwaku Ananse lay awake and listened.

An hour or so later Kwaku Ananse heard voices coming from the children's hut and crept over to listen. The children were talking angrily: "It is the stranger," they grumbled. "He stinks and has no right to come and dirty the sleeping room of the Chief's children. He is old enough to know better or he should have stayed with his mother. Let us beat him and teach him a lesson."

Ananse heard the sound of fists and gave a sigh of relief. He returned to his own room and slept deeply.

In the morning Ananse got up late for he had overslept. There was no sound coming from the children's hut, and many of them were out taking their baths by the stream. He ate his breakfast, waited a bit, and then asked to be taken to the Chief.

The Chief greeted him warmly and immediately asked him how God's son had slept.

"Where is the boy?" he said. "We have prepared gifts for him and soon the official welcome will begin. Did he enjoy the special food we sent to him?"

"I have not seen God's son," said Ananse. "I was sure that he was with you for he is used to visiting me early. Where can he be as late as this? Send someone quickly to look for him, for I fear some harm may have befallen him."

"I expect he is with the other children," smiled the Chief. "Even God's son must play.

"Come, let us look into the sleeping hut, and I will send my servants to look by the stream."

The Chief went to his children's hut, and waiting a moment to get used to the dim light—for the sun was strong outside—he went over to the only sleeping form he could see. He saw it was indeed God's son, wrapped in his cloth. He gently touched the boy's shoulder, but there was no movement. He shook him a little, but still no sign of life. He began to get anxious and pulled back the cloth. Then he saw that the child's body was covered with marks as if it had been beaten. His heart almost stopped beating and he ran to the door and called to Ananse, who hurried to join him.

"There is something wrong," he said. "I beg you to wake the child, for I cannot do so. Look at the marks on his body—I fear he has been beaten."

Ananse tapped the shoulder of the boy three times. There was still no movement. Then he lifted the child and at once both could see that he was dead. The Chief swayed on his feet and stumbled to the door.

Ananse, grim and silent, stood before him. "This was God's favorite child," he said.

Then the Chief broke down altogether. He called to his children, and learning that they had beaten the child he wept bitterly. He called his elders to him and told them what had happened and begged them to kill him then and there that his kingdom might not suffer. He went down on his knees to Kwaku Ananse, great king that he was: "Kwaku Ananse, God's messenger, spare me. Tell me what I can do. How can I save my kingdom and my people? What must I do to turn away the wrath of God? Take my life, take all my possessions, only do not disgrace me before the people. I will make any sacrifice you require. Turn away, oh turn away the wrath of God."

Very sternly Ananse said: "When God hears of this you will face such calamities, such storms of thunder and lightning, such earth-quakes and plague as the country has never known. How can you think that your life can atone for that of God's favorite son? Only in one way can I help you. If you like I will appeal to God's pity. If all your people, your womenfolk and your children, the sick and the aged come with me before the face of God, then will I plead for you and do what I can. There is no choice. Do this or face destruction."

The Chief replied: "O Kwaku Ananse, messenger of God, if you can indeed do this then I will give you all my kingdom. My people shall be yours and my riches I will heap upon you. Only save us from the just wrath of Nyame."

The Chief called together all his people, even from the remotest villages. They came in their thousands, and when they were gathered together, young and old, women and children, the sick on stretchers of boughs, the blind and the dying, then Kwaku Ananse called to Nyame the Sky God. He called to him to witness that he had brought him all the people of the Kingdom Beyond the River, using just the one grain of corn that he had been given.

And Kwaku Ananse brought also the body of the child whom he had promised to take to Nyame. The Sky God had pity on him and breathed into his mouth so that he arose and returned rejoicing to his parents.

Nyame the Sky God kept his promise, as he always does. He gave to Kwaku Ananse the spider so much wisdom that all the people feared him. The Chief heaped upon him riches and gold, so glad was he to escape from the wrath of God.

So Kwaku Ananse returned rich and honored to his family. But he kept most of the riches to himself, as his family had failed to believe in him.

HOW RAVEN BROUGHT FIRE TO THE INDIANS

Cyrus Macmillan

MANY AGES AGO when the world was still young, Raven[1] and White Seagull lived near together in Canada, far in the north country on the shores of the Great Water in the west.[2] They were very good friends and they always worked in harmony and they had much food and many servants in common. White Seagull knew no guile: he was always very open and frank and honest in his dealings with others. But Raven was a sly fellow, and at times he was not lacking in treachery and deceit. But Seagull did not suspect him, and the two lived always on very friendly terms.

In these far-back times in the north country, all the world was dark and there was no light but that of the stars. Seagull owned all the daylight, but he was very stingy and he kept it always locked up in a box. He would give none of it to anyone else, and he never let it out of the box except when he needed a little of it to help himself when he went far away on his journeys.

After a time Raven grew envious of Seagull's possession, and he said, "It is not fair that Seagull should keep the daylight all to himself locked up in a box. It was meant for all the world and not for him alone, and it would be of great value to all of us if he would sometimes let a little of it out." So he went to Seagull and said, "Give me some of your daylight. You do not need it all and I can use some of it with advantage." But Seagull said, "No. I want it all for myself. What could you do with daylight, you with your coat as black as night?" and he would not give him any of it. So Raven made up his mind that he would have to get some daylight from Seagull by stealth.

"How Raven Brought Fire to the Indians" from CANADIAN WONDER TALES by Cyrus Macmillan. Reprinted by permission of The Bodley Head.

1. *Raven*, the principal trickster (see note page 160) in the mythologies of the Indian peoples of the Northwest, from British Columbia to Alaska. 2. *the Great Water in the west*, the Pacific Ocean.

Soon afterwards Raven gathered some prickly thorns and burdocks and scattered them on the ground between Seagull's house and the beach where the canoes were lying. Then he went to Seagull's window and cried loudly, "Our canoes are going adrift in the surf. Come quickly and help me to save them." Seagull sprang out of bed and ran half-asleep on his bare feet. But as he ran to the beach the thorns stuck in his bare flesh and he howled with pain. He crawled back to his house, saying, "My canoe may go adrift if it pleases. I cannot walk because of the splinters in my feet." Raven chuckled to himself and he moved away, pretending to go to the beach to draw up the canoes.

Then he went into Seagull's house. Seagull was still howling with pain; he was sitting crying on the side of his bed and he was trying to pull the thorns from his feet as best he could. "I will help you," said Raven, "for I have often done this before. I am a very good doctor." So he took an awl made from whalebone and he caught hold of Seagull's foot with the pretence of removing the thorns. But instead of taking them out he only pushed them in farther until poor Seagull howled louder than ever. And Raven said, "It is so dark I cannot see to pull these thorns from your feet. Give me some daylight and I will soon cure you. A doctor must always have a little light." So Seagull unlocked the box and lifted the cover just a little bit so that a faint gleam of light came out. "That is better," said Raven. But instead of picking out the thorns he pushed them in as he had done before, until Seagull howled and kicked in pain. "Why are you so stingy with your light?" snapped Raven. "Do you think I am an owl and that I can see well enough in the darkness to heal your feet? Open the box wide and I will soon make you well." So saying, he purposely fell heavily against Seagull and knocked the box on the floor. The cover flew open and daylight escaped and spread quickly over all the world.

Poor Seagull tried his best to lure it back again into the box, but his efforts proved fruitless, for it had gone forever. Raven said he was very sorry for the accident, but after he had taken all the thorns from Seagull's feet, he went home laughing to himself and well pleased because of the success of his trick.

Soon there was light in all the world. But Raven could not see very well, for the light was too bright and his eyes were not accustomed to it. He sat for a time looking towards the east, but he saw there nothing of interest. The next day he saw a bit farther, for he was now getting used to the new conditions. The third day he could see distinctly a line of hills far in the east, rising against the sky and covered with a blue mist. He looked long at the strange sight. Then he saw far away towards the hill a thin column of smoke lifting heavenwards. He had never seen smoke before, but he had often heard of it from travelers in strange places. "That must be the country of which I have been told," he said. "In that land dwell the people who alone possess Fire. We have searched for it for many ages and now I think we have found it." Then he thought, "We now have the daylight, and what a fine thing it would be if we could also have Fire!" And he determined to set out to find it.

On the following day he called his servants together and told them of his plans. He said, "We shall set out at once, for the distance is far." And he asked three of his best servants, Robin, Mole, and Flea, to go with him. Flea brought out his little wagon and they all tried to get into it, but it was much too small to hold them. Then they tried Mole's carriage, but it was much too frail and it had scarcely started to move when it broke down and they all fell out in a heap. Then they tried Robin's carriage, but it was much too high and it toppled over under its heavy load and threw them all to the ground. Then Raven stole Seagull's large strong carriage (for Seagull was asleep) and it did very well, and they started on their journey, taking turns pushing the carriage along with a pole over the flat plain.

After a strange journey in queer places they reached the land of the people who owned Fire, guided along by the thin column of smoke. The people were not people of earth. Some say they were the Fish people, but that no man knows. They sat around in a large circle with Fire in their midst, for it was autumn and the days and nights were chill. And Fire was in many places.

Raven looked on for a while from afar, thinking of the best plan to obtain Fire. Then he said to Robin, "You can move faster than any of us. You must steal Fire. You can fly in quickly, pick it up in your bill and take it back to us, and the people will not see nor hear you." So Robin picked out a spot where there were few people, and he darted in quickly and picked up Fire in a twinkling and flew back unharmed towards his companions. But he had only taken a very little bit of it. When he got halfway back to his friends, Fire was so hot in his bill that it gave him a strange pain and he had to drop it on the ground. It fell to the earth with a crash and it was so small that it flickered faintly. Robin called to his companions to bring the carriage. Then he stood over Fire and fanned it with his wings to keep it alive. It was very hot, but he stood bravely to his task until his breast was badly scorched and he had to move away. His efforts to save Fire were of no avail, and before his companions reached him Fire had died, and only a black coal remained. And poor Robin's breast was singed, and to this day the breasts of his descendants are a reddish-brown colour because he was scorched while trying to steal Fire ages ago.

Then Raven asked Flea to make the attempt to steal Fire. But Flea said, "I am too little. The heat would roast me to death; and, further, I might miscalculate the distance and hop into the flame." Then Raven asked Mole to try, but Mole said, "Oh, no. I am better fitted for other work. My fur would all be singed like Robin's breast."

Raven took good care that he would not go himself, for he was a great coward. So he said, "There is a better and easier way. We will steal the baby of the Chief and hold him for ransom. Perhaps they will give us Fire in exchange for him," and they all thought this was a very good idea. Raven asked, "Who will volunteer to steal the baby?" for he always made the others do all the work. Flea said, "I will go. In one jump I will be into the house, and in another jump I will be out again, for I can hop a great distance." But the others laughed and said, "You could not carry the baby. You are too small." The Mole said, "I will go. I can tunnel a passage very quietly under the house and right up to the baby's cradle. I can then steal the baby and no one will hear me or see me." So it was agreed that Mole should go. In a few minutes Mole made his tunnel, and he was soon back with the baby. Then they got into their carriage and hurried home with their prize.

When the Chief of the Fire People discovered the loss of his child he was very angry. And in all the land there was great sorrow because the Chief's heir, the hope of the tribe, had gone. And the child's mother and her women wept so bitterly that their tears fell like rain on all the land. The Chief said he would give anything he possessed to find his child. But although his people searched far and near, they could not find the baby.

After many days a wayfarer who had come far from the Great Water in the west brought them news that a strange child was living far to the westward in the village by the sea. He said, "He is not of their tribe; he looks like the children of your village," and he advised them to go to see him for themselves. So the Chief sent his men to search for them, guided by the wayfarer. When they reached Raven's village they were told that a strange baby was indeed there; the child was described to them, but he was kept out of sight, and Raven would not tell how he had happened to come there. And Raven said, "How do I know he is your Chief's child? People tell strange lies these days. If you want him you can pay for him, for he has caused us much trouble and expense." So the messengers went back and reported to the Chief what they had heard. From the description the Chief knew that the child was his, so he gave the messengers very valuable presents of pearls and rich robes and sent them back again to ransom his boy. But Raven, when he saw the presents, said, "No, I do not want these gifts; they do not pay me for my trouble," and he would not part with the baby. The messengers again reported to the Chief what had happened. Then the Chief gave them still richer gifts, the best he had in all his land, and sent them back. But again Raven said, "No, your gifts are valueless compared with my trouble and expense. Say this to your Chief."

When the Chief heard this from his messengers he was sore perplexed, for he had offered the best he had, and he thought that he had reached the end of his resources. So he said, "Go back and ask the people to demand what they wish in exchange for my boy and they will receive it if it can be provided." So the messengers went back to Raven and spoke as they had been commanded. And Raven said, "Only one thing can pay for the child, and that is Fire. Give me Fire and you can take the baby." The messenger laughed and said, "Why did you not say so at first and save us all this trouble and anxiety? Fire is the most plentiful thing in our kingdom, and we hold it in no value." So they returned happy to the Chief. And he sent back much Fire and received his child unharmed from Raven in exchange. And he sent Raven two small stones which the messengers taught Raven how to use. And they said, "If you ever lose Fire or if it dies for lack of food, you can always call it back to life with these two little stones." Then they showed him how to make Fire with the two little stones and withered grass and birch-bark and dry pine, and Raven thought it was very easy. And he felt very proud because he had brought Fire and Light to the earth.

He kept Fire for himself for a long time and, although the people clamoured loudly for it, he would not give any of it away. Soon, however, he decided to sell a quantity of it, for he now had the power of making it. So he said to himself, "This is a good way to get many wives," and he announced that he would only sell some of his Fire in return for a wife. And many families bought his Fire and in exchange he received many wives. And to this day he still has many wives and he still moves about from place to place with a flock of them always around him. But the Indians, when they arrived, took Fire away from him. Thus Fire came to the Indians in the olden days. And when it has died, as it often does, they still sometimes use Raven's flint stones to bring it back to life.

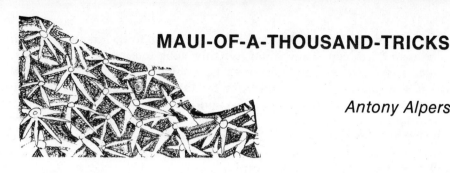

MAUI-OF-A-THOUSAND-TRICKS

Antony Alpers

Maui (mou′ē) is the most widely known figure in the mythologies of the island peoples of Polynesia. His name and the tales of some of his thousand tricks have spread throughout the Pacific.

MAUI MURI[1] LIVED in that land from which our people came, in Rarotonga.[2] Manu ahi whare was his father, Tongo i whare[3] was the mother. They were offspring of the god Great Tangaroa-of-the-tattooed-face.[4]

These were all the children of those two: Maui mua the first-born son; Maui roto the second-born son; Hina ika[5] the daughter; and Maui muri the last-born son, the potiki, his sister's pet.

Those children played at hiding. One day Hina hid small Maui underneath some leaves and rotten wood, and she said to her elder brothers, "Find your brother."

They-two searched and searched, nowhere could they find their little Maui. Therefore Hina pointed to the heap of sticks and leaves. That heap had vanished! All the leaves and sticks were scattered on the ground. No Maui muri!

This was the first time that those three knew what their brother was, what he could do.

Maui muri was his father's favourite; each night he slept by Manu ahi whare on his sleeping-mat. But every day at dawn his father disappeared, he stayed away from their house all day and he only returned at night. No one knew how he went, or how he returned. Therefore Maui wished to find this out.

---

1. *muri*, (mü′rē). 2. *that land . . . Rarotonga.* Rarotonga (rä′rō tong′gä) is the main island of the Cook Islands in the South Pacific. This story comes from Manihiki (mä′nē hē′kē), a group of islands north of the Cook Islands. 3. *Manu ahi whare . . . Tongo i whare,* (mä′nü ä′hē hwä′rä . . . tong′gō ē hwä′rä). 4. *Tangaroa-of-the-tattooed-face.* Tangaroa (täng′gä rō′ä) is the god of the sea. 5. *Maui mua . . . Maui rota . . . Hina ika,* (mou′ē mü′ä . . . mou′ē rō′tō . . . hē′nä ē′kä).

One night he lay awake until his father came to the mat and undid his maro[6] to sleep. Then Maui, secretly, took one end of his father's maro and put it beneath him, so that he would wake up when his father pulled it out. In the morning when his father arose and drew out the maro to put it on, young Maui lay quite still, he breathed like sleep. Through one eye then he saw his father go to the housepost, and he heard him say this chant:

O you housepost, open, open up!
Open so that Manu ahi whare may enter,
May descend to the world below.

That pillar lifted, left a hole, and Maui's father descended to the world below. Then Maui muri closed his eyes again, he slept, he waited for the light.

That day those children played their hiding games once more. Said Maui-the-youngest to his brothers and his sister, "You-three go out-side. I will hide here in the house." They went outside, they wondered where inside the house young Maui could find a hiding-place.

Then Maui went to the housepost and he chanted:

O you housepost, open, open up!
Open so that Maui muri may enter,
May descend to the world below.

That post obeyed, it lifted, left a hole. Small Maui went down there, he went below. He entered the body of a bird and flew to where his father was, became himself again.

Manu was greatly surprised to see his son in the world below. They pressed their noses, made the hongi. Then Manu went on quietly with his work.

Maui muri went to find, he went journeying in the world below. Came he to the house of an old blind woman, she was stooped over a cooking-fire with her fresh green tongs, her piece of kikau midrib split and bent. Fingered she apart the tongs, went to pick up food—picked up burning wood instead!

Maui muri stood there, watched that old blind woman try to pick up food. What she picked was embers with the tongs! She left good food to be burned.

Then Maui spoke to her, he learned her name. She was Hina porari,[7] his ancestor Hina-the-blind.

Old Hina asked the boy his name, but he would not tell it. He stood there watching, sorry for her, sorry for the blindness.

---

6. *maro* (mä′rō), a loincloth worn by men. 7. *Hina porari*, (hē′nä pō rä′rē).

Near that place there grew four nono trees. Maui took a stick, he struck it against the nearest of those trees. Said angry Hina porari: "Who is this, meddling with the nono tree of Maui-the-first?"

Maui muri did not answer; he went back to the next tree, tapped it with his stick. Old Hina shouted angrily, "Who is this that meddles with the nono tree of Maui roto?"

Then Maui struck the third tree, and found that it was the tree of his sister Hina ika. Very angry now, the Old one.

Then did Maui strike the fourth tree, nono tree of Maui muri, last-born child. Cried the Old one, "Who is this maggot who meddles with the sacred tree of Maui muri, here in this world beneath?" Then said the visitor, "I here am Maui muri."

Was then surprised the Old one. "Oh, then," she said, "you are my grandson! And this, here, is your own tree!"

Now when Maui muri first looked at that nono tree it was bare, it had no leaves nor fruit. After Hina-the-blind had spoken to him he looked again, and the tree had leaves, with fruit as well, not ripe.

Therefore Maui climbed up the nono tree and he brought down one of its fruit. He bit off a piece, and threw it into one blind grey eye of Hina. That Old one smarted with the pain, her sight returned. She saw! Then Maui picked another fruit, he bit off a piece and threw it in the Old one's other eye. Her sight was given back, she saw him plain! Delighted then was Hina porari, to see her grandson Maui muri. She said to him:

All that is above here,
All that is below
Now is subject to your sacred mana,[8]
Grandson of Hina porari!

Then Hina-the-Old, once called Hina porari, gave to her grandson Maui muri sacred knowledge of all things that are found in her land in the world below, and power in the world above.

She taught him these things: in Havaiki[9] there are four kinds of nono tree, one for each child of her son Manu ahi whare. In Havaiki also there are four kinds of coconut tree, one for each of those children. There are, besides, four kinds of taro,[10] one kind for each of the children of Manu.

Maui asked this question of his ancestor Hina: "Who is the god from whom fire comes?" She answered, "Your ancestor, Tangaroa tui mata."[11]

"Where does he live?"

---

8. *mana* (mä'nä), supernatural or magical power. 9. *Havaiki* (hä'vä ē'kē), the Underworld. 10. *taro* (tä'rō), a plant whose root is made into an edible starch. 11. *tui mata* (tü'ē mä'tä).

"He lives over there, my grandson," Hina answered. "But do not go to him. Anger is in that god. You would die, being near to him."

"I wish to see him."

"You would die, my grandson. Do not go to him!"

But Maui insisted in his asking, therefore Hina yielded to his wish, yielded to this grandson who restored her sight. She spoke thus:

"There are two roads to the house of Tangaroa-of-the-tattooed-face. One road, my child, is the road of dying; men who go by that path die. The other is the common road. You, Maui—take that common road."

Now Maui did not do as that Old one had told him. He spurned the common road. He chose the path of dying.

Tangaroa tui mata saw this small man coming on the road, he raised his right hand up to kill him. No man had ever lived, struck by that hand of the god of fire. But Maui lifted *his* right hand, he raised it up. Therefore Tangaroa pulled a face of fearful looks and lifted up his right foot, he would kick to death this Maui. But Maui muri lifted his foot also, he showed the god no awe.

Was astounded the god. He asked the visitor to give his name.

"I here am Maui muri, son of Manu ahi whare and Tongo i whare. I have come."

Then Tangaroa tui mata knew his grandson, and they made the hongi, said their greetings, wept.

The god asked Maui: "For what purpose have you come to this place?"

"To get some fire," that young man said.

Then Tangaroa tui mata gave him a burning stick and sent him away. Maui walked a certain distance, he came to water, put the stick in water. Out the fire! Maui returned to Tangaroa tui mata. "Oh sir, my fire went out. The water killed its flame." Therefore Tangaroa gave him another burning stick, but Maui did the thing again, put out the fire, returned to the god for more.

When Maui returned to his ancestor a third time, all the burning sticks were gone. Therefore Tangaroa had to fetch two dry sticks to rub for fire. This, young Maui had wanted, wished to see it done.

"Hold this for me."

So Maui held the grooved piece, kau ati, while Tangaroa with his two hands worked the kau rima; he ground it in the groove until there was smoke. When the dust in the groove was smoking, Maui blew it—*Pu!* He blew the tinder all away.

Was then enraged the god, he drove young Maui off! And he called to his pet tern, his white kakaia, to come and hold the kau ati. The kakaia came; and with her pretty foot she held the grooved piece firm for Tangaroa while he worked the fire-plough with his aged hands. The fire began, the dust was smoking. Tangaroa put it with some dry stuff in an open basket, waved it in the air. It flamed. Fire was.

Then did jealousy of that tern drive Maui to his mischief. He took up the charred fire-stick of the god, and he put two black marks on the beautiful face of that pure white bird. The kakaia flew away, she left that place for ever. That is why the kakaia has a black brow above its eye, and another below. Maui muri put them there.

Then Tangaroa wept because his tern was gone, his favourite bird. And Maui lied to him. "Your bird will come back." But the tern did not; it left Havaiki, the world below, it flew up through a cave to the world of light, this world. It lives above here, in the world of light.

One day Maui said to Tangaroa tui mata, "Let us go up there to where your tern is living." The god asked, "How can we-two go up there?" Said Maui, "I will show you the way." Then he changed himself into a bird and flew high up, toward the entrance which leads to this world from the world below.

Then Tangaroa laughed and was pleased, and Maui flew down and said to him, "Now you will try." The god asked how he should and Maui made him put on his most glorious girdle, his girdle of sacred kura which the people of this world call anuanua, that is rainbow.

Therefore Tangaroa girded on his rainbow; and by its sacred mana rose he above the highest coconut tree in all that land.

They flew, they-two flew high; but Maui flew below the god, he did not fly beside him. They passed beyond the clouds, to open sky, this world of light. Then Maui snatched the loose cord of the girdle of the god, he pulled it sharply; Tangaroa fell, he fell from cloud-height to the ground of world-below. And falling thus, great Tangaroa-of-the-tattooed-face was killed.

Then Maui was pleased and he returned to his parents, he showed them the secret of making fire with wood, which no one in that land had known. He did not tell his parents that he had killed Tangaroa his ancestor.

Maui's parents were filled with happiness because he had brought them the gift of fire, and they-two wished to visit Tangaroa. "But do not go at once," said Maui, "wait until the third day. I myself wish to visit him tomorrow." Those parents agreed. "Very well, we will wait until the third day."

On the next morning Maui went alone to Tangaroa's place, he found that his body was rotten. Only bones. Therefore Maui gathered up the bones and put them inside a coconut shell, he closed up the hole which is known as "Tuna's mouth," and he vigorously shook that shell, he rattled the bones of the god.

When he opened the shell again his grandfather was alive and whole. Then Maui let him out from that degrading place, he washed his body, gave him food; he rubbed scented oil on Tangaroa's skin, and left him in his house to recover from the trouble. Then Maui returned to his parents. They said to him, "Now we must visit your ancestor Tangaroa tui mata. We shall go tomorrow."

But Maui urged them not to go, he asked them: "Wait until the third day, as I said." For Maui feared his parents' anger, knew what they would learn. He wished to reach this world before they-two could speak to Tangaroa.

On the third day Manu and Tongo made their journey, went to Tangaroa's house. When they saw him they-two wept, his mana and his pride were gone from him, his face showed feebleness, its tattoo marks were rotted off.

Then Manu, softly weeping, asked the god what was the cause. "It is that son of yours, he has been ill-treating me. First he scorched the face of my bird, my tern. Then he made me fly, and he pulled my girdle to make me fall, and the great fall killed me. I was dead. Then he gathered up my bones and degraded them—he rattled them around inside a nut! Then he made me come alive again, as you see me now, all scarred and feeble. Aue! Aue! That son of yours!"

Then Maui's parents wept, and they returned to their home in Havaiki to scold their son. But Maui had left that place; he had returned to this world of light, where his brothers and his sister all were weeping for him, mourning for his loss. For they thought their brother dead.

Delighted were those brothers and Hina, filled with joy, when Maui appeared at their house. Their brother then did boast to them, "I have found a new land! I have found how fire is made!"

"Tell us where! Tell us where!"

"The place is down there."

"Down where?"

"Down there—down there below."

Those brothers and Hina did not know of the cave beneath the housepost. Therefore Maui said that if they would promise to follow him he would show them the world below. He went to the post of the house and said this word:

O you housepost, open up,
That we all may enter, go below;
That we may go to Havaiki, the world beneath.

Upon this word of Maui's the housepost lifted up, and all those four went down, they visited Havaiki. When Maui had shown his brothers and his sister the world beneath, they returned to their house and all lived quietly together there.

After Maui had brought back fire from Tangaroa the people of this world ate cooked food. Before that time all food was raw. It was Maui who brought the gift of fire and of cooking to this world above.

One day Maui said to his family, "These days are too short. There is not enough time in the days for men to do their work. There is not enough time in the days for women to cook the food. The sun god goes too quickly across the sky. Before our food is cooked, Ra[12] has gone to the world beneath."

Therefore Maui considered how Ra might be caught and made to move more slowly across the sky. With his brothers he made a great cord of coconut fibre. He took this cord to the far horizon, to that pit from which the sun rises, and he laid the noose around the pit to catch the god. This trick of Maui's did not work. The cord was too weak, it was soon broken.

Maui made himself stronger ropes, he gathered all the coconut husks of this land and rolled the fibre, and he plaited it into ropes of very great strength. But these ropes also were of no use, for the sun god made them frizzle up.

Therefore Maui took the sacred tresses of his sister Hina, he cut off lengths of Hina's hair and plaited it, to make a rope whose mana could not be destroyed by Ra. He took that noose of Hina's hair, he traveled eastward to the border of the sea; he placed his ropes around the pit from which the sun rises, waited there, he waited for the dawn. Then Ra came up, he came up from the spirit-world which lies in the east.

Maui pulled the cord, he caught the sun god by the throat! Ra struggled, kicked, he screamed against the sky.

"Then will you go more slowly if I turn you loose?"

The sun then promised Maui, "Let me go, and I will move more slowly, I will make longer days for your fishing." Since that time, men have had longer days in which to go about their work.

When he had done this task Maui left some ropes of Hina's hair hanging from the sun, and they are still there. We see them when the sun is going down through clouds, outstretching to the sea, the Ropes of Maui.

The first man to find this land of Manihiki was Huku.[13] He found it before Maui did, when it was still beneath the sea.

Huku was a man of Rarotonga. He was fishing for bonito, far out from that land. Looking down, he saw a great coral-head that was growing up in the sea. Then Huku said this word:

Huku looked down and saw
Foundation-of-the-rock.

After that Huku returned to his land, to Rarotonga.

Huku went fishing for atu again; he returned to this place and looked down, his rock had grown, it had moved upwards. Therefore when he

12. *Ra* (rä), the sun god. 13. *Huku*, (hü′kü).

returned to Rarotonga he gave his canoe a new name, he called it Tapuaua—"coral-coral."

Afterwards came Maui and his brothers: they came because they knew of what Huku had seen in this place. They came together in their canoe Pipi mahakohako, and they found the rock, that growing reef.

Then Maui the youngest dived into the sea, he went below to the house of Hina i te papa. And after he had spoken to Hina-in-the-rock he returned to his brothers in the canoe. They started their fishing in this place, threw out their lines.

Maui mua baited his hook and let his line down, chanting:

Maui roto, Maui muri,
Guess the name of my fish—
What is it?

Maui roto could not guess, but Maui muri said:

Your filthy fish is a haha shark—
Then haul it up!

And when that fish was hauled to their canoe they found indeed it was a shark, the haha kind.

Then Maui roto let down his hook, and chanting asked his brothers to name the fish that he had caught. Maui mua could not guess, but Maui-the-youngest said, "Your filthy fish is an urua. Haul it up." And so it was.

Then said Maui muri, "You-two have had your chances, now let me try." And he baited his hook with puroro, that is spathe of coconut, and with aoa, that is sprouting kernel of the nut; these two were wrapped up in a puke leaf by Maui muri.

Maui let down his line so that it would be seen by Hina-in-the-rock. That woman fixed the hook for him, she hooked it on the coral growth. Then Maui asked his brothers:

Maui mua, Maui roto,
Guess the name of my fish,
What is its name?

They-two both said, "Your filthy fish is a haha kakahi." But Maui hauled his line, the weight of his fish was very great. When it came near, the whole sea broke in angry waves, they saw that Maui's fish was land, and were afraid.

Sprang then Maui muri out of the canoe, he leapt on to the rocks. But his brothers Maui mua and Maui roto were dashed on the reef; their canoe broke up, they were hurt in the breakers, and they drowned.

Then Maui named his land Manihiki, and he stayed here looking at it, looking at this land. His only food was fish, the rain from the skies was his drink, no coconuts were growing here in Maui's time. Then Maui said his chant:

The sea was churned, churned up,
It became an angry sea—
Then upward came the land.
I, Maui, severed Manihiki,
Severed it from Rakahanga.
The sea was churned, churned up,
It became an angry sea.

Maui walked about on his land. He came to a house built of earth, and he asked them, "Who are you?" They answered, "We are a house of tupuas."

There were eighty of those spirit-people in the house of earth. Maui also heard the voices of men inside the house, for there were ten-score people living there. Then Maui sang a dancing-song before those tupuas, with gestures of contempt, and he claimed the land for his. Just when he had finished, Huku came back to his reef that he had found. Great was his anger at seeing Maui there! They two fought together! Did come combat, did come combat!

Then Huku chased Maui across the land to Tumukau. Fled Maui from Tumukau to Paahi, chased by Huku's anger. But at Paahi, Maui found that Huku had trodden on the land and spoilt it all. Therefore Maui with a great spring leapt up to the heavens, never was he seen on Manihiki more.

The force of Maui's leaping broke off Rakahanga from Manihiki. These two lands afterwards were separate for ever.

After this Huku returned to Rarotonga, for the land here was barren, no coconuts were growing in this place. It was only later that Huku returned and found that Wheatu, having heard him speak of this land, had come to take it. This led to the great disputes between those two.

LLEU AND THE FLOWERFACE

Gwyn Jones

The tale of the enchanter Gwydion (gwid′yon) and the magical child Lleu Llaw Gyffes (hlī hlou guf′fes) is the last of the "Four Branches of the Mabinogi," the first four stories in the collection of twelve medieval Welsh tales which Lady Charlotte Guest (1812–1895) published with an English translation in 1849 as the Mabinogion *(mab′in nōg′yon). The Four Branches were probably composed by a single author sometime after 1000 A.D., but are a reworking of various elements of Celtic myth of a much earlier date.*

IN THOSE FAR-OFF DAYS when Math son of Mathonwy was lord over Gwynedd,[1] there lived at his court and served him one who was still more of a magician than he. This was his nephew Gwydion son of Dôn,[2] the man who made the circuit of Gwynedd on his behalf and ruled his war-band. It was the same Gwydion who by magic and strength slew Pryderi lord of Dyfed at Maentwrog in north Wales, after carrying off his pigs.[3]

It happened one day when Gwydion was lying in his bed of a morning, half-awake, half-asleep, that he heard a low cry from the chest he kept at his bed's foot. In a moment or two he heard it again, though no cry could ever be quieter. Quickly he stepped out of bed and went to open the chest, and when he had done so, he could see an infant boy lying there in a silken sheet, thrusting his arms through its folds and spreading it apart. He lifted the boy out of the chest and carried him to the light, and it seemed to Gwydion that there was something of his own likeness in the boy's face. "Shame on my beard," said Gwydion, "if I do not maintain him as well as myself." That same

---

"Lleu and the Flowerface" From WELSH LEGENDS AND FOLK-TALES retold by Gwyn Jones. Used by permission of the publishers, Henry Z. Walck, Inc. and Oxford University Press.

1. *Math son of Mathonwy . . . Gwynedd.* Math son of Mathonwy (math *son of* math on ü′ē) was the ruler of Gwynedd (gwin′eth), an ancient kingdom in North Wales. **2.** *Dôn* (dôn, dōn), a goddess. **3.** *Pryderi lord of Dyfed . . . pigs.* The first episode of the Fourth Branch tells the story of how Gwydion managed to carry off the pigs of Pryderi (prü de′rē), king of Dyfed (düv′ed) in South Wales, which were the only pigs in the world at that time. Pryderi pursued Gwydion, they fought, and Pryderi was killed.

day he found a woman to look after the boy, and the boy throve so well that in a year's time one would have remarked on his size had he been twice that age. By the end of his second year he was big and sturdy enough to be sent to the court, and Gwydion received him there and loved him as his own son, and the boy loved Gwydion and called him father, and all who saw them said that there was never such likeness or such love between any other two in the Island of Britain.

Still the boy throve, and so quickly that by the time he was four years old one would have remarked on his size had he been eight. It was now that Gwydion set off one day, and the boy with him, and made his way on foot to the castle of the lady Aranrhod.[4] When they entered the court there, the lady rose up to meet him, to make him welcome and to give him greeting.

"Heaven prosper you, lord," she said. "You do not come as often as you used to do."

"There is a reason for everything," said Gwydion. "Heaven prosper you too, lady."

"But who," she asked, "is the lad who follows you, and bears your likeness in his face?"

"Lady," said Gwydion, "this is your son."

"Alas, man," cried Aranrhod, "why bring such shame upon me as to say he is my son!" And she hid her face in her hands, so great was the shame that possessed her.

"Lady," replied Gwydion, "unless you suffer a greater shame than that I should rear so fine a lad as this, your shame is no great thing. Take him now at my hands."

"What is his name?" asked Aranrhod. "For without a name he is no son of mine, no son of thine, and no kinsman of the king's."

"Faith," said Gwydion, "as yet he has no name. Do you name him, lady."

At this the lady Aranrhod smiled more with her teeth than her eyes. "No," she said, "there is no hope that I will name him. Moreover, I will swear on him a destiny that he shall never get a name unless he gets it from me."

"Wicked woman," cried Gwydion in a rage, "to treat your own son thus! But never fear," he added more quietly, setting his hand on his son's shoulder, "he shall have a name, and sooner than you think." And with that they turned away from the court and went back to Caer Dathyl[5] to spend the night, the boy in sleep, but Gwydion in deep thought and meditation.

On the morrow in the young of the day Gwydion arose and took his son with him and they went walking along the seashore between there and Aber Menai. Wherever he saw dulse and sea girdle[6] on the rocks

---

4. *Aranrhod,* (är an′rōd). 5. *Caer Dathyl* (cär dath′əl), Math's stronghold. 6. *dulse and sea girdle,* seaweeds.

he collected them, and made a ship from them by magic; and wherever he saw seaweed and dulse on the sands those too he collected, and from them he made cordwain.[7] Next he put colours on the cordwain till no one in the world had seen leathers so lovely. He set a sail in the ship, and he and the boy sailed on till they reached the sea-gate of Caer Aranrhod, where they at once began cutting out shoes and stitching them. Watchmen saw them from the castle tower, and as soon as Gwydion knew that they were overlooked he took away their own proper semblance and put another semblance upon them, so that they would not be recognized.

"What men are they in the ship?" asked Aranrhod.

"Shoemakers," they told her.

"I have need of shoes. Go and see what leathers they have, and what kind of work they do."

When the messengers reached the ship, Gwydion was colouring cordwain in gold. They returned and told Aranrhod that they had never seen leathers so lovely and stitching so true.

"Take the measure of my foot," she ordered, "and ask the shoemaker to make shoes for me."

Gwydion fashioned the shoes, but he cut them much bigger than the measure.

"These are the best shoes in the world," said Aranrhod, "and he shall be paid for them. But they are too big. Let him make me shoes that are smaller."

Gwydion fashioned the shoes, but this time he cut them much smaller than the measure.

"He shall be paid for these too," said Aranrhod. "But they are too small and will not go on me."

The messengers reported this to Gwydion. "I waste my craft," he reproved them. "I shall make no more shoes for her until I measure her foot myself."

When she heard this, "Yes," said Aranrhod, "that will be best. Tell him I am on my way."

When she reached the ship Gwydion was cutting out and the boy stitching. "Heaven prosper you, lady," said Gwydion.

"Heaven prosper you, too," she replied. "But I marvel that a man of your craft cannot make shoes to measure."

"There is a reason for everything," said Gwydion. "I think I may succeed now."

At that moment a wren alighted on board the ship. The boy took aim at it with his awl, so that he hit it between the sinew of its leg and the bone. Aranrhod laughed. "Faith," she said, "with a deft hand has the fair one hit it."

"Aye," retorted Gwydion, "he has hit more deftly than you know.

7. *cordwain,* leather.

For he has now got a name, and a very good name. Lleu Llaw Gyffes he shall be called from now on." And as he spoke the wren vanished into air, and the leathers into dulse, and where the ship had been there was only sea-girdle. Then he released his son into his proper semblance, and himself stood revealed in his right aspect. "Lady," he said, "this is your son. It is not too late for you to make him amends."

"There is no hope of that," she vowed. "Moreover, I will swear on him a second destiny, that he shall never bear arms until he gets them from me."

"Cruel woman," cried Gwydion in his anger, "to treat your own son thus! But never fear, he shall have arms, and sooner than you think."

They returned now to Math's court, where Lleu Llaw Gyffes was reared till he could ride every horse and run every course, and till he was perfected in feature, form and favour, even as a man should be. But Gwydion saw that he was pining for want of arms, and at last he found a time to say to him, "Lad, you and I will go a journey tomorrow. I know what you want, and we shall find it before we return. Till then, lad, be of good cheer."

On the morrow in the young of the day they arose and followed the seashore towards Caer Aranrhod. When they were near enough to recognize the place, Gwydion changed their semblance, so that they came riding towards the land-gate of the castle in the guise of young men. Of the two, though, Gwydion was the staider and stouter. "Porter," he ordered, "go in and tell your lady that there are bards here from the south who would gladly entertain her." The porter returned quickly and led them inside.

"A welcome to you both," said Aranrhod, in answer to their greeting. They went to eat, and when that was ended there was much discourse of tales and story-telling, and all the court was happy that night, for Gwydion was the best teller of tales in the world. Later a chamber was made ready for them and they went to sleep. At first cockcrow Gwydion arose by stealth and called up his magic and his power. By early dawn there was a bustling to and fro and trumpets and clamour throughout the countryside. By daylight they heard a knocking at the chamber door, and there was Aranrhod herself bidding them open. The boy arose and opened the door; she came in and a maiden with her.

"Good sirs," she cried, "we are in danger. You must rise and help defend the castle."

"We have heard the trumpets and clamour," Gwydion admitted. "What is the cause of that, lady?"

"Faith," she said, "go to the embrasure and you will not know the colour of the sea for the host of ships you will spy there, making for the land with all the speed they can."

"I see them, lady," said Gwydion, "and they are still more numerous than you say."

"Then what shall we do? I beg you, good sirs, to find a plan for me."

"There is only one plan I know," Gwydion told her. "We must close the castle gates and make the best defence we can. Have you arms? Then bring them here and arm this youth and me."

She went out after the arms and returned, and two maidens with her. "Lady," said Gwydion, "do you arm this youth. I am staider and stouter, and the maidens will help me better than they would help him. Hurry, lady, hurry! Surely I hear men at the gates?"

In haste but with the properest care, Aranrhod armed the youth at all points. "Is his arming completed?" asked Gwydion.

"At all points," said Aranrhod. "Now, acquit yourselves like men."

Gwydion burst out laughing. "It is time to doff our arms," he corrected her, as she stood before him angry and puzzled.

"But why?" she demanded. "Look at the fleet that surrounds us!"

"There is no fleet, lady."

"Then hearken to the land army!"

"There is no army either."

"Alas," asked Aranrhod, "what kind of a mustering was this?"

"A mustering," he replied, "to break the destiny you swore upon your son." As he spoke these words he released his son into his proper semblance, and himself stood revealed in his right aspect. "Here is your son, lady, who has received arms at your hands. Will you still not take him to you and love him as your own?"

"I am so far from doing that," said the angry Aranrhod, "that I will swear on him a third destiny, that he shall never have a wife of all the women that are now on earth."

"Monstrous woman," cried Gwydion, "to treat your own son thus! But never fear, lad," he added more quietly, "you shall have a wife, and sooner than she thinks."

After they had broken their fast they left the castle, and without any halt made their way to the court of Math son of Mathonwy. They told him their troubles, and he commanded that his wand be put in his hand.

"Aye," he told Gwydion, "we shall be too much for her, you and I. Let us seek by our magic and enchantment to make a wife for him out of flowers."

For Lleu was now a man in feature, form and favour, and the handsomest youth that mortal ever saw. They took the flowers of the oak, the broom, and the meadowsweet, and from those they called forth the fairest and the best endowed maiden that was ever seen in Gwynedd, and baptized her with the baptism they used at that time, and the name they gave her was Blodeuedd.[8] Then they gave Lleu Llaw Gyffes a court and its territory, so that he might honourably maintain himself, in the place which is called Mur Castell in the

8. *Blodeuedd* (blô di ′eth), "Flowers."

uplands of Ardudwy, and he settled there and ruled it well, and every one was content with him and his rule.

A year passed, and a second, and then it happened one day that Lleu went to Caer Dathyl to visit Math and Gwydion. That same day, not long after he had gone, Blodeuedd was crossing the courtyard when she heard the blast of a horn, and after the blast she saw a spent stag going by, and after the stag there came dogs and huntsmen, and after these a troop of men on foot moving more slowly. She was curious to know who these men and their lord might be, and sent a lad to inquire. "Gronw Bebyr[9] is our lord here," they told him, "he who is lord of Penllyn."

Meantime Gronw was pursuing the stag. The dogs pulled it down on the bank of Cynfael river, and it was there that he slew it. But what with killing the stag and feeding his dogs and the exhaustion of his horses, he was kept busy there till night closed in on him. Darkness was falling as he again came past the gate of the court.

"Faith," said Blodeuedd, "it would be a great discourtesy to let the chieftain pass by to some other dwelling at this hour of the night." Messengers went out to meet Gronw and invite him to the court. He accepted the invitation gladly, and Blodeuedd herself came forth to meet him at the gate and gave him greeting.

"Lady," he said, "Heaven repay you this noble welcome."

He washed and changed his hunting garb, and then they sat down. Blodeuedd looked on him where he sat, and as she looked she was filled with love of him, so that her cheeks were now red as the reddest foxgloves and now white as the foam of the sea. And Gronw looked on her, and the same thought was in him as in her, so that he might not conceal that he loved her; and from that same moment all their talk was of the love and affection they felt one for the other. And they talked too of how it might come about that they should be together for ever.

"There is only one plan I know," Gronw told her. "We must kill your husband Lleu."

"Only one man in this world knows how his death may come about," replied Blodeuedd. "And Lleu is that man."

"Then under pretence of loving care for him," said Gronw, "you must win his secret from him." And before he rode away from the court he said again, "Remember, lady, what I told you. For you alone can draw from him what way his death may come about."

The first thing Lleu noticed when he reached home was that his wife was sad and silent. "Lady," he asked her, "are you ill or does some trouble oppress you? I cannot bear to see you unhappy."

"I am not ill," she replied, "but I am troubled about you in a way you would never trouble about me. I am troubled about your death, lest you should die sooner than I."

9. *Gronw Bebyr*, (gro′nü be′bər).

"Ah," said Lleu, "Heaven repay you for your loving care. But be happy, for unless God shall slay me, I shall not easily be slain."

"I thank heaven for it," replied his wife. "But tell me how that may be, for my memory should prove a surer safeguard than yours."

"I will, gladly," said Lleu. "First, it will not be easy to kill me with a blow. The spear that would kill me must be a whole year a-making, and never a hand shall be laid to that work except when other folk are at Mass[10] on Sunday."

"I thank heaven for it," replied his wife.

"Further, I cannot be slain inside or outside a house. I cannot be slain on horseback or a-foot."

"Why," she said, "then you cannot be slain at all."

"Yes," he told her, "I can be slain by this means. By making a bath for me on a river bank, and setting a vaulted frame over the tub, and thatching it well and snugly, and then bringing a he-goat and placing it alongside the tub, and then I myself setting one foot on the back of the goat and the other on the edge of the tub. If any one should smite me with a one-year spear when I was standing so, he would bring about my death."

"I thank heaven for it," replied his wife. "For that can be easily avoided."

She had news of this sent to Gronw in Penllyn, and for a whole year Gronw laboured to make the spear, and that same day twelvemonth he had her informed that it was ready.

"Lord," she said to Lleu, "I am still troubled about the manner of your death. That is a thing I would guard against more than my own death or the kingdom's. Will you show me in what manner you would stand on the back of the goat and the edge of the tub, if I prepare the bath?"

"Heaven repay you for your loving care," replied Lleu. "I will show you gladly."

This news too she had sent to Gronw, with an instruction that he should be lying in wait under the lee of a hill on the bank of Cynfael river. Also she had all the he-goats of the district gathered together on the bank facing that hill. Then on the morrow she said to Lleu, "Lord, I have had the bath and the frame prepared, and they are ready for you. Will you look?" So they came to look at the bath. "Will you go into the bath, as you promised, lord?" she asked. He went into the bath. "And here are the animals you called he-goats," she told him. "Shall one of them be fetched here alongside the bath?" A goat was fetched, and Lleu rose up out of the bath and stood with one foot on the back of the goat and the other on the edge of the tub. At that moment Gronw drew himself up on one knee from behind the lee of the hill and took aim at

10. *Mass,* the central service of worship of medieval Christians, consisting of various prayers and ceremonies.

him with the poisoned spear, and smote him in the side, so that the shaft started out of him and the head remained embedded. Instantly he flew up in the form of an eagle and gave a horrid scream. And after that he was seen no more.

The moment he vanished Gronw and Blodeuedd set off for the court, and the next day Gronw rose up and subdued Ardudwy, so that all Lleu's lands were under his sway.

News of these events was brought to Math son of Mathonwy and to Gwydion son of Dôn. Their grief grew heavy upon them. "Lord king," said Gwydion, "I shall never rest till I get tidings of my son. Give me leave that I may make the circuit of Gwynedd."

"Aye," said Math, "may God be your guide." Gwydion set off the same day and traversed Gwynedd and the length and breadth of Powys, but he found no word or whisper of his son Lleu. In time he arrived at the house of a villein[11] in Arfon and took lodging for the night. The goodman came home late, and last of all came the swineherd.

"Fellow," asked the goodman, "has your sow come home tonight?"

"Aye," he replied. "She has just gone into the sty."

"What kind of journey does that sow go on?" asked Gwydion.

"That is what no one knows," was the answer. "Every day when the sty is opened she goes off at such a run that no one has as yet been able to keep up with her. For all I know," said the swineherd, "she might as well disappear into the depths of the earth."

"Do me one favour," asked Gwydion. "Do not open the sty until I am standing there at your side."

"Gladly," said the swineherd, and they named a time of day for tomorrow's morn.

When the swineherd saw the first light of day he roused Gwydion, and they went and stood alongside the sty. The moment the sty was opened out rushed the sow and made upstream at top speed into the valley which is now called Nantlleu, where she slowed down and began to feed under an oak. Gwydion had followed her, and came forward under the tree to see what she was feeding on. Her food, he could see, was rotten flesh and maggots. So he looked up into the tree, and in the tree top he could see an eagle. And whenever the eagle shook himself the worms and the rotten flesh fell from him. Gwydion thought that this eagle must be Lleu, and he sang a verse:

Grows an oak within this glen
'Twixt two lakes (the dark sky lours);
If I speak not falsely, then
This befalls from Lleu's false Flowers.

11, *villein* (vil′ən), a peasant.

When he heard Gwydion's voice the eagle descended till he was in the middle of the tree. Then Gwydion sang a second verse:

Grows an oak on upland plain,
Heat and tempest pass it by;
Of nine-score hardships he'll complain,
In its top, the deft-hand Lleu.

The eagle now let himself down till he was on the lowest branch of the tree. Then Gwydion sang yet a third verse:

Grows an oak upon a hill,
Fair lord's refuge this, maybe;
If I speak not falsely, still
Lleu will light upon my knee.

At these words the eagle came down and alighted on Gwydion's knee. Then Gwydion struck him with his magic wand, so that he was once more in his own likeness. No one ever saw on man a more pitiful sight. He was nothing but skin and bone.

With great tenderness Gwydion conveyed him to Caer Dathyl, to Math's court, and all the physicians of Gwynedd came there to heal him. But it was a full year before he was whole again. As soon as he was whole he came to speak with Math. "Lord king," he said, "it is high time for me to get redress from the man who brought this suffering upon me. And the sooner I get it, the better satisfied I shall be."

Math mustered Gwynedd, and Lleu and his father set out for Ardudwy. Gwydion travelled in front and was soon in sight of Mur Castell. Blodeuedd was informed that they were coming, and such was her fear that she fled across the river with her maidens and far out on to the mountain. Here all her maidens fell into a deep lake and were drowned, and she was alone when Gwydion caught up with her.

"Do not kill me," she begged. "I am young. Why should I die?"

"No," he said, "I will not kill you." At his words she laughed and cried together, but he would not pity her even so. "There is a harder destiny for you by far than to die. I shall release you in the shape of a bird, and because of the dishonour you have done to my son Lleu, you shall never dare show your face by daylight, through fear of other birds, so that it will be their nature to mob and molest you wherever they find you. Nor shall you lose your name Blodeuedd, but I will change it a little even so, so that now and for ever you shall be called Blodeuwedd."[12]

---

12. *Blodeuwedd* (blô di ü′eth), "Flowerface."

And that is the reason why all birds are hostile to the owl, and why the owl is called Blodeuwedd to this present day.

Meantime Gronw Bebyr had fled to Penllyn, whence he sent envoys to ask whether Lleu Llaw Gyffes would accept land or territory or gold or silver for his injury. "Not I," vowed Lleu. "The very least I will accept of him is that he shall stand in the place where I stood, and I in the place where he stood, and that I shall then take aim at him with my spear."

This answer was brought to Gronw. "Aye," he said, "that is the least I can do. My trusty lords, my war band, and my foster-brothers, is there any one of you will take this blow in my stead?"

"Faith," they answered, "there is none." And that is why they have been called from that day to this one of the Three Disloyal War Bands.

"Then if that is so," said Gronw, "I must needs take it myself."

The two of them came to the bank of Cynfael river. Then Gronw stood in the place where Lleu had been when he smote him with the spear, and Lleu in the lee of the hill.

"Lord," said Gronw then, "since it was through a woman's wiles I did you so much hurt, I beg you for pity's sake that you will let me set that great stone I see there between me and the blow."

"I will not refuse you that," said Lleu.

So Gronw took up the stone and set it between him and the blow. Then Lleu rose up on one knee and took aim at him with the spear, and the spear pierced the stone and Gronw too, so that his back was broken and that was the end of him. The stone may be seen there to this day, on the bank of Cynfael river, and the hole goes right through it. And for that reason it is called Llech Ronw.

And when he had slain Gronw, Lleu Llaw Gyffes took possession of the land a second time and ruled over it prosperously. And in the fullness of time, so the tale tells, he succeeded Math as king over Gwynedd. And that is the end of his story.

LOKI
AND THE
GIANTS

Roger Lancelyn Green

Loki (lō′kē) is a curious figure, sometimes identified as one of the Aesir (ā′sir, ē′sir), the Norse gods, sometimes as one of their enemies, the Giants. He is cunning and malicious and equally adept at getting himself and the gods into and out of trouble. For some background in Norse myth and the pronunciation of names see the notes on pages 32 and 333.

Loki NOW LIVED IN ASGARD, accepted as one of the Aesir, and no one seemed to suspect that he had first betrayed Iduna to the Storm Giant and then won her back.[1] Indeed this was ever Loki's way, for he took such a delight in mischief that he would often do whatever came into his head, without counting the cost. Nevertheless his cunning was very great, and his powers were often useful to the Aesir. Indeed at first he was one of the most important guardians of Asgard, and saved them from disaster more than once.

Odin believed that Loki had overcome and would forget his Giant nature; and remembering that he had made him his blood-brother, he saw to it that he was treated as if he were in truth Bestla's child[2] and not merely her cousin's son.

Very early in the history of Midgard, Loki showed his prowess by dealing with the Giant Skrymsli[3] who proved too much for both Odin and Honir. For it chanced that the three Aesir were wandering the earth once more, as they did frequently in those early days, and came to the house of a farmer in the Faroe Islands.[4]

The farmer, who did not recognize them in their disguise, welcomed the three travelers into his kitchen and set a good supper before them. But he did not make one of the party as they made merry round the fire with their horns of mead, and Odin noticed that he turned aside from time to time to weep.

"What troubles you, kind host?" asked Odin at length. "Is there anything in which we can assist or comfort you?"

1. *betrayed Iduna . . . won her back.* The goddess Iduna had in her keeping the golden apples by which the Aesir renewed their youth. She and her apples were carried off to Jotunheim ("Giantland") with Loki's help. He then managed to get her back and save the Aesir from old age. **2.** *Bestla's child.* Odin was the son of Bestla (best′lä), a giantess. **3.** *Skrymsli,* (skrüm′slē). **4.** *the Faroe Islands.* The Faroes (fôr′erz) are a group of islands in the Baltic Sea near Sweden.

"Alas, noble sir," answered the farmer, with the tears streaming down his face, "no mortal man may help us. In the morning the terrible Giant Skrymsli is coming for our darling youngest son Rogner whom he has chosen for his dinner tomorrow, and though we have begged and prayed for mercy, nothing will persuade him to spare our beloved child."

"This must never be!" cried Odin, springing to his feet, and letting fall his disguise. "Tomorrow the boy shall be hidden safely from Skrymsli—and if I cannot hide him, then Honir my brother shall do so!"

Then, while the farmer and his wife knelt before the three Aesir, Odin strode to the door and, holding out his arms, began to chant great rolling Runes which he had learnt from Mimir his uncle, the wise Giant.[5] As he chanted the corn grew over many a wide acre, till, when the sun rose, as far as the eye could see there stretched a great golden harvest ripe for the sickle.

Then Odin took the boy Rogner and hid him in a single grain of corn in one ear on one straw in the midst of the great cornfield. Then the three Aesir stood in the doorway of the farmhouse to see what would happen, and before long the huge Giant came striding down from the mountains.

"Give me the boy Rogner!" cried Skrymsli.

"He is hiding in the cornfield," said the farmer.

"Then I shall find him before sunset," answered the Giant, and drawing his sharp sword he began to reap the corn with it, shaking each sheaf as he gathered it and flinging it aside until he had built a high stack at the end of the field. Evening was falling as Skrymsli cut the fatal stalk of corn, shook the grains into his hand, and picked out the very one in which Rogner was hidden.

In his terror the child called to Odin for help, and one of his ravens[6] flew down, snatched the grain out of Skrymsli's hand, and carried it to the farmhouse, where at once Rogner regained his own shape and size.

"I have done all I can to help you," said Odin to the farmer. "The sun has set, Skrymsli has gone, and the boy is safe."

That night the three Aesir remained in the farmhouse, and in the morning they saw the Giant Skrymsli striding towards them again. Then Honir took Rogner's hand and led him quickly out by the back door and into a wood where two silvery-white swans flew down, and Honir changed the boy into a tiny feather on the neck of one of them.

Meanwhile the Giant had come to the farmhouse door.

---

5. *great rolling Runes . . . the wise Giant.* In search of wisdom Odin had gone to the well guarded by the Giant Mimir, whose waters gave knowledge of the past, present, and future. Mimir asked Odin for his right eye in exchange for a drink from the well, to which Odin agreed. Runes (rünz) are magic spells. **6.** *ravens.* A raven perched on each of Odin's shoulders. These two birds, named Hugin ("Thought") and Munin ("Memory"), flew about the different worlds gathering news which they reported to Odin.

"Give me the boy Rogner!" he cried.

"He is hiding in the greenwood," said the farmer.

"Then I shall find him before sunset," answered Skrymsli, and away he went into the wood.

All day he searched among the birds and the beasts who dwelt there, and in the evening he caught the very swan on whose neck Rogner was hidden. With a shout of triumph he raised the bird to his lips and bit at it. But Honir was watching, and sent a gust of wind which blew the feather away from the Giant's lips and carried it to the farmhouse, where the terrified boy became himself again.

"I have done all I can to help you," said Honir to the farmer. "The sun has set, Skrymsli has gone, and the boy is safe."

Yet the three Aesir tarried still another night in the farmhouse, and next morning they saw the Giant Skrymsli striding towards them once more. This time Loki took Rogner's hand and led him quickly out by the back door and down to the sea-shore. He set him in a boat, rowed out to sea, and casting his line soon caught three flounders. He hid the boy in the tiniest egg in the roe of one of them, and threw the three fishes overboard.

Meanwhile the Giant had come to the farmhouse door.

"Give me the boy Rogner!" he cried.

"He has gone out fishing," said the farmer.

"Then I shall find him before sunset," answered Skrymsli, and away he went down to the sea-shore, where he got into his boat and rowed out from land. When he reached deep water he met Loki, who instantly steered his own boat so that Skrymsli's crashed into it and sank it.

Loki climbed into the Giant's boat, and sat shivering in the stern, begging Skrymsli to take him back to the shore before he died of cold.

But Skrymsli ignored him and rowed on until he was well out to sea, and there he anchored and cast his line.

Very soon he caught three flounders, and amongst them Loki recognized the fish in which he had hidden Rogner.

"Good master Giant," begged Loki, "give me that little fish. There's nothing like raw fish for a man who's just been half-drowned."

"So you're hungry, are you?" growled Skrymsli, picking up the fish. "Well, I am afraid you will have to wait until sunset!"

With that he opened the three fishes and counted every egg in their roes until he came to the one in which Rogner was hidden.

But Loki was watching carefully, and the moment he saw that Skrymsli had the egg he turned himself into a falcon, snatched it from the Giant's hand, and flew with it to the shore.

There he turned Rogner back into his own shape and size and said to him: "Wait where you are until the Giant actually sets foot on shore, then run your fastest across that stretch of very white sand and put up this iron pole at the far end of it." Rogner did as he was told, and the sand seemed to move and whistle strangely beneath his feet as he sped across. But when he had turned and stuck in the iron pole as he had been instructed, he saw that the giant was sinking in the sand.

Down went Skrymsli to his knees, and then with a tremendous effort and a fearful roar of rage, he dragged out one leg and plunged forward. He tripped and fell, and put out his hands to save himself. But both his hands and arms went down into the quicksand as though it had been water, and he struck his head so hard on the iron pole that he knocked himself unconscious. Before he could recover his wits, he had gone down head first into the quicksand and was smothered. Only his legs stuck up out of the ground, and Loki came along with the Giant's own sharp reaping hook and cut them both off.

After Loki had dealt so successfully with Skrymsli, Odin and the other Aesir were still more inclined to take his advice in matters concerning Giants—and very soon his cunning was again put to the test, but in a far more serious matter.

This time it was not merely a farmer's son, but the very existence of Asgard which was in danger. It happened that Odin and the other Aesir were met in council to decide how to build a wall round Asgard to be a sure defence against their enemies.

While they were discussing the difficulties of this undertaking, Heimdall, the guardian of the Bridge Bifrost, came to them and said:

"Father Odin, there stands a man in the plain below the gate of Asgard who offers to build a wall that shall keep out both the Hill Giants and the Rime Giants. But he would speak with you all and make a bargain over the price you are to pay for his labours."

So Odin and the other Aesir came to the gate of Asgard and looked down to where the man stood, his arm through the reins of a fine white stallion. He was tall and grim-looking, but there seemed to be nothing unusual about him, except that he was in an exceedingly bad temper.

"Are you the master mason who offers to build our wall?" asked Odin.

"I am," answered the man. "And I swear to build the whole wall in three years, strong enough and high enough to keep out all the Giant race."

"And what is your price for doing so great a feat of building?" asked Odin.

"Your solemn oath to give me Freya, Lady of the Vanir, as my bride," answered the man, "as well as the Sun and the Moon."

When the Aesir heard this, they were about to treat it as a joke and send the man away with a warning against such impudence.

But Loki said: "Perhaps there is more to this. You know very well that none of us could build such a wall in three years. It is not possible that a man should either, but he may know some craft which we lack. So agree to his terms, but insist that he must build the wall to the very last stone in one winter, with no one to help him, and that if on the first day of summer any part of the work remains undone, he will receive no wages. . . . He cannot possibly complete it, but he may at least lay a good foundation, which we shall get for nothing."

It seemed as if Loki had drunk of Kvasir's Blood,[7] for the Aesir were persuaded by his words, and Odin proposed the conditions to the man.

"To all this will I agree," he replied, "and no man shall help me. But you must allow me to use my horse here."

There seemed no harm in this, so all the Aesir swore solemn oaths to give him Freya, with the Sun and the Moon, if the work were completed by the first day of summer.

The next day was the beginning of winter, and the strange mason set to work. By nightfall the watching Aesir were already feeling uneasy, for the mason's horse Svadilfari[8] carried and hauled such amazing quantities of such huge stones that it seemed little short of miraculous. Moreover the mason himself squared every one of those stones before morning and set each in position, firmly mortared to the next.

So the work went on. Every day Svadilfari hauled vast loads of stone, and night after night his master built them up until, as winter drew towards an end, the wall was nearing completion.

Then the Aesir met in council once more, in a great state of alarm and consternation. "It is only three days until the beginning of summer," said Odin, "and you can all see that this mason will easily finish the wall by then. Shall we therefore be obliged to give one of our number, Freya the Beautiful, to a stranger from Midgard? And must we destroy both Midgard and Asgard by losing the Sun and the Moon—which this wizard may sell to the Giants our enemies?"

"But we have sworn an oath—we cannot break that," the son of bright Baldur, Forseti the Oath-keeper, reminded him.

"Why did we ever swear so foolish—so wicked an oath?" asked Tyr, the War-lord, angrily. "We could have fought the Giants without a wall!"

"We were persuaded to it by cunning Loki," said Odin slowly.

"You all agreed that what this mason offered was an impossible boast," Loki reminded the Aesir. "You must not blame me for what was only a suggestion—which you were quite ready to follow."

"I was not here," grumbled Thor, his red beard bristling. "I was away guarding against Giants. And I'm certain Loki, the son of Laufey, tricked you. He got us into this trouble, he must get us out of it—or he'll have me to reckon with."

Most of the Aesir seemed to agree with Thor, and Loki began to feel frightened. "I had no more idea than you that the man's horse had

---

7. *Kvasir's Blood.* Kvasir (kväs′er) was famous for his wisdom and goodness. The Dwarfs coveted his knowledge and killed him to gain it, mixing his blood with honey to make a magical drink, which gave the power of poetic inspiration to anyone who drank it. **8.** *Svadilfari,* (sväd il fär′ē).

magic powers," he protested. "I'm sure I can think of a way to prevent the mason from earning his prize—my mind is full of schemes. But it pains me to think that you suspect me of bringing this terrible danger upon us by anything but the merest accident."

"No one distrusts you, Loki," answered Odin. "You are one of us, and my brother by blood. But Thor is right; in you there is more cunning than any of us possess. You advised us to make this bargain— and you must save us from having to keep it."

"But without breaking our oath or staining our honour," murmured Forseti. And to this the Aesir agreed, and the council broke up.

Loki at once went away out of Asgard by himself and Thor muttered suspiciously that he was taking refuge with the Giants, and that Heimdall the Watchman of Asgard should not have let him cross Bifrost.

But the other Aesir said nothing: only they took their places on the almost completed wall and looked down to see what would happen.

As night fell the mason arrived leading the great stallion Svadilfari with another load of stones. They had almost reached the foot of the wall, when suddenly, out of a little wood nearby, sprang another horse, a beautiful white mare, neighing and prancing.

At once Svadilfari seemed to go mad. He reared up, neighing in answer to the white mare, and with a sudden plunge broke his traces, oversetting the load of stones, and dashed away into the darkness.

All that night and all the next day Svadilfari followed the white mare, and Svadilfari's master followed him, shouting and cursing in vain. But on the last night of winter he came limping back to Asgard without his horse. Over Bifrost he strode, and stood in the midst of the Aesir, and cursed them as cheats and oathbreakers. Greater and greater grew his fury; until suddenly it overcame all his cunning, and he grew greater too, huger and uglier and more evil. Then the Aesir knew him for one of their enemies the Rime Giants from Jotunheim, and they gathered round him angry and threatening.

But Odin in his wisdom placed the shield Svalin in the eastern sky to hide the rising sun. Suddenly the Giant paused in his threats of tearing down Asgard and casting the Aesir except Freya into Nifelheim, and with a cry of dismay he sprang up on to his new wall for he had seen the sun shining round the edge of the shield. Then Odin cast down Svalin, and the risen sun shone on the Giant and turned him into a stone, which tipped forward off the wall, fell down, down to the plain of Midgard far below, and broke into a mass of splinters.

But Loki came back to Asgard some months later leading the wonderful grey horse Sleipnir, the fastest horse in the world, which had eight legs. It was the foal of Svadilfari and the white mare, and it became Odin's horse and bore him ever afterwards through the clouds and over Midgard, wherever he had a mind to go.

THE TRICKSTER

Few myths have so wide a distribution as the one known by the name of The Trickster . . . For few can we so confidently assert that they belong to the oldest expressions of mankind. Few other myths have persisted with their fundamental content unchanged.

Paul Radin, *The Trickster*

The figure of the Trickster has had a remarkable hold over the imagination of mankind. This is attested to by the fundamental consistency of his character in his appearances in the literatures, both oral and written, of a great variety of peoples and periods. His role is basically unchanged in mythologies from the simplest to the most evolved.

Put most simply, this role is that of a principle of disorder, of incoherence, of accident. He represents that contradictory face of events which perplexes all men, from the most primitive to most civilized; which bespeaks neither providence nor malevolence, but only the rule of chance, that "even-handed justice" which perpetually frustrates the designs of men.

Psychologically, the Trickster represents the factors of inferiority, irrationality, and selfishness that exist in human nature. He is greedy, violent, lecherous, and cunning, though his cunning is often ineffectual. He personifies that "house divided against itself" which confronts men within their own character. He expresses man's feelings of insufficiency in the face of the forces behind events. Sometimes he becomes master of the situation through trickery, as often he is bested. He is the original anarchist, the original clown, the embodiment of the darkly humorous, of the antiheroic.

From THE TRICKSTER, A STUDY IN AMERICAN INDIAN MYTHOLOGY by Paul Radin. Routledge & Kegan Paul Ltd., 1956.

A POETICS FOR BULLIES

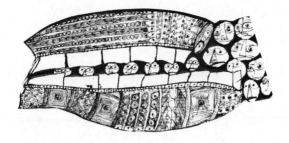

Stanley Elkin

I'M PUSH THE BULLY, and what I hate are new kids and sissies, dumb kids and smart, rich kids, poor kids, kids who wear glasses, talk funny, show off, patrol boys and wise guys and kids who pass pencils and water the plants—and cripples, *especially* cripples. I love nobody loved.

One time I was pushing this red-haired kid (I'm a pusher, no hitter, no belter; an aggressor of marginal violence, I hate *real* force) and his mother stuck her head out the window and shouted something I've never forgotten. *"Push,"* she yelled. *"You, Push.* You pick on him because you wish you had his red hair!" It's true; I *did* wish I had his red hair. I wish I were tall, or fat, or thin. I wish I had different eyes, different hands, a mother in the supermarket. I wish I were a man, a small boy, a girl in the choir. I'm a coveter, a Boston Blackie[1] of the heart, casing the world. Endlessly I covet and case. (Do you know what makes me cry? The Declaration of Independence. "All men are created equal." That's beautiful.)

If you're a bully like me, you use your head. Toughness isn't enough. You beat them up, they report you. Then where are you? I'm not even particularly strong. (I used to be strong. I used to do exercise, work out, but strength implicates you, and often isn't an advantage anyway—read the judo ads. Besides, your big bullies aren't bullies at all—they're *athletes.* With them, beating guys up is a sport.) But what I lose in size and strength I make up in courage. I'm very brave. That's a lie about bullies being cowards underneath. If you're a coward, get out of the business.

1. *Boston Blackie,* reformed safecracker who was the hero of a series of detective films made in the 1940's.

I'm best at torment.

A kid has a toy bow, toy arrows. "Let Push look," I tell him.

He's suspicious, he knows me. "Go way, Push," he says, this mama-warned Push doubter.

"Come on," I say, "come on."

"No, Push. I can't. My mother said I can't."

I raise my arms, I spread them. I'm a bird—slow, powerful, easy, free. I move my head offering profile like something beaked. I'm the Thunderbird.[2] "In the school where I go I have a teacher who teaches me magic," I say. "Arnold Salamancy, give Push your arrows. Give him one, he gives back two. Push is the God of the Neighborhood."

"Go way, Push," the kid says, uncertain.

"Right," Push says, himself again. "Right. I'll disappear. First the fingers." My fingers ball to fists. "My forearms next." They jackknife into my upper arms. "The arms." Quick as bird-blink they snap behind my back, fit between the shoulder blades like a small knapsack. (I am double-jointed, protean.[3]) "My head," I say.

"No, Push," the kid says, terrified. I shudder and everything comes back, falls into place from the stem of self like a shaken puppet.

"The arrow, the arrow. Two where was one." He hands me an arrow. *"Trouble, trouble, double rubble!"* I snap it and give back the pieces.

Well, sure. There *is* no magic. If there were I would learn it. I would find out the words, the slow turns and strange passes, drain the bloods and get the herbs, do the fires like a vestal.[4] I would look for the main chants. *Then* I'd change things. *Push* would!

But there's only casuistical[5] trick. Sleight-of-mouth, the bully's poetics.

You know the formulas:

"Did you ever see a match burn twice?" you ask. Strike. Extinguish. Jab his flesh with the hot stub.

"Play 'Gestapo'?"[6]

"How do you play?"

"What's your name?"

"It's Morton."

I slap him. "You're lying."

"Adam and Eve and Pinch Me Hard went down to the lake for a swim. Adam and Eve fell in. Who was left?"

"Pinch Me Hard."

I do.

---

2. *Thunderbird,* a being who causes thunder and lightning, occurring in the mythologies of some North American Indian peoples. **3.** *protean* (prō'tē ən, prō tē'ən), readily assuming different forms or characters. Proteus was a sea-god in Greek mythology who had the power of assuming different shapes. **4.** *a vestal,* one of the virgin priestesses of the Roman goddess of the hearth, Vesta. Six vestal virgins tended an undying fire in honor of the goddess at her temple in ancient Rome. **5.** *casuistical,* (cazh'ü is'tik əl). Casuistry is clever but false reasoning, especially in regard to right and wrong. **6.** *Gestapo* (gə stä'pō, gə shtä'pō), an official organization of secret police in Nazi Germany.

Physical puns, conundrums.[7] Push the punisher, the conundrummer!

But there has to be more than tricks in a bag of tricks.

I don't know what it is. Sometimes I think *I'm* the only new kid. In a room, the school, the playground, the neighborhood, I get the feeling I've just moved in, no one knows me. You know what I like? To stand in crowds. To wait with them at the airport to meet a plane. Someone asks what time it is. I'm the first to answer. Or at the ball park when the vendor comes. He passes the hot dog down the long row. I want *my* hands on it, too. On the dollar going up, the change coming down.

I am ingenious, I am patient.

A kid is going downtown on the elevated train. He's got his little suit on, his shoes are shined, he wears a cap. This is a kid going to the travel bureaus, the foreign tourist offices to get brochures, maps, pictures of the mountains for a unit at his school—a kid looking for extra credit. I follow him. He comes out of the Italian Tourist Information Center. His arms are full. I move from my place at the window. I follow for two blocks and bump into him as he steps from a curb. It's a *collision*—The pamphlets fall from his arms. Pretending confusion, I walk on his paper Florence. I grind my heel in his Riviera. I climb Vesuvius and sack his Rome and dance on the Isle of Capri.

The Industrial Museum is a good place to find children. I cut somebody's five- or six-year-old kid brother out of the herd of eleven- and twelve-year-olds he's come with. *"Quick,"* I say. I pull him along the corridors, up the stairs, through the halls, down to a mezzanine landing. Breathless, I pause for a minute. "I've got some gum. Do you want a stick?" He nods; I stick him. I rush him into an auditorium and abandon him. He'll be lost for hours.

I sidle up to a kid at the movies. "You smacked my brother," I tell him. "After the show—I'll be outside."

I break up games. I hold the ball above my head. "You want it? Take it."

I go into barber shops. There's a kid waiting. "I'm next," I tell him, "understand?"

One day Eugene Kraft rang my bell. Eugene is afraid of me, so he helps me. He's fifteen and there's something wrong with his saliva glands and he drools. His chin is always chapped. I tell him he has to drink a lot because he loses so much water.

"Push? Push," he says. He's wiping his chin with his tissues. "Push, there's this kid—"

"Better get a glass of water, Eugene."

"No, Push, no fooling, there's this new kid—he just moved in. You've got to see this kid."

---

7. *conundrums* (kə nun′drəmz), riddles whose answers involve puns or plays on words.

"Eugene, get some water, please. You're drying up. I've never seen you so bad. There are deserts in you, Eugene."

"All right, Push, but then you've got to see—"

"Swallow, Eugene. You better swallow."

He gulps hard.

"Push, this is a kid and a half. Wait, you'll see."

"I'm very concerned about you, Eugene. You're dying of thirst, Eugene. Come into the kitchen with me."

I push him through the door. He's very excited. I've never seen him so excited. He talks at me over his shoulder, his mouth flooding, his teeth like the little stone pebbles at the bottom of a fishbowl. "He's got this sport coat, with a patch over the heart. Like a king, Push. No kidding."

"Be careful of the carpet, Eugene."

I turn on the taps in the sink. I mix in hot water. "Use your tissues, Eugene. Wipe your chin."

He wipes himself and puts the Kleenex in his pocket. All of Eugene's pockets bulge. He looks, with his bulging pockets, like a clumsy smuggler.

"Wipe, Eugene. Swallow, you're drowning."

"He's got this funny accent—you could die." Excited, he tamps at his mouth like a diner, a tubercular.

"Drink some water, Eugene."

"No, Push. I'm not thirsty—really."

"Don't be foolish, kid. That's because your mouth's so wet. Inside where it counts you're drying up. It stands to reason. Drink some water."

"He has this crazy haircut."

"Drink," I command. I shake him. *"Drink!"*

"Push, I've got no glass. Give me a glass at least."

"I can't do that, Eugene. You've got a terrible sickness. How could I let you use our drinking glasses? Lean under the tap and open your mouth."

He knows he'll have to do it, that I won't listen to him until he does. He bends into the sink.

"Push, it's *hot,*" he complains. The water splashes into his nose, it gets on his glasses and for a moment his eyes are magnified, enormous. He pulls away and scrapes his forehead on the faucet.

"Eugene, you touched it. Watch out, please. You're too close to the tap. Lean your head deeper into the sink."

"It's *hot,* Push."

"Warm water evaporates better. With your affliction you've got to evaporate fluids before they get into your glands."

He feeds again from the tap.

"Do you think that's enough?" I ask after a while.

"I do, Push, I really do," he says. He is breathless.

"Eugene," I say seriously, "I think you'd better get yourself a canteen."

"A canteen, Push?"

"That's right. Then you'll always have water when you need it. Get one of those Boy Scout models. The two-quart kind with a canvas strap."

"But you hate the Boy Scouts, Push."

"They make very good canteens, Eugene. *And wear it!* I never want to see you without it. Buy it today."

"All right, Push."

"Promise!"

"All right, Push."

"Say it out."

He made the formal promise that I like to hear.

"Well, then," I said, "let's go see this new kid of yours."

He took me to the schoolyard. "Wait," he said, "you'll see." He skipped ahead.

"Eugene," I said, calling him back. "Let's understand something. No matter what this new kid is like, nothing changes as far as you and I are concerned."

"Aw, Push," he said.

"Nothing, Eugene. I mean it. You don't get out from under me."

"Sure, Push, I know that."

There were some kids in the far corner of the yard, sitting on the ground, leaning up against the wire fence. Bats and gloves and balls lay scattered around them. (It was where they told dirty jokes. Sometimes I'd come by during the little kids' recess and tell them all about what their daddies do to their mommies.)

"There. See? Do you see him?" Eugene, despite himself, seemed hoarse.

"Be quiet," I said, checking him, freezing as a hunter might. I stared.

He was a *prince,* I tell you.

He was tall, tall, even sitting down. His long legs comfortable in expensive wool, the trousers of a boy who had been on ships, jets; who owned a horse, perhaps; who knew Latin—what *didn't* he know?— somebody made up, like a kid in a play with a beautiful mother and a handsome father; who took his breakfast from a sideboard, and picked, even at fourteen and fifteen and sixteen, his mail from a silver plate. He would have hobbies—stamps, stars, things lovely dead. He wore a sport coat, brown as wood, thick as heavy bark. The buttons were leather buds. His shoes seemed carved from horses' saddles, gun-stocks. His clothes had once grown in nature. *What it must feel like inside those clothes,* I thought.

I looked at his face, his clear skin, and guessed at the bones, white as beached wood. His eyes had skies in them. His yellow hair swirled on his head like a crayoned sun.

"Look, look at him," Eugene said. "The sissy. Get him, Push."

He was talking to them and I moved closer to hear his voice. It was clear, beautiful, but faintly foreign—like herb-seasoned meat.

When he saw me he paused, smiling. He waved. The others didn't look at me.

"Hello there," he called. "Come over if you'd like. I've been telling the boys about tigers."

"Tigers," I said.

"Give him the 'match burn twice,' Push," Eugene whispered.

"Tigers, is it?" I said. "What do you know about tigers?" My voice was high.

"The 'match burn twice,' Push."

"Not so much as a Master *Tugjah.* I was telling the boys. In India there are men of high caste—*Tugjahs,* they're called. I was apprenticed to one once in the Southern Plains and might perhaps have earned my mastership, but the Red Chinese attacked the northern frontier and . . . well, let's just say I had to leave. At any rate, these *Tugjahs* are as intimate with the tiger as you are with dogs. I don't mean they keep them as pets. The relationship goes deeper. Your dog is a service animal, as is your elephant."

"Did you ever see a match burn twice?" I asked suddenly.

"Why no, can you do that? Is it a special match you use?"

"No," Eugene said, "it's an ordinary match. He uses an ordinary match."

"Can you do it with one of mine, do you think?"

He took a matchbook from his pocket and handed it to me. The cover was exactly the material of his jacket, and in the center was a patch with a coat-of-arms identical to the one he wore over his heart.

I held the matchbook for a moment and then gave it back to him. "I don't feel like it," I said.

"Then some other time, perhaps," he said.

Eugene whispered to me. "His accent, Push, his funny *accent.*"

"Some other time, perhaps," I said. I am a good mimic. I can duplicate a particular kid's lisp, his stutter, a thickness in his throat. There were two or three here whom I had brought close to tears by holding up my mirror to their voices. I can parody their limps, their waddles, their girlish runs, their clumsy jumps. I can throw as they throw, catch as they catch. I looked around. "Some other time, perhaps," I said again. No one would look at me.

"I'm *so* sorry," the new one said, "we don't know each other's names. You are?"

"I'm so sorry," I said. "You are?"

He seemed puzzled. Then he looked sad, disappointed. No one said anything.

"It don't sound the same," Eugene whispered.

It was true. I sounded nothing like him. I could imitate only defects, only flaws. A kid giggled.

"Shh," the prince said. He put one finger to his lips.

"Look at that," Eugene said under his breath. "He's a sissy."

He had begun to talk to them again. I squatted, a few feet away. I ran gravel through my loose fists, one bowl in an hourglass feeding another.

He spoke of jungles, of deserts. He told of ancient trade routes traveled by strange beasts. He described lost cities and a lake deeper than the deepest level of the sea. There was a story about a boy who had been captured by bandits. A woman in the story—it wasn't clear whether she was the boy's mother—had been tortured. His eyes clouded for a moment when he came to this part and he had to pause before continuing. Then he told how the boy escaped—it was cleverly done—and found help, mountain tribesmen riding elephants. The elephants charged the cave in which the mo—the *woman*—was still a prisoner. It might have collapsed and killed her, but one old bull rushed in and, shielding her with his body, took the weight of the crashing rocks. Your elephant is a service animal.

I let a piece of gravel rest on my thumb and flicked it in a high arc above his head. Some of the others who had seen me stared, but the boy kept on talking. Gradually I reduced the range, allowing the chunks of gravel to come closer to his head.

"You see?" Eugene said quietly. "He's afraid. He pretends not to notice."

The arcs continued to diminish. The gravel went faster, straighter. No one was listening to him now, but he kept talking.

"—of magic," he said, "what occidentals call 'a witch doctor.' There are spices that induce these effects. The *Bogdovii* was actually able to stimulate the growth of rocks with the powder. The Dutch traders were ready to go to war for the formula. Well, you can see what it could mean for the Low Countries. Without accessible quarries they've never been able to construct a permanent system of dikes. But with the *Bogdovii's* powder"—he reached out and casually caught the speeding chip as if it had been a ping-pong ball—"they could turn a grain of sand into a pebble, use the pebbles to grow stones, the stones to grow rocks. This little piece of gravel, for example, could be changed into a mountain." He dipped his thumb into his palm as I had and balanced the gravel on his nail. He flicked it; it rose from his nail like a missile and climbed an impossible arc. It disappeared. "The *Bogdovii* never revealed how it was done."

I stood up. Eugene tried to follow me.

"Listen," he said, "you'll get him."

"Swallow," I told him. "Swallow, you pig!"

I have lived my life in pursuit of the vulnerable: Push the chink seeker, wheeler dealer in the flawed cement of the personality, a collapse maker. But what isn't vulnerable, *who* isn't? There is that which is unspeakable, so I speak it, that which is unthinkable, which I think. Me and the devil, we do God's dirty work, after all.

I went home after I left him. I turned once at the gate, and the boys were around him still. The useless Eugene had moved closer. *He* made room for him against the fence.

I ran into Frank the fat boy. He made a move to cross the street, but I had seen him and he went through a clumsy retractive motion. I could tell he thought I would get him for that, but I moved by, indifferent to a grossness in which I had once delighted. As I passed he seemed puzzled, a little hurt, a little—this was astonishing—guilty. *Sure* guilty. Why *not* guilty? The forgiven tire of their exemption. Nothing could ever be forgiven, and I forgave nothing. I held them to the mark. Who else cared about the fatties, about the dummies and slobs and clowns, about the gimps and squares and oafs and fools, the kids with a mouthful of mush, all those shut-ins of the mind and heart, all those losers? Frank the fat boy knew, and passed me shyly. His wide, fat body, stiffened, forced jokishly martial when he saw me, had already become flaccid as he moved by, had already made one more forgiven surrender. Who cared?

The streets were full of failure. Let them. Let them be. There was a paragon, a paragon loose. What could he be doing here, why had he come, what did he want? It was impossible that this hero from India and everywhere had made his home here; that he lived, as Frank the fat boy did, as Eugene did, as *I* did, in an apartment; that he shared our lives.

In the afternoon I looked for Eugene. He was in the park, in a tree. There was a book in his lap. He leaned against the thick trunk.

"Eugene," I called up to him.

"Push, they're closed. It's Sunday, Push. The stores are closed. I looked for the canteen. The stores are closed."

"Where is he?"

"Who, Push? What do you want, Push?"

"*Him.* Your pal. The prince. Where? Tell me, Eugene, or I'll shake you out of that tree. I'll burn you down. I swear it. Where is he?"

"No, Push. I was wrong about that guy. He's nice. He's really nice. Push, he told me about a doctor who could help me. Leave him alone, Push."

"Where, Eugene? *Where?* I count to three."

Eugene shrugged and came down the tree.

I found the name Eugene gave me—funny, foreign—over the bell in the outer hall. The buzzer sounded and I pushed open the door. I stood inside and looked up the carpeted stairs, the angled banisters.

"What is it?" She sounded old, worried.

"The new kid," I called, "the new kid."

"It's for you," I heard her say.

"Yes?" His voice, the one I couldn't mimic. I mounted the first stair. I leaned back against the wall and looked up through the high, boxy banister poles. It was like standing inside a pipe organ.

"Yes?"

From where I stood at the bottom of the stairs I could see only a boot. He was wearing boots.

"Yes? What is it, please?"

"*You,*" I roared. "Glass of fashion, mold of form,[8] it's me! It's Push the bully!"

I heard his soft, rapid footsteps coming down the stairs—a springy, spongy urgency. He jingled, the bastard. He had coins—I could see them: rough, golden, imperfectly round; raised, massively gowned goddesses, their heads fingered smooth, their arms gone—and keys to strange boxes, thick doors. I saw his boots. I backed away.

"I brought you down," I said.

"Be quiet, please. There's a woman who's ill. A boy who must study. There's a man with bad bones. An old man needs sleep."

"He'll get it," I said.

"We'll go outside," he said.

"No. Do you live here? What do you do? Will you be in our school? Were you telling the truth?"

"Shh. Please. You're very excited."

"Tell me your name," I said. It could be my campaign, I thought. His *name.* Scratched in new sidewalk, chalked onto walls, written on papers dropped in the street. To leave it behind like so many clues, to give him a fame, to take it away, to slash and cross out, to erase and to smear—my kid's witchcraft. "Tell me your name."

"It's John," he said softly.

"What?"

'It's John."

"John what? Come on now. I'm Push the bully."

"John Williams," he said.

"John Williams? John Williams? Only that? Only John Williams?" He smiled.

"Who's that on the bell? The name on the box?"

"She needs me," he said.

---

8. *"Glass of fashion, mould of form,"* Hamlet, act 3, scene 1, line 161. These phrases are from Ophelia's grandiloquent description of her former lover, Hamlet, the young prince of Denmark.

"Cut it out."

"I help her," he said.

"You stop that."

"There's a man that's in pain. A woman who's old. A husband that's worried. A wife that despairs."

"You're the bully," I said. "Your John Williams is a service animal," I yelled in the hall.

He turned and began to climb the stairs. His calves bloomed in their leather sheathing.

"Lover," I whispered to him.

He turned to me at the landing. He shook his head sadly.

"We'll see," I said.

"We'll see what we'll see," he said.

That night I painted his name on the side of the gymnasium in enormous letters. In the morning it was still there, but it wasn't what I meant. There was nothing incantatory in the huge letters, no scream, no curse. I had never traveled with a gang, there had been no togetherness in my tearing, but this thing on the wall seemed the act of vandals, the low production of ruffians. When you looked at it you were surprised they had gotten the spelling right.

Astonishingly, it was allowed to remain. And each day there was something more celebrational in the giant name, something of increased hospitality, lavish welcome. John Williams might have been a football hero, or someone back from the kidnapers. Finally I had to take it off myself.

Something had changed.

Eugene was not wearing his canteen. Boys didn't break off their conversations when I came up to them. One afternoon a girl winked at me. (Push has never picked on girls. *Their* submissiveness is part of their nature. They are ornamental. Don't get me wrong, please. There is a way in which they function as part of the landscape, like flowers at a funeral. They have a strange cheerfulness. They are the organizers of pep rallies and dances. They put out the Year Book. They are *born* Gray Ladies.[9] I can't bully them.)

John Williams was in the school, but except for brief glimpses in the hall I never saw him. Teachers would repeat the things he had said in their other classes. They read from his papers. In the gym the coach described plays he had made, set shots he had taken. Everyone talked about him, and girls made a reference to him a sort of love signal. If it was suggested that he had smiled at one of them, the girl referred to would blush or, what was worse, look aloofly mysterious. (*Then* I could have punished her, *then* I could.) Gradually his name began to appear on all their notebooks, in the margins of their texts. (It annoyed me to remember what *I* had done on the wall.) The big canvas books,

9. *Gray Ladies*, women workers in the American Red Cross who serve as volunteer aides in medical services.

with their careful, elaborate J's and W's, took on the appearance of ancient, illuminated fables. It was the unconscious embroidery of love, hope's bright doodle. Even the administration was aware of him. In Assembly the principal announced that John Williams had broken all existing records in the school's charity drives. She had never seen good citizenship like his before, she said.

It's one thing to live with a bully, another to live with a hero.

Everyone's hatred I understand, no one's love; everyone's grievance, no one's content.

I saw Mimmer. Mimmer should have graduated years ago. I saw Mimmer the dummy.

"Mimmer," I said, "you're in his class."

"He's very smart."

"Yes, but is it fair? You work harder. I've seen you study. You spend hours. Nothing comes. He was born knowing. You could have used just a little of what he's got so much of. It's not fair."

"He's very clever. It's wonderful," Mimmer says.

Slud is crippled. He wears a shoe with a built-up heel to balance himself.

"Ah, Slud," I say, "I've seen him run."

"He has beaten the horses in the park. It's very beautiful," Slud says.

"He's handsome, isn't he, Clob?" Clob looks contagious, radioactive. He has severe acne. He is ugly *under* his acne.

"He gets the girls," Clob says.

He gets *everything*, I think. But I'm alone in my envy, awash in my lust. It's as if I were a prophet to the deaf. Schnooks, schnooks, I want to scream, dopes and settlers. What good does his smile do you, of what use is his good heart?

The other day I did something stupid. I went to the cafeteria and shoved a boy out of the way and took his place in the line. It was foolish, but their fear is almost all gone and I felt I had to show the flag. The boy only grinned and let me pass. Then someone called my name. It was *him*. I turned to face him. "Push," he said, "you forgot your silver." He handed it to a girl in front of him and she gave it to the boy in front of her and it came to me down the long line.

I plot, I scheme. Snares, I think; tricks and traps. I remember the old days when there were ways to snap fingers, crush toes, ways to pull noses, twist heads and punch arms—the old-timey Flinch Law I used to impose, the gone bully magic of deceit. But nothing works against him, I think. How does he know so much? He is bully-prepared, that one, not to be trusted.

It is worse and worse.

In the cafeteria he eats with Frank. "You don't want those potatoes," he tells him. "Not the ice cream, Frank. One sandwich, remember. You

lost three pounds last week." The fat boy smiles his fat love at him.
John Williams puts his arm around him. He seems to squeeze him thin.

He's helping Mimmer to study. He goes over his lessons and teaches him tricks, short cuts. "I want you up there with me on the Honor Roll, Mimmer."

I see him with Slud the cripple. They go to the gym. I watch from the balcony. "Let's develop those arms, my friend." They work out with weights. Slud's muscles grow, they bloom from his bones.

I lean over the rail. I shout down, "He can bend iron bars. Can he peddle a bike? Can he walk on rough ground? Can he climb up a hill? Can he wait on a line? Can he dance with a girl? Can he go up a ladder or jump from a chair?"

Beneath me the rapt Slud sits on a bench and raises a weight. He holds it at arm's length, level with his chest. He moves it high, higher. It rises above his shoulders, his throat, his head. He bends back his neck to see what he's done. If the weight should fall now it would crush his throat. I stare down into his smile.

I see Eugene in the halls. I stop him. "Eugene, what's he done for you?" I ask. He smiles—he never did this—and I see his mouth's flood. "High tide," I say with satisfaction.

Williams has introduced Clob to a girl. They have double-dated.

A week ago John Williams came to my house to see me! I wouldn't let him in.

"Please open the door, Push. I'd like to chat with you. Will you open the door? Push? I think we ought to talk. I think I can help you to be happier."

I was furious. I didn't know what to say to him. "I don't want to be happier. Go way." It was what little kids used to say to me.

"Please let me help you."

"Please let me—" I begin to echo. "Please let me alone."

"We ought to be friends, Push."

"No deals." I am choking, I am close to tears. What can I do? *What?* I want to kill him.

I double-lock the door and retreat to my room. He is still out there. I have tried to live my life so that I could keep always the lamb from my door.

He has gone too far this time; and I think sadly, I will have to fight him, I will have to fight him. Push pushed. I think sadly of the pain. Push pushed. I will have to fight him. Not to preserve honor but its opposite. Each time I see him I will have to fight him. And then I think—*of course!* And *I* smile. He has done *me* a favor. I know it at once. If he fights me he fails. He fails if he fights me. *Push pushed pushes!* It's physics! Natural law! I know he'll beat me, but I won't prepare, I won't train, I won't use the tricks I know. It's strength against strength, and my strength is as the strength of ten because my jaw is glass! *He doesn't know everything, not everything he doesn't.* And I think, I could go out now, he's still there, I could hit him in the hall, but I think, No, I want them to see, I want *them* to see!

The next day I am very excited. I look for Williams. He's not in the halls. I miss him in the cafeteria. Afterward I look for him in the schoolyard where I first saw him. (He has them organized now. He teaches them games of Tibet, games of Japan; he gets them to play lost sports of the dead.) He does not disappoint me. He is there in the yard, a circle around him, a ring of the loyal.

I join the ring. I shove in between two kids I have known. They try to change places; they murmur and fret.

Williams sees me and waves. His smile could grow flowers. "Boys," he says, "boys, make room for Push. Join hands, boys." They welcome me to the circle. One takes my hand, then another. I give to each calmly.

I wait. *He doesn't know everything.*

"Boys," he begins, "today we're going to learn a game that the knights of the lords and kings of old France used to play in another century. Now you may not realize it, boys, because today when we think of a knight we think, too, of his fine charger, but the fact is that a horse was a rare animal—not a domestic European animal at all, but Asian. In western Europe, for example, there was no such thing as a work horse until the eighth century. Your horse was just too expensive to be put to heavy labor in the fields. (This explains, incidentally, the prevalence of famine in western Europe, whereas famine is unrecorded in Asia until the ninth century, when Euro-Asian horse trading was at its height.) It wasn't only expensive to purchase a horse, it was expensive to keep one. A cheap fodder wasn't developed in Europe until the tenth century. Then, of course, when you consider the terrific risks that the warrior horse of a knight naturally had to run, you begin to appreciate how expensive it would have been for the lord—unless he was extremely rich—to provide all his knights with horses. He'd want to make pretty certain that the knights who got them knew how to handle a horse. (Only your knights errant—an elite, crack corps—ever had horses. We don't realize that most knights were *home* knights; *chevalier chez*[10] they were called.)

"This game, then, was devised to let the lord, or king, see which of his knights had the skill and strength in his hands to control a horse. Without moving your feet, you must try to jerk the one next to you off balance. Each man has two opponents, so it's very difficult. If a man falls, or if his knee touches the ground, he's out. The circle is diminished but must close up again immediately. Now, once for practice only—"

---

10. *chevalier chez*, (shèr va′lyā′ shā). [*French*]

"Just a minute," I interrupt.

"Yes, Push?"

I leave the circle and walk forward and hit him as hard as I can in the face.

He stumbles backward. The boys groan. He recovers. He rubs his jaw and smiles. I think he is going to let me hit him again. I am prepared for this. He knows what I'm up to and will use his passivity. Either way I win, but I am determined he shall hit me. I am ready to kick him, but as my foot comes up he grabs my ankle and turns it forcefully. I spin in the air. He lets go and I fall heavily on my back. I am surprised at how easy it was, but am content if they understand. I get up and am walking away, but there is an arm on my shoulder. He pulls me around roughly. He hits me.

"*Sic semper tyrannus*,"[11] he exults.

"Where's your other cheek?" I ask, falling backward.

"One cheek for tyrants," he shouts. He pounces on me and raises his fist and I cringe. His anger is terrific. I do not want to be hit again.

"You see? You see?" I scream at the kids, but I have lost the train of my former reasoning. I have in no way beaten him. I can't remember now what I had intended.

He lowers his fist and gets off my chest and they cheer. "Hurrah," they yell. "Hurrah, hurrah." The word seems funny to me.

He offers his hand when I try to rise. It is so difficult to know what to do. Oh God, it is so difficult to know which gesture is the right one. I don't even know this. He knows everything, and I don't even know this. I am a fool on the ground, one hand behind me pushing up, the other not yet extended but itching in the palm where the need is. It is better to give than receive, surely. It is best not to need at all.

Appalled, guessing what I miss, I rise alone.

"Friends?" he asks. He offers to shake.

"Take it, Push." It's Eugene's voice.

"Go ahead, Push." Slud limps forward.

"Push, hatred's so ugly," Clob says, his face shining.

"You'll feel better, Push," Frank, thinner, taller, urges softly.

"Push, don't be foolish," Mimmer says.

I shake my head. I may be wrong. I am probably wrong. All I know at last is what feels good. "Nothing doing," I growl. "No deals." I begin to talk, to spray my hatred at them. They are not an easy target even now. "Only your knights errant—your crack corps—ever have horses. Slud may dance and Clob may kiss but they'll never be good at it. *Push is no service animal.* No. No. Can you hear that, Williams? There isn't any magic, but your no is still stronger than your yes, and distrust is where I put my faith." I turn to the boys. "What have you settled for? Only your knights errant ever have horses. *What have you*

---

11. *Sic semper tyrannus*, "Ever thus to tyrants," the motto of the state of Virginia. [*Latin*]

settled for? Will Mimmer do sums in his head? How do you like your lousy hunger, thin boy? Slud, you can break me but you can't catch me. And Clob will never shave without pain, and ugly, let me tell you, is *still* in the eye of the beholder!"

John Williams mourns for me. He grieves his gamy grief. No one has everything—not even John Williams. He doesn't have *me*. He'll never have me, I think. If my life were only to deny him that, it would almost be enough. I could do his voice now if I wanted. His corruption began when he lost me. "You," I shout, rubbing it in, "*indulger,* dispense me no dispensations. Push the bully hates your heart!"

"Shut him up, somebody," Eugene cries. His saliva spills from his mouth when he speaks.

"Swallow! *Pig, swallow!*"

He rushes toward me.

Suddenly I raise my arms and he stops. I feel a power in me. I am Push, Push the bully, God of the Neighborhood, its incarnation of envy and jealousy and need. I vie, strive, emulate, compete, a contender in every event there is. I didn't make myself. I probably can't save myself, but maybe that's the only need I don't have. I taste my lack and that's how I win—by having nothing to lose. It's not good enough! I want and I want and I will die wanting, but first I will have something. This time I will have something. I say it aloud. "This time I will have something." I step toward them. The power makes me dizzy. It is enormous. They feel it. They back away. They crouch in the shadow of my outstretched wings. It isn't deceit this time but the real magic at last, the genuine thing: the cabala[12] of my hate, of my irreconcilableness.

Logic is nothing. Desire is stronger.

I move toward Eugene. "*I will have something,*" I roar.

"Stand back," he shrieks, "I'll spit in your eye."

"*I will have something.* I will have terror. I will have drought. I bring the dearth. Famine's contagious. Also is thirst. Privation, privation, barrenness, void. I dry up your glands, I poison your well."

He is choking, gasping, chewing furiously. He opens his mouth. It is dry. His throat is parched. There is sand on his tongue.

They moan. They are terrified, but they move up to see. We are thrown together. Slud, Frank, Clob, Mimmer, the others, John Williams, myself. I will not be reconciled, or halve my hate. *It's* what I have, all I can keep. My bully's sour solace. It's enough, I'll make do.

I can't stand them near me. I move against them. I shove them away. I force them off. I press them, thrust them aside. *I push through.*

---

12. *cabala* (kab/ə lə, kə bä/lə), a system of interpretation of the Scriptures based on the numerical rather than the alphabetical values of the Hebrew letters, developed in the Middle Ages by certain rabbis.

4

TRIALS
AND
COMBATS

TESILYA,[1]
SUN'S DAUGHTER

Theodora Kroeber[2]

THERE IS A VARIETY of large cane growing in brakes and thickets along the Colorado River which, beyond its many practical daily uses, is said by the river people to possess a powerful magic for one who knows how to use it. This cane is named for Ahta,[3] a hero who lived in the far-off times. Nowadays the story of Ahta (Cane) and of Ahta-hana[4] (son of Cane) is renewed for the river people of each generation in a dream which comes to one or another of them, usually to someone already skilled in the practice of magic and storytelling.

The dream is of Ahta and his son, their journeyings and fights and great exploits. Only by the way does Tesilya, the wife of Ahta, or indeed any woman come into the dream at all.

Of Tesilya we know only that she was beautiful and gracious, that she was joyous when her world was good, that she was quiet and strong when her world was evil, that she was so in age as in youth. And perhaps that is as much as a dream need tell of a woman.

The dream usually begins with Ahta already grown, living with his elder brother Hotpa[5] and his uncle in the shadow of the sacred mountain of the river people.

The uncle watched over the two boys with loving care. Hotpa was skilled in magic, but his uncle saw with sorrow that he was cruel and of an unhappy disposition, and that he was already jealous of his younger brother, knowing as he did that Ahta was born a hero, that he was gentle and brave, and beloved of all who knew him.

Each night the three of them came home to an empty, cheerless house, the food for the evening meal yet to be cooked. At last the uncle said, "Look at us! We are three men here with no woman. We come home and there is no wood, no water, no food. I am old. But go, you two young ones, tomorrow, and find, one or both of you, a wife."

The brothers took their uncle's advice, and early the next morning set out, travelling east from the sacred mountain. Ahta had heard of old man Sun's daughter, and it was in his mind to find her.

1. *Tesilya*, (tə sil'yä). 2. *Kroeber*, (krō'bẽr). 3. *Ahta*, (ä'tä). 4. *Ahta-hana*, (ä'tä hä'nä). 5. *Hotpa*, (hot'pä).

They walked all day and slept the night on the open desert. As soon as it was light they went on again, always east, until toward midday they reached Sun's house. Ahta and Hotpa stopped before its door of plaited willowbark.

Tesilya, Sun's daughter, lived there with her father. Sun was often away from home and Tesilya had as a pet and guardian a yellow-hammer woodpecker whose cage hung high above the door. No one but Tesilya ever touched the yellow-hammer, and if a stranger approached or if all seemed not right when she was alone inside, he cried out in his hoarse voice and beat against the sticks of his cage to warn her.

This morning, though two strangers came up to the door, the yellow-hammer made no sign, no sound. Ahta lifted down his cage and took him out, and it was only after he had set him on the ground in front of the door that the bird gave his usual cry. Tesilya heard the hoarse, familiar voice, and glancing warily between the willow plaits, she saw where he was. She remembered that this was a sign that someone outside there wished her for his wife—someone the yellow-hammer was not afraid of—so she looked much more closely from behind her screen.

She looked first to the north, and there she saw Ahta standing, facing her door expectantly. Then she looked to the south where Hotpa stood, also facing her door expectantly. Her bright gaze turned back to the north, to Ahta the young hero. As she looked toward him a second time, she laughed softly. This made the brothers laugh aloud and caused the yellow-hammer to sing. And so they waited as they were, the brothers and the woodpecker, for the willow screen to be lifted.

They had to wait quite a while. First Tesilya poured water into a bowl blackened inside with charcoal. Using this for a mirror, she made herself up carefully. She painted two small red triangles on her forehead between the arched black eyebrows and the short black bangs, and with the same red, a small curving-out bow down each cheek. Then she encircled her eyes and breasts with narrow lines of yellow paint. She dressed herself in a new fringed willowbark skirt and a new little front apron, fringed also, and a wide braided belt. She put earrings in her ears and hung many heavy strings of beads around her neck and wrists. Close about her throat she clasped an enormous clam shell, carved in a frog pattern. She tied two small bags of face paint, one red, one yellow, to her belt; and she peeled a fresh willow switch with which to sweep her skirt smoothly under her so as not to crumple it when sitting.

Ready at last, she raised the slatted screen and came out of the house. First, she picked up the woodpecker and put him back in his cage; then, with the cage on her arm, she went to Ahta and stood before him and looked into his face. Ahta was smiling, and she was smiling, too.

Ahta asked her if she would go home with him to the sacred mountain, and she answered, "Yes. I am ready to go."

Hotpa was angry. He grabbed Tesilya's arm, shouting, "She is mine! She is mine! I am older than you and she is mine!"

But Ahta held Tesilya and would not give her up. He said, "No. She chose. She came to me. She belongs to me."

Hotpa struck Ahta and tried to drag Tesilya away from him but Ahta was too strong for him and beat him off. At last Hotpa stopped dragging at her and fighting his brother and said, "Very well! Let us go home."

They started in the direction of the sacred mountain, but they had not gone many steps west when Tesilya stopped and looked back to her home. "I thought my house was already far away, but it is only a little distance," she said. "Will you wait, you two, while I sing the song of my house?" The brothers waited and listened to Tesilya's song. She sang of her father, his house, and her life there as a child and a young woman, and of how she was leaving now, never to return, never to see her father or the house again.

Her song finished, they turned again to the west and walked on all through the day. As they walked, the brothers sang to Tesilya to make the way seem shorter. They sang her the song of Mountain Sheep and the song of Vulture and the songs of all the other stars until the stars themselves came out and night was upon them, far from any house or people.

Ahta made a bed on the open desert and took Tesilya to it. As in the morning, Hotpa fought with his younger brother over her, but again Ahta was too strong for him. In the end, Hotpa went off and slept alone, and in the morning Tesilya was much relieved to have him speak to her as "My Sister-in-law."

The three of them continued their journey in the morning, and when the sun was overhead they reached the sacred mountain, and there outside their house, they found their uncle sitting, waiting for them.

Tesilya was shy before her new uncle and hid her face behind her hair which hung, black and shining, almost to her knees. The uncle took her hand in greeting between both of his. Then, gently, he parted the heavy hair and uncovered her face, saying, "Come! Let me see my younger brother's daughter-in-law!"

He led her into the house and showed her over her new home and talked to her in his quiet way. Shyness left her, and soon she was grinding corn, singing as she worked. The three men smiled, repeating to one another, "See how beautiful she is!"

When it was supper time, the uncle helped Tesilya make mush of the fresh-ground corn. He poured the corn slowly into the pot of boiling water while she stirred it and added salt. Together they tasted it to be sure it was right.

From that time, when the men came home they found a warm fire and fresh water and a supper ready, and a happy woman singing at her work. But when it was bed-time the uncle saw the soreness in Hotpa's heart renewed each night, for Tesilya went always with Ahta to the southwest corner of the house, which was his sleeping place. The uncle did what he could. When he learned that his friend Jaguar had a marriageable daughter, he sent the two brothers to the west to Jaguar's house to bring her as wife to Hotpa. And so, at last the uncle thought his household was complete and at peace. When he settled himself for the night on his pallet at the center of the house, Ahta would be lying in his corner with Tesilya, and Hotpa in his with Jaguar's daughter.

But there was to be no peace in this house. Hotpa could not forget his humiliations in the journeys with Ahta. It had happened at Jaguar's house as at Sun's house: Jaguar's daughter, too, had chosen Ahta first, and it was only when Ahta said that he did not want her that she turned to Hotpa. Even when this was all past and over and Jaguar's daughter was his wife and content, Hotpa could not forgive Ahta and Tesilya. He hated them as together they became ever more beautiful, and happiness was in them, and all the river people loved them. In their happiness they forget to fear and to watch Hotpa.

Hotpa put a powerful ghost illness on Ahta, which no one recognized for a magic spell until it was far advanced. It caused Ahta to have terrible nightmares; then he became delirious, and at last mortally weak. Secretly, Hotpa kept a close watch on his younger brother. There came a morning when Tesilya and the uncle left Ahta alone for a while. He was asleep, and in any case too weak to cry out or to defend himself. With savage swiftness, Hotpa cut off a piece of Ahta's scalp, and, while his brother yet lived, hacked out the shinbone and kneecap from one of Ahta's legs. Tesilya was not gone for long, but when she returned, this violence had been done, Hotpa was nowhere to be seen, and her husband Ahta was dead.

Hotpa, a man possessed, waved the bloody shinbone over his head, and running from house to house, called out to whoever was inside to come with him for a game of shinny.[6] Threatening and promising, he found players for his shinny game, for he was greatly feared. Never was there such a game, for Hotpa used Ahta's shinbone for a shinny stick, and his kneecap for a ball.

But when the people found that Ahta was dead they fled in panic from Hotpa, out onto the desert. And Hotpa and his shinny players ran away from the sacred mountain, too, hiding in the mountains far to the north. Jaguar's daughter did not go with Hotpa. She went home to her father's house in the west, and the old uncle and Tesilya were left alone.

Alone, they did all that must be done for a hero's passage from this

6. *shinny*, a simple form of hockey, played with a ball and a curved stick.

world. When they had sung the songs for the newly dead and performed the other rites, they laid Ahta's body on a funeral pyre along with his clothing and blankets and ornaments, his bows and arrows and his war clubs: everything that had belonged to him. They burned everything, even his house, in a great and inclusive and cleansing fire which translated him wholly into the world of the dead. They cut their hair to mourning shortness, and together they cried and sang the mourning songs for Ahta, and cried and sang and cried again. They built themselves another house and lived on there, mourning and missing him always in their hearts.

The moons came and went until one morning Tesilya wakened in heavy pain. Her uncle cared for her gently as a loving woman might, and he told her that her baby would be born soon. The day passed and night came and the baby was not yet born, but they heard him plainly, singing and talking inside her. This frightened Tesilya, but her uncle reassured her. "This is good," he said to her. "It means that your son will have much power and be a hero."

Toward dawn of the next day the baby stopped singing and spoke plainly, saying, "Be quiet, you two! Let no one come near! I am coming out into the world."

And so it was that the son of Ahta and Tesilya was born. His great-uncle laid him gently on a bed of warmed sand and covered him to his neck with more warmed sand, that he might rest and become accustomed to the outside world. Tesilya saw that her son was beautiful and like his father, and she named him Ahta-hana.

The night Ahta-hana was born, it rained and rained in the mountains where Hotpa was hiding, although it was not the season of rainfall. Hotpa took this to be some sort of a portent. He sent a messenger to see if Tesilya's baby had been born. If so, and if it were a boy—something Hotpa greatly dreaded—he meant to have the baby killed.

The baby's great-uncle was sitting in the doorway when the messenger arrived before Tesilya's house. He greeted him courteously and listened while the messenger told him that Hotpa wanted to know how Tesilya fared, and if her baby was born.

"Yes. She was born last night," said the uncle. "I will bring her for you to see so that you can tell Hotpa of his niece." So saying, he went into the house, returning shortly with Ahta-hana, bound to a cradle-board with the diamond pattern of cross-strapping used only for girl babies. He even gave the baby on its board to Hotpa's messenger to hold, all the while appearing at ease and open.

The messenger returned to Hotpa, telling him that his brother's child was a girl, and Hotpa's fears were put to rest.

Once he was born, Tesilya's baby did not talk as he had in her womb. Within six days he smiled and within twelve days he laughed aloud. With the return of the moon of his birth he ran about alone and talked plainly. During the passing of many placid seasons he grew under the tender care and teaching of mother and great-uncle, without particular event to mark the seasons.

But the time came when Hotpa could no longer stifle the homesickness of those who had fled with him, and he returned with them to the sacred mountain.

Ahta-hana was much interested in these people, new to him. Tesilya dressed him in a girl's willowbark skirt and let him go among them. Hotpa gave him a doll carefully carved from bone, and Ahta-hana watched his uncle's people play shinny. When Tesilya was putting him to bed that night, he showed her his new doll and he told her of the new sort of shinny game his uncle's people played.

Tesilya knew there was evil in all this. She said nothing that night or the next or the next. But the fourth night, when she was talking to Ahta-hana at his bedtime, she told him the truth: that the bone doll, the shinny stick, and the shinny ball were made from his own father's bones. It saddened and dismayed Tesilya to do this, but she had no power to protect her son, and she feared greatly for him.

Ahta-hana cried all through the night, and when it was light he wandered out onto the desert still crying. Worn out, he crept under a mesquite bush and went to sleep. As he slept, he dreamed that a beetle crawled off a branch of the mesquite bush to his upper lip. There the beetle sat and talked to him, telling him all about his father and his father's death.

When he wakened, Ahta-hana lay quiet awhile thinking over his dream. At last he understood the meaning of Hotpa's shinny game. And he understood that Hotpa would surely destroy whatever had been dear to his dead brother.

Ahta-hana laid aside his girl's willowbark skirt and went home to his mother and great-uncle, and when he spoke to them they knew he was no longer a child in his mind.

They listened to Ahta-hana's words, and they did as he said. His great-uncle was to stay as always by the sacred mountain. To his mother, Ahta-hana said, "But you, my mother, you must go back to my grandfather's house. My uncle will try to kill you; he will surely harm you if you stay here. Go—and when I have done all I must do, I will come to you."

Tesilya filled her mirror bowl with glowing coals from the fire. She would replenish the coals with twigs and sticks from time to time as she travelled. Holding it close to her, it would warm her and light her way across the desert. She said a quiet goodbye to her uncle and to her son. Without tears that could be seen, without a backward glance, Tesilya opened the door of her house and stepped outside. Straight and firm, she walked to the east, the bowl of coals held in both her hands.

She walked back over the way she had come with Ahta, toward the house she had thought never to see again.

Ahta-hana watched her until he could no longer catch the faintest glimmer from the bowl of glowing coals, far, far out on the desert. Then he cried, "O, why have I sent my mother away like a bird?

A bird's nest is on the desert.
It sleeps on the desert
Where no one lives.

And Ahta-hana cried and sang songs of lonesomeness for his mother.

Tesilya found her way back to Sun's house, and, again with a yellow-hammer for a pet, she lived on, dreaming of Ahta-hana, fearful of all that might befall him, waiting for him to return to her some day as he had promised.

As soon as Tesilya was safely out of reach of Hotpa and his evil magic, Ahta-hana did the only thing he would be able to do until more age and wisdom and power were his: he hid himself close to the shinny field, and when the play passed his way, he stole the shinny ball. No one saw him take it or run home with it. The players were still looking for it in the grass when Ahta-hana appeared outside his house door, the ball in his hand. Hotpa dared not interfere while Ahta-hana offered the kneecap ball to the Four Directions, singing a prayer to each, nor when he laid it on the ground and struck it as hard as he could with a cane such as his father had carried. The ball flew like a meteor to the west, falling somewhere in the mountains there. This done, Ahta-hana went indoors and was not seen any more. Hotpa came to kill him, but he found only his old uncle alone in the house. His uncle told him that Ahta-hana had gone to be with his mother in Sun's house, and Hotpa was afraid to follow him there.

Ahta-hana went on a long journey which took him to the very end of the earth where it meets the ocean. He learned many things on his travels. He came to know the properties of plants and springs and mountains and deserts. He subdued Rattlesnake, and thereby his own fears. He crossed and re-crossed the Colorado River until it was no longer a barrier, and its total course was known to him. He reached the sea, staying there until the shells along its shore and the life in its waters seemed no longer strange to him, but were known and within his control, just as he came to know the water birds, so different from the birds of the desert.

At last he turned his steps toward home. Wisdom and magical power and doctoring skill were now his. Young as he was, he was already full grown, for he had grown at a hero's rate of growth. Around his neck he wore many strings of shell beads and a thick feather rope, and on his head a headdress of square-clipped raven's wings. He was as beautiful as his father before him.

On his return journey, he encountered Kwayu[7] the Cannibal and Kwayu's four daughters, all of whom fell in love with him. Because they so much wished it, and he felt sorry for them, he married them all even though the eldest of the sisters was his favorite and the one of his own choosing.

Now Ahta-hana was weary of wandering, and it seemed to him that he had surely learned enough that he might return home. He dreamed, and afterwards he said to his wives, "I know that my mother is dreaming of me. I must go to her." All four wives wished to go with him and he consented to their going. But it was as he had feared, their strength and endurance were far less than his, and he felt so much encumbered by them that he thought of leaving them and going on alone. To make this appear more reasonable, he caused a cold rain to fall, until they could scarcely drag their feet through the mud. He went on ahead; but he looked back and saw them still struggling after him. He was ashamed of what he had willed and done, and he knew at last that he truly loved them. For the remainder of the journey he made no more cold rains; rather he learned something of their needs and natures as he had of other life in the world different from himself, and he was no longer impatient with them nor did he think again of leaving them behind.

For many days they travelled north, until one morning a yellow-hammer flew out of the east toward them. He flew straight to Ahta-hana who took him in his hands, saying, "This must be my mother's pet, and the bird who guards her. That is why he comes to me. My mother cannot be far from here." They turned to the east, going the way the woodpecker had flown, and by noon of that day they reached Sun's house with the willowbark door, and the bird cage hanging there in its old place. Ahta-hana set the yellow-hammer on the ground outside the door of Sun's house, as had his father long, long ago. And the bird gave his familiar, hoarse cry.

Tesilya came to the door to look through its slats. When she saw Ahta-hana, she raised the door and ran to him, holding him close and crying, "My son—it is you! The time was so long—I thought you must have been killed—I thought I was never to see you again!" She stood back a little from him and looked at him. She saw that he was become indeed beautiful and a hero, and she said exultingly, "You have dreamed well! It is good!" Then she turned to greet her son's wives, saying apologetically to them, "You have come far and stood long. You are tired. Sit down. When you have rested, I have corn and wheat inside. It is yours—grind it, make mush of it, cook it anyway you like it. Take all you want."

7. *Kwayu.* (kwä′yü).

The oldest of the sisters thanked Tesilya and followed her into the house and set herself to parching corn. She was not shy with her mother-in-law because she knew she was her husband's favorite. Of her he said to his mother, "I knew I should love her before I saw her because I dreamed of her. And she loved me and cared for me when I was bewitched and sick on my way home, and looked like nothing but a bundle of dead, dried cane." And he told his mother that his other wives were this one's younger sisters.

Those others remained outside, standing, ashamed before their mother-in-law, unsure of their welcome. Seeing them so, Tesilya went quickly to them and put out her hands to them leading them inside the house, and saying in her gentle voice, "My daughters-in-law!"

Sun came home, and they talked of many things, on into the night. Ahta-hana told his grandfather and his mother of his journeyings, and Tesilya learned how he had stolen the shinny ball as a beginning toward avenging his father's murder. Now he said he was almost ready to go on with that task. Two things more he needed: good supplies of thunder and of lightning. And his grandfather told him of a pit where they were to be found.

His wives slept, weary from their travels, and while they slept Ahta-hana went swiftly, alone, farther to the east till he came to the pit his grandfather had told him of. His wives were alarmed when they wakened and found him gone, but Tesilya reassured them and comforted them, and, as she had said, he was back home again before night, his arrow case bulging with lengths of hollow cane, each filled with thunder or lightning from the pit. Now, he said, he was ready to meet Hotpa. So the next day, he bid good-bye to Sun and set out over Ahta's and Tesilya's old route westward to the river and the sacred mountain. Tesilya sang a song of farewell to her father and his house, and followed after her son, his four young wives with her.

Word of their coming preceded them. Hotpa and the shinny players stayed close by the sacred mountain, setting up a pole in an open space before their houses and tying Ahta's scalp piece to it. While they sang and danced around the scalp, Hotpa prepared to use the most powerful magic he knew against Ahta-hana.

All the other people came pouring over the desert and across the river. When Ahta-hana and Tesilya reached the river, their relatives and friends were waiting there to give them joyful greeting. Even Ahta's uncle was there. Very old and frail, he did not cry when he saw Tesilya and Ahta-hana; he embraced them, touching their faces and hands again and again, reassuring himself in this way that they were truly come back to him.

When the greetings were over, Ahta-hana left his family and friends where they were on the riverbank. He said that no one was to go with him or to follow after him. Alone, he crossed the river he had come to know so well, and he went close to the dancers and Hotpa. So swiftly and quietly had he come that they only realized he was there when, using his long powerful cane—the one like his father's—as if it were a spear thrower, he threw all of the thunder and lightning he had brought in his arrow case amongst them, causing such a hot and destroying fire that not one of his enemies survived it. Hotpa and the shinny players were consumed in the flames, and every house and article belonging to them was burned down to the ground.

The fire he had started swept out over the desert, and Ahta-hana was barely able with all his strength and power to stop it at the river's edge. But at last it burned itself out. Ahta's death was avenged, and his people came home to live out their lives within the shadow of the sacred mountain.

Under Ahta-hana's guidance, they followed the way of life which is right for the river people, and continued to dream the dreams which belong to them. Ahta-hana wished his people not to forget their beginnings, nor to lose all memory of their early heroes. To this end he put it into their hearts to be reminded of the good and faithful uncle whenever they heard the soft call of the snowy owl of the Colorado. The river cane of daily use was already, in his time, called by his father's name, and the great red rock by the river's edge would be named for himself when it came time for him to die. As for his wives and his mother, the river people were to see them as the cluster of the Pleiades,[8] Tesilya the brightest star of the tiny constellation. It seemed fitting to her son to think of his mother so, shining softly, high in the winter sky.

Today, the great red rock is called Ahta-hana. The river people smile in remembrance of the old uncle whenever they hear the snowy owl. And they look up often during the clear, dark nights of winter to where the wives of Ahta-hana dance around his mother—the one in the center, the brightest one—Tesilya.

---

8. *Pleiades* (plē′ə dēz′, pli′ə dēz′), a group of stars in the constellation Taurus.

JACK
THE GIANT-KILLER

Joseph Jacobs

WHEN GOOD KING ARTHUR[1] REIGNED, there lived near the Land's End of England, in the county of Cornwall,[2] a farmer who had one only son called Jack. He was brisk and of ready, lively wit, so that nobody or nothing could worst him.

In those days the Mount of Cornwall was kept by a huge giant named Cormoran. He was eighteen feet in height, and about three yards round the waist, of a fierce and grim countenance, the terror of all the neighbouring towns and villages. He lived in a cave in the midst of the Mount, and whenever he wanted food he would wade over to the main-land, where he would furnish himself with whatever came in his way. Everybody at his approach ran out of their houses, while he seized on their cattle, making nothing of carrying half-a-dozen oxen on his back at a time; and as for their sheep and hogs, he would tie them round his waist like a bunch of tallow-dips. He had done this for many years, so that all Cornwall was in despair.

One day Jack happened to be at the town-hall when the magistrates were sitting in council about the Giant. He asked, "What reward will be given to the man who kills Cormoran?" "The giant's treasure," they said, "will be the reward." Quoth Jack, "Then let me undertake it."

So he got a horn, shovel, and pickaxe, and went over to the Mount in the beginning of a dark winter's evening, when he fell to work, and before morning had dug a pit twenty-two feet deep, and nearly as broad, covering it over with long sticks and straw. Then he strewed a little mould over it, so that it appeared like plain ground. Jack then placed himself on the opposite side of the pit, farthest from the giant's lodging, and, just at the break of day, he put the horn to his mouth, and blew, Tantivy, Tantivy. This noise roused the giant, who rushed from his cave, crying, "You incorrigible villain, are you come here to disturb my rest? You shall pay dearly for this. Satisfaction I will have, and this it shall be, I will take you whole and broil you for breakfast." He had no sooner uttered this, than he tumbled into the pit, and made the very

"Jack the Giant-Killer." Reprinted by permission of G. P. Putnam's Sons from ENGLISH FAIRY TALES collected by Joseph Jacobs.

1. *King Arthur*, legendary king of Britain who is believed to have lived around the beginning of the sixth century. See note page 56. 2. *Land's End . . . Cornwall.* Land's End is the tip of the peninsula of Cornwall in southwestern England.

foundations of the Mount to shake. "Oh Giant," quoth Jack, "where are you now? Oh, faith, you are gotten now into Lob's Pound,[3] where I will surely plague you for your threatening words; what do you think now of broiling me for your breakfast? Will no other diet serve you but poor Jack?" Then having tantalised the giant for a while, he gave him a most weighty knock with his pickaxe on the very crown of his head, and killed him on the spot.

Jack then filled up the pit with earth, and went to search the cave, which he found contained much treasure. When the magistrates heard of this they made a declaration he should henceforth be termed

JACK THE GIANT-KILLER,

and presented him with a sword and a belt, on which were written these words embroidered in letters of gold:

Here's the right valiant Cornish man,
Who slew the giant Cormoran.

The news of Jack's victory soon spread over all the West of England, so that another giant, named Blunderbore, hearing of it, vowed to be revenged on Jack, if ever he should light on him. This giant was the lord of an enchanted castle situated in the midst of a lonesome wood. Now Jack, about four months afterwards, walking near this wood in his journey to Wales, being weary, seated himself near a pleasant fountain and fell fast asleep. While he was sleeping, the giant, coming there for water, discovered him, and knew him to be the far-famed Jack the Giant-killer by the lines written on the belt. Without ado, he took Jack on his shoulders and carried him towards his castle. Now, as they passed through a thicket, the rustling of the boughs awakened Jack, who was strangely surprised to find himself in the clutches of the giant. His terror was only begun, for, on entering the castle, he saw the ground strewed with human bones, and the giant told him his own would ere long be among them. After this the giant locked poor Jack in an immense chamber, leaving him there while he went to fetch another giant, his brother, living in the same wood, who might share in the meal on Jack.

After waiting some time Jack, on going to the window beheld afar off the two giants coming towards the castle. "Now," quoth Jack to himself, "my death or my deliverance is at hand." Now, there were strong cords in a corner of the room in which Jack was, and two of these he took, and made a strong noose at the end; and while the giants were unlocking the iron gate of the castle he threw the ropes over each of their heads. Then he drew the other ends across a beam, and pulled

---

3. *Lob's Pound*, difficulty or disgrace.

with all his might, so that he throttled them. Then, when he saw they were black in the face, he slid down the rope, and drawing his sword, slew them both. Then, taking the giant's keys, and unlocking the rooms, he found three fair ladies tied by the hair of their heads, almost starved to death. "Sweet ladies," quoth Jack, "I have destroyed this monster and his brutish brother, and obtained your liberties." This said he presented them with the keys, and so proceeded on his journey to Wales.

Jack made the best of his way by travelling as fast as he could, but lost his road, and was benighted, and could find no habitation until, coming into a narrow valley, he found a large house, and in order to get shelter took courage to knock at the gate. But what was his surprise when there came forth a monstrous giant with two heads; yet he did not appear so fiery as the others were, for he was a Welsh giant, and what he did was by private and secret malice under the false show of friendship. Jack, having told his condition to the giant, was shown into a bedroom, where, in the dead of night, he heard his host in another apartment muttering these words:

Though here you lodge with me this night,
You shall not see the morning light:
My club shall dash your brains outright!

"Say'st thou so," quoth Jack; "that is like one of your Welsh tricks, yet I hope to be cunning enough for you." Then, getting out of bed, he laid a billet in the bed in his stead, and hid himself in a corner of the room. At the dead time of the night in came the Welsh giant, who struck several heavy blows on the bed with his club, thinking he had broken every bone in Jack's skin. The next morning Jack, laughing in his sleeve, gave him hearty thanks for his night's lodging. "How have you rested?" quoth the giant; "did you not feel anything in the night?" "No," quoth Jack, "nothing but a rat, which gave me two or three slaps with her tail." With that, greatly wondering, the giant led Jack to breakfast, bringing him a bowl containing four gallons of hasty pudding. Being loth to let the giant think it too much for him, Jack put a large leather bag under his loose coat, in such a way that he could convey the pudding into it without its being perceived. Then, telling the giant he would show him a trick, taking a knife, Jack ripped open the bag, and out came all the hasty pudding. Whereupon, saying, "Odds splutters her nails, hur can do that trick hursely," the monster took the knife, and ripping open his belly, fell down dead.

Now, it happened in these days that King Arthur's only son asked his father to give him a large sum of money, in order that he might go and seek his fortune in the principality of Wales, where lived a beautiful lady possessed with seven evil spirits. The king did his best to persuade his son from it, but in vain; so at last gave way and the prince set out with two horses, one loaded with money, the other for himself to ride upon. Now, after several days' travel, he came to a market-town in Wales, where he beheld a vast crowd of people gathered together. The prince asked the reason of it, and was told that they had arrested a corpse for several large sums of money which the deceased owed when he died. The prince replied that it was a pity creditors should be so cruel, and said: "Go bury the dead, and let his creditors come to my lodging, and there their debts shall be paid." They came, in such great numbers that before night he had only twopence left for himself.

Now Jack the Giant-Killer, coming that way, was so taken with the generosity of the prince, that he desired to be his servant. This being agreed upon, the next morning they set forward on their journey together, when, as they were riding out of the town, an old woman called after the prince, saying, "He has owed me twopence these seven years; pray pay me as well as the rest." Putting his hand into his pocket, the prince gave the woman all he had left, so that after their day's food, which cost what small store Jack had by him, they were without a penny between them.

When the sun got low, the king's son said, "Jack, since we have no money, where can we lodge this night?"

But Jack replied, "Master, we'll do well enough, for I have an uncle lives within two miles of this place; he is a huge and monstrous giant with three heads; he'll fight five hundred men in armour, and make them to fly before him."

"Alas!" quoth the prince, "what shall we do there? He'll certainly chop us up at a mouthful. Nay, we are scarce enough to fill one of his hollow teeth!"

"It is no matter for that," quoth Jack; "I myself will go before and prepare the way for you; therefore stop here and wait till I return." Jack then rode away at full speed, and coming to the gate of the castle, he knocked so loud that he made the neighbouring hills resound. The giant roared out at this like thunder: "Who's there?"

Jack answered, "None but your poor cousin Jack."

Quoth he, "What news with my poor cousin Jack?"

He replied, "Dear uncle, heavy news, God wot!"

"Prithee," quoth the giant, "what heavy news can come to me? I am a giant with three heads, and besides thou knowest I can fight five hundred men in armour, and make them fly like chaff before the wind."

"Oh, but," quoth Jack, "here's the king's son a-coming with a thousand men in armour to kill you and destroy all that you have!"

"Oh, cousin Jack," said the giant, "this is heavy news indeed! I will immediately run and hide myself, and thou shalt lock, bolt, and bar me in, and keep the keys until the prince is gone." Having secured the giant, Jack fetched his master, when they made themselves heartily merry whilst the poor giant lay trembling in a vault under the ground.

Early in the morning Jack furnished his master with a fresh supply of gold and silver, and then sent him three miles forward on his journey, at which time the prince was pretty well out of the smell of the giant. Jack then returned, and let the giant out of the vault, who asked what he should give him for keeping the castle from destruction. "Why," quoth Jack, "I want nothing but the old coat and cap, together with the old rusty sword and slippers which are at your bed's head." Quoth the giant, "You know not what you ask; they are the most precious things I have. The coat will keep you invisible, the cap will tell you all you want to know, the sword cuts asunder whatever you strike, and the shoes are of extraordinary swiftness. But you have been very serviceable to me, therefore take them with all my heart." Jack thanked his uncle, and then went off with them. He soon overtook his master and they quickly arrived at the house of the lady the prince sought, who, finding the prince to be a suitor, prepared a splendid banquet for him. After the repast was concluded, she told him she had a task for him. She wiped his mouth with a handkerchief, saying, "You must show me that handkerchief to-morrow morning, or else you will lose your head." With that she put it in her bosom. The prince went to bed in great sorrow, but Jack's cap of knowledge informed him how it was to be obtained. In the middle of the night she called upon her familiar spirit[4] to carry her to Lucifer. But Jack put on his coat of darkness and his shoes of swiftness, and was there as soon as she was. When she entered the place of the demon, she gave the handkerchief to him, and he laid it upon a shelf, whence Jack took it and brought it to his master, who showed it to the lady next day, and so saved his life. On that day, she gave the prince a kiss and told him he must show her the lips to-morrow morning that she kissed last night, or lose his head.

"Ah!" he replied, "if you kiss none but mine, I will."

"That is neither here nor there," said she; "if you do not, death's your portion!"

At midnight she went as before, and was angry with the demon for letting the handkerchief go. "But now," quoth she, "I will be too hard for the king's son, for I will kiss thee, and he is to show me thy lips." Which she did, and Jack, when she was not standing by, cut off Lucifer's head and brought it under his invisible coat to his master, who the next morning pulled it out by the horns before the lady. This broke the enchantment and the evil spirit left her, and she appeared in all her beauty. They were married the next morning, and soon after went to the Court of King Arthur, where Jack for his many great exploits, was made one of the Knights of the Round Table.

---

4. *familiar spirit*, a devil who serves a witch.

Jack soon went searching for giants again, but he had not ridden far, when he saw a cave, near the entrance of which he beheld a giant sitting upon a block of timber, with a knotted iron club by his side. His goggle eyes were like flames of fire, his countenance grim and ugly, and his cheeks like a couple of large flitches of bacon, while the bristles of his beard resembled rods of iron wire, and the locks that hung down upon his brawny shoulders were like curled snakes or hissing adders. Jack alighted from his horse, and, putting on the coat of darkness, went up close to the giant, and said softly: "Oh! are you there? It will not be long before I take you fast by the beard." The giant all this while could not see him, on account of his invisible coat, so that Jack, coming up close to the monster, struck a blow with his sword at his head, but, missing his aim, he cut off the nose instead. At this, the giant roared like claps of thunder, and began to lay about him with his iron club like one stark mad. But Jack, running behind, drove his sword up to the hilt in the giant's back, so that he fell down dead. This done, Jack cut off the giant's head, and sent it, with his brother's also, to King Arthur, by a waggoner he hired for that purpose.

Jack now resolved to enter the giant's cave in search of his treasure, and, passing along through a great many windings and turnings, he came at length to a large room paved with freestone, at the upper end of which was a boiling caldron, and on the right hand a large table, at which the giant used to dine. Then he came to a window, barred with iron, through which he looked and beheld a vast number of miserable captives, who, seeing him, cried out, "Alas! young man, art thou come to be one amongst us in this miserable den?"

"Ay," quoth Jack, "but pray tell me what is the meaning of your captivity?"

"We are kept here," said one, "till such time as the giants have a wish to feast, and then the fattest among us is slaughtered! And many are the times they have dined upon murdered men!"

"Say you so," quoth Jack, and straightway unlocked the gate and let them free, who all rejoiced like condemned men at sight of a pardon. Then searching the giant's coffers, he shared the gold and silver equally amongst them and took them to a neighbouring castle, where they all feasted and made merry over their deliverance.

But in the midst of all this mirth a messenger brought news that one Thunderdell, a giant with two heads, having heard of the death of his kinsmen, had come from the northern dales to be revenged on Jack, and was within a mile of the castle, the country people flying before him like chaff. But Jack was not a bit daunted, and said, "Let him come! I have a tool to pick his teeth; and you, ladies and gentlemen, walk out into the garden, and you shall witness this giant Thunderdell's death and destruction."

The castle was situated in the midst of a small island surrounded by a moat thirty feet deep and twenty feet wide, over which lay a drawbridge. So Jack employed men to cut through this bridge on both sides, nearly to the middle; and then, dressing himself in his invisible coat, he marched against the giant with his sword of sharpness. Although the giant could not see Jack, he smelt his approach, and cried out in these words:

Fee, fi, fo, fum!
I smell the blood of an Englishman!
Be he alive or be he dead,
I'll grind his bones to make me bread!

"Say'st thou so," said Jack; "then thou art a monstrous miller indeed."

The giant cried out again, "Art thou that villain who killed my kinsmen? Then I will tear thee with my teeth, suck thy blood, and grind thy bones to powder."

"You'll have to catch me first," quoth Jack, and throwing off his invisible coat, so that the giant might see him, and putting on his shoes of swiftness, he ran from the giant, who followed like a walking castle, so that the very foundations of the earth seemed to shake at every step. Jack led him a long dance, in order that the gentlemen and ladies might see; and at last to end the matter, ran lightly over the drawbridge, the giant, in full speed, pursuing him with his club. Then, coming to the middle of the bridge, the giant's great weight broke it down, and he tumbled headlong into the water, where he rolled and wallowed like a whale. Jack, standing by the moat, laughed at him all the while; but though the giant foamed to hear him scoff, and plunged from place to place in the moat, yet he could not get out to be revenged. Jack at length got a cart rope and cast it over the two heads of the giant and drew him ashore by a team of horses, and then cut off both his heads with his sword of sharpness, and sent them to King Arthur.

After some time spent in mirth and pastime, Jack, taking leave of the knights and ladies, set out for new adventures. Through many woods he passed, and came at length to the foot of a high mountain. Here, late at night, he found a lonesome house, and knocked at the door, which was opened by an aged man with a head as white as snow. "Father," said Jack, "can you lodge a benighted traveller that has lost his way?" "Yes," said the old man; "you are right welcome to my poor cottage." Whereupon Jack entered, and down they sat together, and the old man began to speak as follows: "Son, I see by your belt you are the great conqueror of giants, and behold, my son, on the top of this mountain is an enchanted castle; this is kept by a giant named Galligantua, and he, by the help of an old conjurer, betrays many knights and ladies into his castle, where by magic art they are transformed into sundry shapes and forms. But above all, I grieve for a duke's daughter, whom they fetched from her father's garden, carrying her through the air in a burning chariot drawn by fiery dragons, when they secured her within the castle, and transformed her into a white hind. And though many knights have tried to break the enchantment, and work her deliverance, yet no one could accomplish it, on account of two dreadful griffins[5] which are placed at the castle gate and which destroy every one who comes near. But you, my son, may pass by them undiscovered, where on the gates of the castle you will find engraven in large letters how the spell may be broken." Jack gave the old man his hand, and promised that in the morning he would venture his life to free the lady.

In the morning Jack arose and put on his invisible coat and magic cap and shoes, and prepared himself for the fray. Now, when he had reached the top of the mountain he soon discovered the two fiery griffins, but passed them without fear, because of his invisible coat. When he had got beyond them, he found upon the gates of the castle a golden trumpet hung by a silver chain, under which these lines were engraved:

Whoever shall this trumpet blow,
Shall soon the giant overthrow,
And break the black enchantment straight;
So all shall be in happy state.

Jack had no sooner read this but he blew the trumpet, at which the castle trembled to its vast foundations, and the giant and conjurer were in horrid confusion, biting their thumbs and tearing their hair, knowing their wicked reign was at an end. Then the giant stooping to take up his club, Jack at one blow cut off his head; whereupon the conjurer, mounting up into the air, was carried away in a whirlwind. Then the enchantment was broken, and all the lords and ladies who had so long been transformed into birds and beasts returned to their proper shapes, and the castle vanished away in a cloud of smoke. This being done, the head of Galligantua was likewise, in the usual manner, conveyed to the Court of King Arthur, where, the very next day, Jack followed, with the knights and ladies who had been delivered. Whereupon, as a reward for his good services, the king prevailed upon the duke to bestow his daughter in marriage on honest Jack. So married they were, and the whole kingdom was filled with joy at the wedding. Furthermore, the king bestowed on Jack a noble castle, with a very beautiful estate thereto belonging, where he and his lady lived in great joy and happiness all the rest of their days.

---

5. *griffins,* mythical creatures with the heads, wings, and forelegs of eagles, and the bodies, hind legs, and tails of lions.

THE TRIALS
OF LEMMINKAINEN

Babette Deutsch[1]

The adventures of Lemminkainen (lem′ min kī′nen) form part of the Kalevala, *a collection of Finnish folk songs first published in 1835 by Elias Lönnrot (lėm′rōt), a doctor and folklorist. The word* Kalevala *can be translated as "The Land of Heroes." For more information on Lönnrot and the* Kalevala *see the note on page 204.*

WHEN LEMMINKAINEN FIRST CAME TO MANHOOD he was a gay fellow who liked fooling and fighting. He was so handsome and merry that he had only to look at a girl for her to fall in love with him. But he did not want to marry any of the girls on the island where he had his home. The bride he wanted lived in far-off Saari,[2] and her name was Kylliki.[3] She was of noble birth, and so lovely that she was called the Flower of Saari.

Kylliki had had many suitors, but she had refused them all.

When Lemminkainen told his mother that he was going to woo Kylliki, his mother said the proud beauty would never have him.

"She comes of a noble house," said his old mother. "You should not try to marry above your station."

"My humble birth does not matter," answered Lemminkainen. "She will take me for my good looks."

And in spite of his mother's warnings, he harnessed his stallion, mounted his sledge, and drove off to Saari. He was in such a hurry that when he came clattering up to Kylliki's gateway, his sledge overturned and he fell out. All the girls laughed to see him tumble onto the road.

Lemminkainen did not like to be laughed at. He made up his mind that they would pay for their mockery. He engaged himself as a herd, and spent his days in the meadows with the cattle and his nights dancing as always. Soon all the girls of Saari were in love with the handsome youth. But though he danced with each one in turn, his heart was set upon Kylliki.

1. *Deutsch,* (doich). 2. *Saari* (sa′ri). 3. *Kylliki,* (kүl′li ki).

One fine evening, not a month after his arrival, the girls were dancing together on the heath near a little grove. Kylliki was there too, the most graceful of them all. Suddenly who should come driving up to the dancing-space but Lemminkainen, his swift horse harnessed to his sledge. This time he did not tumble out. He leaned from his sledge, snatched up Kylliki from among her companions, cracked his whip-lash, and drove off with her. Now it was his turn to laugh.

"Keep this a secret!" he called to the girls over his shoulder, "or I will sing all your sweethearts off to the wars and you will never hear of them again!"

Poor Kylliki wept and sobbed and begged Lemminkainen to set her free. When he would not listen, she threatened him with the vengeance of her five strong brothers and the seven strong sons of her uncle. But Lemminkainen paid no attention.

"Unhappy girl that I am!" cried Kylliki. "I, who was so gently reared, to be forced to marry a worthless fellow, a rude quarrelsome churl!"

But Lemminkainen spoke to her tenderly and promised to cherish her always, to take her to a kind house, where there was great plenty of everything needful.

"And if I am not of noble birth," he said, "I have a noble sword, no man living has a better."

At this Kylliki, who was beginning to be comforted, sighed sadly.

"If you want me to love you," she said, "and be a good wife to you, promise me that you will forget that sword of yours. Swear to me that you will not be lured into battle, for the sake of silver or of gold."

Lemminkainen was so glad to have won Kylliki that he promised readily.

"But you must promise me something, too," he said. "Never go out in the evening to dance with the village girls." For he thought this did not befit a married woman, and besides, he wanted to keep Kylliki all to himself. She was quite willing to satisfy Lemminkainen on this score, and so they pledged their troth.

He brought her home, and his mother was full of praise for his beautiful bride, the Flower of Saari.

For a while the young couple lived contentedly enough. The lively Lemminkainen did not go forth to battle, and the lovely Kylliki stayed away from the village dances.

But one morning early Lemminkainen went out to fish. He was gone all day and when night came he had not returned. Kylliki did not like being left alone. She forgot her promise and went off to the village to join the girls at their dances. It was not long before Lemminkainen learned of what she had done. He was enraged. If she could break her promise, why should he keep his?

"Mother!" he cried, "wash my shirt in the venom of the black snake, and dry it quickly so that I may wear it in battle. I am going to the North Country[4] to fight."

All his mother's pleas were in vain. He was bound to go, and when he had fought the young men, he declared, and won fame as a warrior, he would find a maiden who would love and honor and obey him, and who would make a happy home for him.

"But you already have a wife," said Lemminkainen's mother.

"Kyllikki is no wife of mine," he stormed. "Let her go to all the dances and sleep where she likes. I do not want to see her any more."

His mother warned him of the sorcerers he would meet in the North Country, and of their wicked enchantments, but Lemminkainen said he had met sorcerers before this and conquered them with magic of his own, singing them into the whirlpools of Tuoni's dark river,[5] where they were asleep forever. With this Lemminkainen turned away, and unconcernedly began to brush his hair. Still his mother, afraid of what might befall him, tried to hold him back, but this only made the stubborn Lemminkainen angrier than before. In his fury he flung his hair-brush at the stove, and the comb after it.

"When you see that brush running with blood and blood dripping from the comb, then you may know that harm has come to Lemminkainen!" he cried. "My armor is magic enough against magicians. My sharp sword is sufficient enchantment for me."

Then he harnessed his fiery horse to his sledge, cracked his whip, and was off for the North Country. The silver sand scattered under his sledge-runners. The golden heather crackled as he passed.

He drove for a day and for another day and for a third day, and on the third day he came to a homestead. At once Lemminkainen stopped the mouth of the watch-dog at the gate with a magic spell, so that none should be warned of his coming. Then he stood outside of the house and listened.

He heard many people talking within. The sound of music came through the walls. The sound of singing came through the shutters. Lemminkainen stepped up softly and looked in. The house was full of wizards. Singers crowded the benches. Musicians sat along the walls. Beside the hearth sat a Northern sorcerer, making songs of Hiisi, the Evil One,[6] in a hoarse voice.

Lemminkainen thrust boldly into the room.

"A song is good when it is finished," he said. "The shortest verses are the finest, and the greatest wisdom is unspoken."

Now the house he had entered was that of old Louhi[7] herself, the crafty Mistress of the North Country. She was angry at these rude words of the stranger.

---

4. *the North Country,* Lapland. **5.** *Tuoni's dark river,* the boundary of the Underworld. Tuoni (tu′ō ni) is the ruler of the dead. **6.** *Hiisi, the Evil One.* Hiisi (hi′si) is a demon, a hideous spirit who haunts the woods. **7.** *Louhi,* (low′hi).

"We have a watch-dog," said she, "who loves to bite bones. He is a great licker-up of fresh blood. How is it that he never warned us of your coming? And who are you who push thus boldly into the house, without a dog to lift his voice against you?"

"I have not come without a store of magic," replied Lemminkainen. "Many the songs my mother taught me, many the songs that I know."

And with eyes shining like flame, and fire flashing from his furred cloak, the lively Lemminkainen began to sing. He sang the best singer in the house to silence. He filled the mouths of the wizards with pebbles. He piled rocks over the cleverest magicians, and sang the sorcerers from their benches onto the treeless plains and away from the hearthstone into roaring whirlpools. He sang the young warriors weaponless and the strong men helpless. Only one man he spared, a wretched cowherd, old and blind and mean-hearted.

"You have banished the young men and the old men," said the cowherd. "Why have you left only me?"

"You were not worth banishing," said the lively Lemminkainen. "You do not know any spells now, old and blind as you are. You were always the worst of cowherds and now you are of no account."

The blind herdsman was deeply angered by these words, but he made no answer. He slipped quickly out of the door and made for the open country, and hid himself by the dread River of Tuoni, Lord of the Dead. There he bided his time, lying in wait for Lemminkainen.

Satisfied that the wizards were banished, the lively Lemminkainen now bethought him of his errand. He turned to old Louhi and asked for her tallest, fairest daughter in marriage.

"Indeed, no," said the Mistress of the North Country. "You have a wife already."

"Kylliki is no wife of mine now," said Lemminkainen. "All she can think of is to go dancing with the girls of the village. I want a better wife than that."

"Well," said crafty old Louhi, "if you really want a wife, I may perhaps give you my daughter. But first you must prove worthy of her. First you must go out and capture the elk of Hiisi."

Lemminkainen was ready enough to undertake this task. And how he performed it, and what followed after, you shall hear.

Lemminkainen pointed his javelin, sharpened the bone tips of his arrows, and strung his bow with strong sinew. But he could not hunt the elk of Hiisi without snow-shoes.

So he commanded a smith famous for this work to fashion him a pair of splendid snow-shoes. The smith spent a whole autumn shaping the left shoe and a whole winter carving the right shoe. He fixed the frames and fitted the rings, and lined the frames with otter-skin and the rings with the skin of the red fox. Then he smeared the runners well with grease made of reindeer fat.

Lemminkainen tried the shoes and they fitted perfectly. He bound his quiver on his back, flung his bow over his shoulder, grasped his pole firmly, and pushed forward, first on his left shoe, then on his right.

"There is not a four-footed creature running," he cried, "who can escape Lemminkainen on his snow-shoes."

And he started off.

But his boast was heard by Hiisi, the Evil One, and Hiisi at once set about making the task hard for Lemminkainen.

He formed a magic elk, using willow branches for the horns and the bark of the pine for the back. He shaped ears of the leaves of the water-lily and the eyes were water-lily flowers. Then Hiisi spoke to the elk and bade it run to the breeding-place of the reindeer, to the grassy plains of the North Country.

"Run fast!" said Hiisi. "Run till the men who follow you are sweating with the chase. Above all, run from Lemminkainen!"

At once Hiisi's elk rushed away, past the barns and over the plains. He ran so fast that he kicked over the tubs in the houses and upset the kettles on the fire, and the meat was thrown out and the soup spilt in the cinders. Then the children began to laugh and the women began to cry and the dogs began to bark and the old people grumbled.

Lemminkainen chased the elk, gliding over the marshes till sparks flew from his snow-shoes and smoke rose from his staff with the speed of his going. He traveled over hill and dale, and finally he came to the far end of the North Country. There he heard the dogs barking and the children laughing and the women crying and the old people complaining. He asked what all the commotion was about.

"It is all because of the elk of Hiisi, the Evil One," they told him. "He charged in here and kicked over the tubs and upset the kettles and spilt all our dinners into the ashes."

Lively Lemminkainen struck his left snow-shoe into a drift and pushed his pine-wood staff forward like a living serpent and glided swiftly away.

"Let the men come and help me bring the elk home," he shouted as he went. "Let the women wash the kettles and set all the children to gathering firewood. You will need all your pots to cook the elk's meat after I capture him."

He speeded forward so fast that at the first stride he could no longer be heard and at the second stride he could no longer be seen and at the third stride he had leapt up to Hiisi's elk. Lemminkainen promptly threw a collar of birch-wood about his neck and tethered him to a maple pole in an oaken pen. Then he stroked the elk's back and patted him gently on the belly.

"I should like to rest here awhile," said Lemminkainen, thoughtfully, well content that he had caught the elk. "It is very pleasant here. If only I had a pretty girl to keep me company!"

At that the elk grew furious.

"Can you think of nothing but pretty girls?" cried the creature. "What sort of fellow are you, anyway!"

In his fury he tore away from his tether and broke out of the pen and went rushing wildly over the plains and marshes till he could no longer be seen.

Lemminkainen was vexed. He chased after the elk, but in his haste he plunged his left snow-shoe into a hole and it broke, and the frame of his right snow-shoe was dashed to pieces against the ground. He did not know where to turn.

He thought for a long while as to whether he should give up the chase and go home, or whether he should try once more. Finally he decided to ask the favor of the god who ruled the forest and begged the nymphs[8] of the wood to turn the game in his direction, driving the quarry straight into the hands of the hunter. The forest deities were pleased by his words and listened graciously to his prayers. Then with powerful enchantments he mended his broken snow-shoes and glided forward through the depths of the woods.

For a whole week he traveled, singing as he went. His songs delighted the wood-nymphs, and they lured Hiisi's elk from his lair and drove him over the tree-covered hills and delivered him up to Lemminkainen. The hunter threw his lasso over the creature's neck and stroked its back. Then, having rewarded his helpers, he journeyed swiftly to old Louhi's homestead and claimed her daughter for his bride.

But crafty old Louhi said that first Lemminkainen must perform another task. He must bring back to her the wild horse of Hiisi.

Lemminkainen thought this could not be any more difficult than capturing Hiisi's elk. Forth he went with a golden bridle slung over his shoulder and a silver bit in his hand, and after traveling for a day and another day and a third day he caught sight of Hiisi's wild horse. Fiery sparks flew from its mane and smoke issued from its nostrils. But with the help of Ukko the Creator,[9] and with wise words of magic, Lemminkainen bitted the wild steed and bridled it, and mounted on its back, he went riding gaily back to old Louhi to claim her daughter for his bride.

Again crafty old Louhi put him off. She would give him her daughter, said she, only when he had brought back to her the swan that swam on the river of Tuoni, Lord of the Dead.

This was the most dangerous task that Lemminkainen had been asked to perform. But he was willing enough to attempt it if only he

---

8. *nymphs,* minor goddesses, guardians of the forest. 9. *Ukko the Creator.* The name Ukko (ŭk′kō) literally means "old man." He is the god of the sky.

could win the wife he sought. So he took his cross-bow and hurried to the banks of the dread river of Tuoni, Lord of the Dead.

Now Lemminkainen knew what risks he ran in undertaking this task. But one danger he did not know. He had forgotten the slight he had put upon the blind cowherd when he had banished all the wizards and paid no heed to him. But the cowherd had not forgotten. Lemminkainen thought no more of the insulting words he had spoken to the blind herdsman. But the herdsman had not forgotten them. At the turn of the murky river of Tuoni the blind herd lay in wait for Lemminkainen, to do him injury.

The cowherd had the keen hearing of the blind, and when Lemminkainen, bow in hand, approached the turn of Tuoni's dreadful river, the herdsman recognized his tread at once. With a cry of vengeance he summoned from the foaming cataract a serpent, and bade it strike Lemminkainen in the arm-pit and the shoulder, and plunge its venom through his heart and his liver.

Against this hurt all Lemminkainen's spells were useless. He was stricken unto death. Then the blind cowherd seized the young man and threw him into the midst of Tuoni's whirlpool. The bloodstained son of Tuoni, Lord of the Dead, caught him on his sword-point and hacked him into five pieces and hewed him into eight fragments, and sent them floating down Tuoni's dark river.

Now every morning and every evening that Lemminkainen had been absent, his old mother, remembering his parting words, had looked at his brush and his comb, for if they were as before, then she knew her son was safe. But on this evening she saw blood flowing from the comb and red drops oozing from the brush. So she knew that mortal hurt had come to Lemminkainen. Weeping and lamenting, she set out at once for the North Country, to discover what had befallen her son.

At last she came to the house of crafty old Louhi.

"Where is my son?" asked Lemminkainen's mother. "Where is he who is my silver staff and my golden apple?"

"Perhaps he has been eaten by a wolf. Maybe he has been devoured by a bear," said old Louhi.

"My son could crush a wolf between his fingers. He could master a bear without any weapon," said the old mother. "Tell me the truth."

Finally old Louhi said that Lemminkainen had gone to fetch the swan from Tuoni's river, but she did not know why he had never returned. Sadly the old mother turned her steps in the direction of Tuoni's dark river, asking of all whom she met whether they had seen Lemminkainen. The oak-tree answered that it had troubles of its own, for it was always being chopped up for faggots. The path said that it could not fret for any but itself, for it was always being trampled by heavy feet. The moon only sighed over its own lonely journey through the sky. Then the old mother asked the sun:

"Have you seen my Lemminkainen? Have you seen him who is my golden apple and my staff of silver?"

And the sun told her what had happened. At once Lemminkainen's mother went to Ilmarinen[10] the smith, and begged him to forge her a mighty rake, with steel teeth a hundred fathoms long and a copper handle of five hundred fathoms. With this she would rake the dread river of Tuoni. And she prayed the sun to shine with all his strength that the sultry heat might put to sleep the evil race of Tuoni, Lord of the Dead. The smith forged the rake for her, and the sun shone so fiercely that all the wicked warriors of the Kingdom of Death fell into a deep slumber.

The old mother stood on the bank of Tuoni's river and raked the waters for her lost Lemminkainen. But she found nothing. She waded stocking-deep into the water. She stood waist-deep among the waves. At last she raked up Lemminkainen's shirt. She raked again, and drew up his stockings. A third time, and she raked up his hat. Full of sorrow, she waded further and raked deeper, and drew up here a finger and there the toes of his left foot, until, piece by piece, she had raked up all that was left of Lemminkainen.

"How shall I make a man again of these pieces?" wept his old mother. "How shall I create the hero anew?"

"You cannot make a man out of these pieces," croaked a raven perched on a bush nearby. "Cast them back into Tuoni's river: perhaps they can be fashioned into a codfish or maybe even a whale."

But the old mother did not heed the raven. Patiently she gathered the fragments, here a rib and there a hand, here the bits of backbone, and there the head, and fitted them all together, bone by bone, and joint by joint. She knit the veins and bound them, and made the flesh firm, with skill and prayer and magic spells. But when all was finished, Lemminkainen remained speechless and without breath.

Then the old mother called upon the bee, the bird of honey, and sent him to fetch nectar from distant flowers, that she might brew a magic ointment that would bring breath and speech back to Lemminkainen. Once and yet again the bee fared forth to collect honey for the precious salve. Once and yet again the old mother tried to brew the wonderful ointment. But in vain.

At last she bade the bee fly over the moon and under the sun and across the shoulder of the Great Bear[11] to the halls of Ukko the Creator, where nectar was boiled in pots of silver and ointment bubbled in kettles of gold. This bee must fetch for her son's healing. The bee did as she asked, and brought back the precious ointment that had been breathed upon by Ukko, the Creator himself. The old mother smelt it and tasted it and found it good.

---

10. *Ilmarinen* (il′ma rin′ən), a great smith, one of the heroes of the *Kalevala*. **11.** *the Great Bear*, a constellation of the Northern Hemisphere.

She anointed Lemminkainen with the salve in every part, smoothly and surely, and when all was done she spoke to him and said:

"Rise, my son, from your sleep. Waken from your dreams, and come away from this wicked place."

Lemminkainen woke and rubbed his eyes and lifted his voice.

"I have been sleeping a long time," he said. "I have been having very painful dreams."

"You might have slept longer still," said his mother, "you might have had worse dreams yet, if it had not been for your unhappy mother."

Lemminkainen thanked his mother politely for having restored him to life and speech, and related all that had befallen him. His mother listened to his story and rejoiced that he was alive and well, and even handsomer and stronger than before.

"Is there anything further that you want, my son?" she asked. "Is there anything more that you need now?"

"There is one thing," answered Lemminkainen. "My heart is fixed on the beautiful Maiden of the North Country. But her ugly old mother will not give her to me for a wife until I shoot the swan on Tuoni's river and take it back to her as a bride-offering."

"Leave the poor swans in peace," said Lemminkainen's mother. "Have nothing further to do with Tuoni's river, or with anything that swims in its depths or even floats on its surface. Be grateful to Ukko the Creator, with whose help I have brought you back to the light of day. And now come home with me quietly, and go fishing in the clear streams of your own country."

For once Lemminkainen was ready to listen to his old mother's advice and he went quietly home with her. He gave up all thought of wooing the daughter of crafty old Louhi.

FINNISH FOLKLORE / ELIAS LÖNNROT AND THE *KALEVALA*

Beginning with the work of Jacob and Wilhelm Grimm, who had published their first collection of German folk tales by 1822, the nineteenth century was a period of intense activity by folklorists throughout Europe. The work of Elias Lönnrot (lėrn′rōt) (1802-1884), a Finnish doctor, is among the most important.

In 1832 Lönnrot was appointed the physician of a town in central Finland. This appointment was very useful to Lönnrot in his researches because the vicinity was particularly rich in folkways. In arranging the folk songs he collected, Lönnrot grouped together those which dealt with the adventures of individual heroes. By 1833 he had assembled a cycle of sixteen songs centered around the figure of the magician Väinämöinen. In 1835 he published an expanded version of this collection as the *Kalevala* (kä′le vä′le), which was translated as "The Land of Heroes."

The essence of the *Kalevala* is magic. The heroes are magicians primarily, and then warriors, or lovers, or craftsmen. The songs are of the combats of sorcerers, the search for a lost spell, the forging of the enchanted Sampo, a magic mill which ground out treasure. It is also a great treasury of the spells and incantations by which the Finnish magicians claimed to control the powers of nature and the lives of human beings.

Lönnrot continued his collecting trips, traveling as far as Lapland, the "North Country" of the *Kalevala.* In addition to folk songs, he made collections of folk tales, proverbs, and riddles, collections of which he published in the 1840's. His last great work was to assemble a new edition of the *Kalevala* which would include the materials he had collected since 1835 and reveal what he believed would form a national "epic," like the *Iliad* or the *Aeneid.* This was an enormous undertaking. When the final (and present) work was published in 1849 it was a cycle of fifty songs.

The impact of Lönnrot's work was enormous. Finnish nationalism was given a powerful thrust by the publication of the national "epic." Finnish artists turned to the Kalevala for inspiration. The greatest of these, Jean Sibelius (1865-1957), wrote a number of musical works based on themes drawn from it. The caption of a cartoon published in 1847 and picturing a barefoot Lönnrot with a rucksack on one of his collecting trips captures the attitude of the Finns toward this scholar: "One man, by running around, has set things to rights for us."

LONG, BROAD, AND QUICK-EYE

Marjory Bruce

MANY YEARS AGO there lived in the land of Bohemia[1] a King who had an only son whom he, and all his people, loved very dearly. When the King felt old age creeping upon him he called the young man to his bedside and said, "Beloved son, I cannot remain with you much longer now, but before I die I would fain see you happily wedded."

"Dear father," replied the Prince, "I ask nothing better than to do your bidding, but it will not be very easy, for I have never seen anyone I should care to ask to marry me."

"My son," said the old King, drawing a golden key from beneath his pillow, "here I may be able to help you. Go to the highest tower in this castle, climb to the very top, look well, and then tell me what you like best of that which you shall see."

Now until that moment he had always forbidden the Prince to explore that tower, so it was with great eagerness that the young man, clutching the golden key, began to mount the winding stone stairs. Up and up he went, round and round twisted the stairs, until he felt quite dizzy. Then, at last, he reached an iron door.

"Maybe this iron door will yield to my golden key," thought the Prince. So he thrust the key into the lock, and immediately the door swung open, and he passed through.

The Prince now found himself in a circular room lit by twelve beautiful windows of stained glass. In each window there was the figure of a young girl, wrought in clear colours with wondrous skill. The Prince looked earnestly at each in turn, and he was just trying to decide which was the most lovely of the twelve when he noticed that there was a thirteenth window, hidden by a curtain of pure white silk.

"I must not disobey my father," thought the Prince, "and his orders certainly were to *look well.*"

"Long, Broad, and Quick-Eye" from A TREASURY OF TALES FOR LITTLE FOLKS, selected and edited by Marjory Bruce, published by Thomas Y. Crowell Co., 1927.

1. *Bohemia* (bō hē′ mē ə), a former country in central Europe, now part of Czechoslovakia.

He drew back the curtain, and saw before him the image of a young girl a thousand times more beautiful than any of the others. They had either golden or chestnut hair, and hers was black as a raven's plume; they had brown or blue eyes, and hers were as pure a purple as the hyacinth; they wore robes of gay colours and coronets of gold, and her robe was of grey silk, and her coronet was of pearls. But what struck the Prince more than anything else was the strange sadness in the maiden's hyacinth eyes.

"This lady will I wed, and no other!" he exclaimed aloud. And then, to his astonishment, the pale cheeks of the glass image were flooded with rose-colour, while all the other windows grew suddenly blank, as the pictures upon them faded away.

When the Prince came down from the tower and told his father what had befallen there, the old King began to weep.

"You did ill, my son," said he; "you should not have touched that curtain. She whom you love is in the power of a fearful wizard who lives in a castle built of black iron. There you must go and seek her, and heaven knows if you will ever return."

The Prince was a hopeful young fellow, and not easily daunted. With many cheering vows he bade his father farewell, then he buckled on his sword, mounted his good steed, and rode forth in quest of the iron castle.

When he had been riding for some time he found himself in a thick wood which he did not remember to have seen before. Deeper and deeper he rode into the wood, and more and more tangled and confusing did the track become. Just as he was beginning to wonder if he would ever find his way out, he saw a man coming toward him.

"God save you, Sir," said the man, "do you want a servant?"

"Not at this moment," returned the Prince. "Do you want a master, friend?"

"That do I. But I shall not want one for many days, I am such a clever person."

"What can you do?"

"I can stretch myself to any height I please. Look—I can get you that bird's nest from the top of that pine without troubling to climb the tree."

And as the Prince sat watching him he grew, and grew, until the top of the pine-tree was on a level with his shoulder; then he stretched out his hand, seized the nest, and a moment later had shrunk to his usual size.

"You are certainly a clever fellow," said the Prince, "but, unfortunately, I don't collect birds' eggs. Now, if you could guide me out of this wood I might, indeed, take you into my service."

"That's easy," returned the man. And up he shot into the air again, till he was taller than even the tallest trees. When he had looked all round him, he dwindled to his former height, seized the bridle of the Prince's horse, and said,

"Here lies our way. And now I am your servant. Long is my name. You will see that I shall serve you well yet."

They were soon clear of the woods, and Long then remarked to his new master, "I see my old comrade yonder. I wish, my lord, that you would take him into your service also."

The Prince gazed about, but could see nobody.

"Call to him to come, so that I may have a look at him," said he.

"He is too far away to hear me if I call," returned Long, "but your lordship shall soon see him, none the less."

Then Long grew, and grew, till his head was hidden by the clouds. With his long legs he took three enormous steps forward, seized his friend, who was half a mile off, took three enormous steps back again, and said, "Your lordship, this is my comrade, Broad."

"What can *you* do?" asked the Prince of the very fat man who stood bowing before him.

"My lord, I can make myself as wide as I please."

"I should like to see you do it," said the Prince.

"Very good, my lord—but you had better get into the shelter of that wood first."

Long had already darted between the trees, so the Prince touched his steed with the spur and followed. Then Broad drew a deep breath and puffed himself out, and grew bigger, and bigger, and *bigger* until he filled the whole landscape like some huge mountain.

"That's enough," cried the Prince, who was anxious to get out of the wood again and continue his quest of the iron castle. "Return to your usual size, and I will take you into my service."

So they went on their way together, and presently they met a man with his eyes blindfolded.

"My lord," said Long, "this is our third comrade. You would be wise to take him also into your service, for he is the cleverest of us three."

"Who are you, friend?" asked the Prince, as the stranger drew near. "How can you see your way with that kerchief over your eyes?"

"My name is Quick-Eye," replied the man, "and I can see more clearly through this kerchief than another man could see through spectacles. Without it, my eyes are *too* strong. Whatever I fix them upon either catches fire or splits asunder."

"I should like to see that," said the Prince, "only pray do not fix your eyes upon *me.*"

So Quick-Eye untied his bandage, and looked toward a lofty rock. And a moment later the rock cracked from top to bottom. In the crack something glittered. Quick-Eye drew it forth and brought it to the Prince—it was a nugget of good red gold.

"I will certainly take you into my service," said the Prince, "And, as your sight is so keen, you may perhaps be able to tell me if we are anywhere near the iron castle for which I am bound."

"That is easy," returned Quick-Eye, "though the castle is many hundreds of leagues away. I can see it now. They are just making supper ready."

"Can you see the magician to whom the castle belongs?"

"Oh, yes, my lord—and a fearfully ugly old man he is."

"And," asked the Prince, in a trembling voice, "can you see the Princess whom he holds captive there?"

"That I can. She is in a high tower, barred with brazen bars. Her hair is like a raven's plume, and her eyes are like hyacinths."

"My friends," said the Prince to his three queer companions, "I have sworn to free that Princess from the clutches of that evil creature. Will you all help me?"

"We will!" promised Long, Broad and Quick-Eye with one voice.

Then Long put the Prince and his horse on one shoulder, took Broad on the other, and Quick-Eye on his back, and grew, and grew, until his legs were such a length that he could cover fifty leagues at each stride.

The sun was setting by the time they reached the iron castle, and its great black towers rose grimly against the golden sky. The Prince and his three servants went forward unafraid, and the moment they had crossed the drawbridge it drew itself up behind them, shutting off their only way of escape.

Long led the Prince's horse into the stables, and then he, and Broad, and Quick-Eye, followed their master into the great hall of the castle, where they found several men in rich garments, sitting or standing in groups. But when they went up to these men they found that they had been turned into stone. On a table in the centre of the hall a banquet was spread, with places laid for four guests. Torches flamed on the walls, the roasted meats were smoking hot, but not a living creature was to be seen. After waiting a little while, the hungry travellers decided to taste the good fare so temptingly set before them.

Hardly had they finished their supper when the door flew open with a loud crash, and the lord of the iron castle entered, leading by the hand a grey-clad princess in a pearl crown. The lord of the castle was a dreadful-looking old man, with a glossy bald head, and a white beard which fell below his knees. He wore a flowing black robe, and three rings of iron encircled his body by way of a girdle.

When the Prince beheld the lady of his dreams he would fain have fallen on one knee at her feet, but the wizard waved him back.

"Beware," said the wizard, sternly, "stir but one inch, and you and your servants shall be turned into stone. I know why you have come hither. And if you can fulfil the task which I shall set you, the Princess shall be yours."

"What is the task?" enquired the young Prince, eagerly.

"For three nights running," returned the wizard, "you must keep watch in this hall. If you can prevent the Princess from escaping, you may claim her hand."

"Is it the wish of the Princess that she should escape?" asked the puzzled Prince.

"No," replied the wizard, grimly, "it is *mine*—for though she may, by my magic art, escape from *you*, she cannot—as yet—escape from *me*."

"Very well," said the Prince, "but you must let my three servants share my watch."

"Provided they are willing to share your punishment if you fail," growled the wizard.

"We are willing," cried Long, Broad, and Quick-Eye with one voice.

The wizard, after handing the Princess quite politely into a chair, withdrew from the hall. Long then stretched himself to his utmost extent and lay curving round the walls, Broad puffed himself out till he completely filled the doorway, and Quick-Eye leant against the central pillar which upheld the vaulted roof. Meanwhile the Prince approached the Princess with many gallant and graceful words, which she heeded no more than if her ears had been made of marble. Realizing that she was under a spell, and could neither see nor hear him, he seated himself on a footstool at her feet, and resolved that, come what might, he would not close even one eye that night. But, strange to relate, in five minutes he and his three servants were fast asleep, nor did they budge until the first faint silver streaks of dawn began to gleam through the lancet windows.

"The Princess!" exclaimed the young Prince, in despair. "She is gone!"

"She is certainly gone, my lord," said Quick-Eye, "but if Long will take me on his back, we shall soon bring her hither again."

"Where is she?" asked the bewildered Prince, gazing all round him.

"A hundred leagues from here," said Quick-Eye, "I can see a forest; in that forest there is an ancient oak-tree; on the top of the tree is a little golden acorn. In that acorn the wizard has hidden the princess."

Away went Long with Quick-Eye on his shoulders, and in a few minutes they returned, bearing the little golden acorn, which Quick-Eye handed to his master.

"Throw it upon the ground, my lord," he said.

The Prince obeyed, and as the acorn touched the ground, the Princess appeared at his side.

"Ha, ha, ha," laughed a gruff voice on the further side of the door, and in walked the old wizard, chuckling wickedly. But his chuckles changed to a howl of dismay when he saw the Princess, and a moment later one of his iron girdles split asunder and fell with a crash upon the stone floor. Seizing the Princess by the hand, the wizard hurried from the room, and the Prince was left alone with his three trusty serving-men. They spent an interesting day exploring the many rooms in the castle, but no living creature did they meet. Thrice in the day food appeared by magic on the table in the great hall, and toward sunset the wizard returned, leading the Princess.

"Watch well, ye wakeful fellows!" said the wizard mockingly, as he installed the silent Princess in her chair.

The Prince and his three companions made great resolutions not to sleep, but no sooner had the wizard withdrawn than they fell into a deep slumber which lasted until dawn. Then the Prince sprang up with a cry of dismay.

"Wake up, Quick-Eye, wake up—the Princess is gone!"

"To be sure she is," returned Quick-Eye "but Long and I will soon bring her back. Two hundred leagues from here there is a mountain; in the mountain there is a rock; in the rock there is a precious jewel—and in that jewel the Princess is hidden."

Away went Long, with his comrade on his shoulders, and as they approached the rock Quick-Eye untied his bandage, and gazed keenly at it. And the rock was split asunder, so that Long was able to snatch up the jewel and bear it back to the Prince.

"Throw it upon the ground, my lord," said Long.

The Prince obeyed, and in a twinkling the Princess stood beside him. When the wizard entered a few moments later he uttered two loud howls of anger, and the second of his iron girdles broke asunder and clashed upon the same floor. Once more he dragged the Princess away with him, and once more his four guests were left to their own devices until dusk.

Then the wizard returned to the hall, leading the Princess.

"You are very clever fellows," he said, grimly, "let us see if my cleverness will not be a match for yours *this* time."

No sooner had he withdrawn than the Prince and his servants, in spite of their desperate struggles, fell fast asleep. When the first silver streaks of dawn began to steal through the lancet-windows, the Prince leapt up with a cry.

"Quick-Eye, Quick-Eye, where is my Princess?"

Quick-Eye untied his bandage, shaded his eyes with his hand, and peered out.

"I see her, my lord, but she is very far away. Three hundred leagues from here there is a deep, dark sea; in the middle of the sea lies a little pink shell; in the middle of the shell is a golden ring, and in that ring the Princess is hidden. Long must take Broad with him as well as me to-day."

Off ran Long, with Quick-Eye on one shoulder and Broad on the other. When they reached the deep, dark sea Long waded in, and Quick-Eye told him where to stop, as there lay the little pink shell. But try as he would, Long could not reach the little pink shell, as it was on the sand in the bed of the sea.

"Courage," cried Broad, "this is where *I* can help!"

So he puffed himself out, and grew bigger, and bigger, and *bigger,* and then he stooped down and drank and drank, and *drank,* until the waves had sunk low enough for Long to reach the little pink shell. Then they turned back toward the iron Castle, and Long ran faster than he had ever run in his life before, covering twenty leagues at every stride. Nevertheless the sun had risen before they reached the wizard's stronghold. At the very moment when the golden beams fell through the lancet-windows, the wizard entered the great hall, and his glee was wild when he saw that the Prince was sitting alone, wringing his hands in despair.

"Ha, ha, ha," chuckled the wizard, "so you see which is cleverer, I or——"

Before he could add "or you," there was a loud crackle of breaking glass, and a gold ring came spinning through the window. As it touched the floor the Princess appeared, no longer pale and silent, but with joyful colour in her cheeks. Quick-Eye had told Long what was happening, and Long had thrown the ring a whole league, so that it fell into the hall in the very nick of time. The wizard uttered three low howls of rage. Then his third iron girdle split asunder, and to the amazement of everyone he himself suddenly turned into a crow, and flew away through the broken window, croaking with fury.

Then all the marble suitors and their servants were restored to life, and yawned, and rubbed their eyes, and asked each other where they were. And the gaunt, bare trees in the garden of the iron castle burst into green leaf, and birds began to sing among their boughs. The unsuccessful suitors all crowded round the Prince to thank him for breaking the spell.

"Do not thank me, gentle Sirs," said the Prince. "But for my three trusty servants, Long, Broad, and Quick-Eye, I, too, should have been turned into stone."

So he went to the stables, and Long led forth his good steed, and the Prince mounted, and took the Princess before him on the saddle, while Long planted Broad and Quick-Eye on his shoulders, and, after bidding the suitors and their serving-men farewell, they all set off, as fast as the good steed could gallop and Long could run, for the kingdom of the Prince's father.

Great was the joy of the old King when he welcomed his son and his beautiful daughter-in-law, and great were the rewards showered upon Long, Broad, and Quick-Eye. The Prince tried to persuade his three faithful friends to stay in his service, but they thanked him and said they preferred to go forth again, and seek for more adventures. And no doubt they found as many as they could desire!

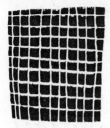

JOE MAGARAC,
MAN OF STEEL

Charlotte Huber

In PITTSBURGH, where the flames from the blast furnaces paint the sky red at night and the tall chimneys of the steel mills belch smoke and sparks into the air, people will never forget Joe Magarac.[1] You can hear the open-hearth crews talk about him to this day.

Sometimes the boss of the furnace crews will say, "Well, boys, that was a pretty good heat of steel you just made, but it's not like the steel Joe Magarac used to make."

Over at the blast furnaces, it's the same story. The tall, burly men in goggles who feed ore, limestone, and coke into the roaring hot furnaces like to talk about Joe Magarac, too. "He was a one-man steel mill," they say. "That Magarac was a giant who could stir up boiling steel with his fingers and never feel it. He even used his bare hands when he was making ingots."

"What a man!" the people in the rolling mills say, as they sit in the control cages pressing buttons and levers to guide machinery that turns red-hot steel into beams for skyscrapers. "That giant Magarac didn't need any rolling mill to make steel. He made steel nails just by pressing the fiery metal through his own steel fingers."

"They don't make steel the Magarac way any more, and there aren't any men like him left either," the oldest men on the night shift say a little sadly. "Those were the days of giants," they tell each other as they unpack their lunch boxes at midnight and bite into thick meat sandwiches in the glare of the Bessemer converters.[2]

Sometimes, if things are going well, one of the eight Mestrovich[3] boys will stop to talk. The boys, all foremen now, like to tell about the good old days when their grandfather, Big Steve Mestrovich, worked beside Joe Magarac in front of open-hearth furnace Number Seven.

"Joe Magarac, Man of Steel" by Charlotte Huber from THESE ARE THE TALES THEY TELL, adapted from "The Saga of Joe Magarac" by Owen Francis, Scribner's Magazine, Vol. 90, no. 5 is reprinted by permission of Charles Scribner's Sons.

1. *Magarac,* (mag/ə rak). 2. *Bessemer converters,* large furnaces for making molten iron into steel. 3. *Mestrovich,* (mes/trō vich).

Big Steve Mestrovich came from the old country many years ago. In Europe he had been a steelmaker; so naturally he came to Pittsburgh. Pretty soon he got a job on the open hearth and rented a little wooden house down by the mill gates. Then he sent for his bride back in Bohemia,[4] and they settled down and raised a family. They had nine boys and a beautiful little girl with golden hair, whose name was Mary. The children grew up. The boys all got jobs in the steel mill, and Mary became the prettiest girl in Steeltown, which was the place where all the steel-mill men and their families lived.

On Mary Mestrovich's eighteenth birthday, Big Steve gave a picnic. Nobody in Steeltown will ever forget that day. They'll never forget it for two reasons: first, it was the day that beautiful Mary Mestrovich got married; second, it was the first time that anybody in this world ever saw Joe Magarac, the giant made out of steel.

When Steve Mestrovich came off the night shift one hot morning in August, he said to his friends, "Do you know what day next Sunday is? Well, it's my daughter Mary's birthday. Yes, she'll be eighteen years old Sunday. Do you know what I'm going to do?"

"No, Steve," the men answered. "What are you going to do, have a cake and a little party, maybe?"

"Little party!" Steve said scornfully. "What do you think I am, a cheap skate, maybe? I'm going to have the biggest picnic you ever saw. I've saved up two hundred dollars, and I'm going to spend it all on a picnic for my Mary. I've rented the baseball park, and I want you all to come. Everything's free—free cold drinks and all the free food you can eat. We're going to have baked ham, and we're going to have sausage cooked like they cook it in the old country. Then, by and by," he ended with a wink, "I may have an announcement to make."

"Well, well, Steve, certainly we'll come," the men from the open-hearth furnaces said. "We wouldn't miss your picnic for the world. Maybe you're going to pick a husband for Mary, yes?"

"Could be," Steve answered. "Mary's a big girl now and so beautiful! I think maybe it's time she got engaged to a good man with a steady job in the steel mill."

"Look, Steve," young Pete Pussick spoke up, "you know I want to marry Mary. I've been trying to get your permission to ask her to marry me for months. How about it? All you have to do is say the word."

"Yes, I know that, Pete," Steve Mestrovich answered. "You want to marry her. So does Eli Stanoski, and maybe a hundred other young men. They are all nice boys and have good jobs in the steel mill. Now, how am I going to decide which boy would make the best husband for my girl?"

No one could answer him, so Steve went on. "Besides, my Mary is

---

4. *Bohemia* (bō hē/mē ə), a former country in central Europe, now part of Czechoslovakia.

one very fine girl and the prettiest girl in Steeltown. She's got to have one very fine husband. The man who marries her has to be strong as anything. No weak little man that can't stand up to eight hours' work in front of a blast furnace is going to marry my daughter. To tell the truth, the man who gets my daughter for a wife must be even stronger than I am."

Steve Mestrovich puffed out his big chest and bent his arms to show muscles as hard as bridge cables.

"I don't have to tell you," Steve continued, "how strong I am. Just ask any steel man up or down the river. From Johnstown to Wheeling, they'll all say that Steve Mestrovich is the strongest man that ever tapped a furnace or poured an ingot."

"Sure, Steve, you are one strong man," his friends agreed. "Everybody knows you are one of the best that ever cooked a heat of steel. But tell us, Steve, how are you going to find another man as strong as you to be a husband for Mary?"

"I've got a plan," Steve said as they all walked through the mill gate, swinging their empty lunch boxes. "Next Sunday you come to the ball park, and you'll see. I'm going to get a good strong husband for my girl."

When Sunday came, all Steve's friends were at the ball park on the river. They had on their best clothes, and the young men who hoped to marry Mary Mestrovich had curled their mustaches and had parted their hair neatly. My, but they were fine-looking young fellows, big, husky, and as strong as anything! Most of them wore stylish straw hats, brightly colored shirts, and fine gold rings from the company store.

Steve Mestrovich was there in his best clothes, too. He smoked a long cigar and tipped his derby hat politely as his guests arrived. "Hello, there, Mrs. Horkey," he said. "How's the new baby? And there's Stanislau. How are you, Stan?"

As the guests arrived, Steve led them to the refreshment tables. "Eat a lot, friends," he said, "particularly you young fellows. You're going to need all your strength this afternoon."

The young men took him at his word and helped themselves to large servings of baked ham, sausages, stuffed cabbage, pickles, and the flaky pastries that Mrs. Mestrovich had stayed up all night to bake. They washed the food down with gallons of lemonade and soda water. Then the young men went over to talk to Mary Mestrovich.

On a little platform, draped in red, white, and blue streamers, sat Mary. My, but she looked pretty, just like a queen on a throne! Her hair was as yellow and shining as hot steel. Her eyes were as big and round and blue as china saucers. Her skin was as white as milk, and her fine strong teeth shone like a string of pearls. She was wearing a new red silk dress, and around her shoulders was a white lace shawl her grandmother had made in Bohemia long ago. Mary was laughing and her cheeks were pink with excitement as her father stepped up on the platform and began to make a speech.

"Ladies and gentlemen," said Steve, "you all know that my daughter Mary is eighteen years old today. She's a fine girl, and she deserves a fine husband. Lots of you young men, you've come to me, and you all say the same thing. 'Steve,' you say, 'I want to marry your daughter Mary. I've got a good job in the rolling mill. I work hard and make good money. What's the matter you won't let me marry your daughter?'

"Now, every time you young men ask me that question, I always give you the same answer," Steve Mestrovich went on. "I say, 'Young man, if you want to marry my daughter, you've got to be a good steelmaker, and you've got to be strong as anything, stronger even than I am. You've got to be the strongest man in the mills, or you don't marry my daughter.' So now I'm tired of all these questions. I've made up my mind to find out who is the strongest man in the mills, and, when I find him, that's the man who is going to be my son-in-law."

"How are you going to find out who that man is, Steve?" the young men all asked at once.

"Very simple," said Steve Mestrovich. He called to Mary's big brothers, "Drive the truck up here and those three dolly bars from the mill."

As her brothers drove the truck up to the platform, Mary Mestrovich smiled at Pete Pussick. She liked Pete Pussick and hoped he would win. She wanted to marry this handsome young man, but she had been brought up strictly, and she wouldn't think of disobeying her father.

With the help of a number of other men, the Mestrovich boys unloaded the dolly bars onto the platform. The dolly bars were long rods of steel with weights at each end, and they were mighty heavy.

The smallest dolly bar weighed three hundred and fifty pounds, and the next weighed five hundred pounds. The third dolly bar weighed a thousand pounds, and it took all the men, working together, to lift it.

"Now," said Steve Mestrovich, "let all the young men who want to marry my daughter step forward."

A number of handsome young men came up to the platform. First of all was Pete Pussick, who looked at Mary with love in his eyes. Then came Eli Stanoski and many other men from the Pittsburgh mills.

There were men from other mills, too, from Johnstown and from Homestead, and from all the mills up and down the Monongahela River. Mary Mestrovich was the prettiest girl in Steeltown, and word had gone out that today her father was going to pick a husband for her.

"All right," said Steve. "Now we'll see who is the strongest man and who is going to marry my daughter. First, you'll have to lift this little dolly bar. It's a small thing, and it only weighs three hundred and fifty pounds. A baby could lift it."

One by one, the young men peeled off their shirts and stepped forward to lift the three-hundred-and-fifty-pound dolly bar. The first man up was Pete Pussick. He gave Mary a little smile and turned all the way around to make sure everybody was looking. Then he lifted the dolly bar as easily as anything.

Next came Eli Stanoski, and he, too, lifted the bar without much effort. All the men from the Pittsburgh mills and the Johnstown mills lifted the dolly bar. Then came two men from Homestead. They tugged and grunted, but neither one of them could lift the bar.

The crowd whistled and booed. "Ha, ha, ha!" laughed Steve Mestrovich. "What kind of men do you have up there at Homestead? You must make pins, not steel ingots. You are too weak for this contest. I think maybe you'd better go and sit down with the babies. This is men's work, and you might get hurt." Without a word, the men from Homestead left the platform and sat down.

Next came the lifting of the five-hundred-pound dolly bar. Pete Pussick was the first to try. He flexed his muscles. Then he spat on his hands and lifted the big dolly bar, but everybody could see that he had to strain to do it. Of all the men who tried to lift the second dolly bar, only three could do it. They were Pete Pussick, Eli Stanoski, and a man from Johnstown.

The crowd grew silent as these three prepared to lift the thousand-pound dolly bar. The Pittsburgh people were not happy at the prospect that the Johnstown man might win and take their Mary Mestrovich away from Steeltown.

"Look here!" yelled the friends of the Johnstown man to the people from Steeltown. "You Steeltown men, you think you're so strong. We've got two-year-old boys back home in Johnstown that can lift more than your men can. You little boys ought to come to the Johnstown mills and watch men work. Why, the Johnstown steel men are so strong that every night they tear down the mill at the end of the night shift and put it up again before the day shift comes on, just for the fun of it."

Then everyone grew quiet as Eli Stanoski bent down and took hold of the thousand-pound dolly bar. He pulled and he pulled, but he couldn't budge it. As he gave up, shaking his head, the people from Steeltown groaned in sympathy.

Next it was Pete Pussick's turn. "Yeah, Pete! Come on, Pete, you'll show them!" the Steeltown men and girls yelled.

Pete Pussick rubbed dirt on his hands so that they would not slip. Slowly he braced his feet and leaned over, bending his knees to take the strain of the thousand-pound weight. He tried to lift the bar. Nothing happened. Taking a deep breath, he tried again. He gave a long hard pull this time. He pulled so hard that his breath came in quick pants and his eyes popped out like apples on a stick. The sweat ran down his face and shoulders as if he were standing in front of a blast furnace in July. But Pete Pussick could not move the thousand-pound dolly bar. Mary Mestrovich cried quietly to herself as the Johnstown man walked up to the big dolly bar. His friends cheered. All the Steeltown people were silent.

The Johnstown man curled his mustache and bowed to the people. He flexed his muscles and smiled. When he was sure everybody was looking at him, he braced his feet and bent down to the thousand-pound chunk of steel. He pulled once, and nothing happened.

Grunting like a pig, the Johnstown man pulled again. Still he could not budge the thousand-pound weight. Finally he took a deep breath and pulled once more. The bar did not rise an inch! As he pulled, something inside his right arm snapped, and he gave up.

Just as the crowd let out a loud sigh of relief, they heard a deep rumbling laugh, "Ha, ha, ha!" The laugh came from somewhere back in the crowd.

Everybody turned around to see who it was that had laughed. The man from Johnstown shook his one good fist and yelled, "Who's that laughing at me? If the fellow that's laughing at me thinks he's so smart, let him come up here and lift this thousand-pound dolly bar. And after he does, I'm going to break his big smart neck!"

Then, out of the crowd, walked the biggest man anyone had ever seen. He had a back as broad as the gate to the steel mill. When he knotted up the muscles in his arms, each arm was bigger around than a man's waist. His chest was as broad and deep as the bottom of a blast furnace.

"Who is that fellow?" people asked each other, but no one had ever seen him before.

"Isn't he just about the prettiest and the biggest man you ever saw?" Steve Mestrovich said to his daughter. "Now, there's a man fit to work in the steel mills. He'd make a mighty good husband for you." Mary Mestrovich shivered, but she said nothing.

"Ha, ha, ha!" laughed the big man as he walked slowly up to the platform. He was still laughing when he stooped to pick up the dolly bar. At this moment the man from Johnstown tried to hit him.

Quick as a jungle cat, the big man reached out with one hand and grabbed the Johnstown man by the scruff of the neck. With the other hand he picked up all three of the dolly bars. Then he stood up, with one hand holding the dolly bars and with the other holding the man from Johnstown and shaking him until his teeth chattered. The Johnstown man was so afraid that he yelled for mercy.

Everybody in the crowd was as white as a sheet. Never in their lives had they seen anything like it. Most of the steel men were strong. Each one of them weighed more than two hundred pounds, and they all had had their share of fights. But there was not a man in the crowd who was a match for the giant on the platform.

"Ha, ha, ha!" laughed the big man. Then he set the man from Johnstown down on the ground. He handled him as gently as a mother putting her baby to bed.

"Be still, little man," he said in his deep voice. "Don't go around saying you're going to break my neck or anybody else's; and I don't like men who slip up behind and try to take unfair advantage."

"Yes, sir. Excuse me, sir, I'll never say or do such things again," the Johnstown man said very politely as soon as he stopped shaking. Then he quietly melted away into the crowd.

"Now, folks," went on the giant in his big rumbling voice, "don't go away and don't be afraid. Nobody's going to get hurt, and I don't want to make any trouble. I was just having a little fun, that's all."

Then Steve Mestrovich walked over. He looked the big fellow up and down. Then he smiled and offered him a drink of lemonade. "What kind of man are you?" Steve Mestrovich asked. "What mill do you come from?"

After drinking a barrel of lemonade, the big fellow answered, "My name is Joe Magarac. What do you think of that, eh?"

At the word "magarac," the crowd burst out laughing because in the old country, where Steve and his friends came from, the word "magarac" means "donkey" or "mule."

"Joe Donkey!" all the people said as they laughed even louder.

"Sure!" Joe Magarac laughed back. "Joe Donkey, that's me. I eat like a donkey, and I work like a mule. That's all I do, eat and work. Me, I'm a steel man. To tell the truth, I'm the only genuine steel man in the world. Look, I'll show you."

With that, Joe Magarac pulled off his shirt. He thumped his chest, and it gave off a hollow metallic ring, like a steel barrel. His chest was all steel, and so were his arms and his hands. His whole body was steel. He was a steel man!

"What do you think of that!" the crowd of picnickers gasped.

"That's all right. No need to be embarrassed or to feel sorry for me," Joe Magarac laughed in friendly fashion. "Me, I like to be a steel man. I can do more things with my steel body than any man made of flesh and blood, and I have just as much fun as you do. I was born inside an ore mountain, away up in northern Minnesota. Today I came down from that mountain on an ore train. I was lying over there on the ore pile at the mill, taking a little nap when all the yelling waked me up. I thought I'd just step over and have a little fun. Don't you worry, I won't hurt you." Then he picked up the thousand-pound dolly bar as easily as if it were a lead pencil and playfully twisted it in two.

Steve Mestrovich, with a big smile on his face, took his daughter Mary by the hand and led her up to Joe Magarac. Putting her little white hand in Joe Donkey's big steel paw, Steve said, "She's yours,

Joe. This time I've found the best and strongest man in all the world to be the husband of my little girl. I know a big strong fellow like you can make plenty big wages at the mill. You'll never be out of work. You're even a better steel man than I am. Come to the mill with me tomorrow, and I'll see that you get a good job right away. Then you and my Mary can get married."

Mary, who was a dutiful girl and always obeyed her father, tried to smile. But the smile froze on her face, and she looked very unhappy.

Joe Magarac took a long look at her. Then, gently dropping Mary Mestrovich's hand, he said, "Oh, boy! I've never seen such a pretty girl in all my life. She'll make a fine wife for some man, but not for me! I won't marry her. No hard feelings, Steve Mestrovich, I hope. You have a fine daughter, but Joe Magarac hasn't time to marry any woman. I'm a man of steel, and I can't waste time getting married. I just have time to work night and day, twenty-four hours every day, to make steel. That's my life."

Mary looked at Joe with a timid little smile, and the big man went on, "But your Mary, Steve, is a fine girl and ought to have a husband. I think I saw her get a little dizzy in the head when she looked at that handsome young Pete Pussick. That's good, for, after me, Pete Pussick is the best man in the country. I think you ought to let Mary marry him right away." Then Joe Magarac winked at Pete Pussick, and Pete Pussick winked back and took Mary Mestrovich in his arms.

Steve Mestrovich sent for the preacher, and Pete and Mary were married that night on the platform. The Mestrovich boys jumped into their truck and went home for more refreshments. Somebody brought an accordion, and the dancing started. The first man to dance with the bride was Joe Magarac, and he was as light as a feather on his feet. That was a good thing, for it certainly would have been a calamity if the steel man had stepped on the toes of any of the girls.

The next day Joe Magarac went down to Mrs. Horkey's boarding-house by the mill gate.

"How do you do, Mrs. Horkey?" said Joe. "My, but you look nice this morning. My nose tells me that you are cooking breakfast. Ham and eggs, isn't it? And griddle cakes, and the best coffee I ever smelled anywhere! Well, Mrs. Horkey, you have a new boarder. I'm going to work in the steel mill, and I'm looking for a nice place to eat. How much would you charge for five meals a day? I don't want a room because I work both the day shift and the night shift. A man of steel like me doesn't have to sleep, but I certainly do like to eat."

"All right," Mrs. Horkey said, "I'll take you as a boarder. Breakfast is served from five to seven in the morning. You can have a second breakfast at ten o'clock. Dinner is at twelve sharp, and I like my boarders to be prompt."

"Yes, ma'am," Joe Magarac answered. "I like my meals on time, too. Now I'm going down to the steel mill to get a job, but I'll be back in time for second breakfast."

Joe Magarac was back in time for second breakfast. It did not take him long to get a job at the steel plant. The minute the melter boss saw the man of steel, he said, "Come right in, big man, and sign the payroll. We need a man made out of steel to stand in front of Number Seven. That's the hottest, crankiest open hearth in the works, but it makes a mighty fine heat of steel if you know how to handle it."

"Don't worry about me, boss," said Joe Magarac. "I know how to make steel. I can make hard steel for armor plate. I can make tough steel for skyscraper girders. I can make steel, without any flaws, for bridges; and I can make steel plate for automobile bodies. You just tell me what kind of steel you want, and leave the rest to me. I want to work both the day and the night shifts. One more thing, boss; please don't put any helpers in with me. They just get in my way. I'm a one-man furnace crew all by myself."

"Suit yourself, Joe Donkey," the melter boss said to the man of steel.

Joe Magarac put on his work clothes, swallowed a couple of hundred salt tablets, and went to work in front of Number Seven. Night and day he worked, stopping just long enough to run down to Mrs. Horkey's for his five meals every day.

When Joe Magarac was charging his furnace, he would pick up the scrap steel and the limestone and other minerals, a ton at a time, in his bare hands. Then he would throw the charge into the red-hot open-hearth furnace. Joe Magarac called the charging boxes used in loading the other furnaces "sissy stuff."

When he was ready for the molten pig iron, Joe Magarac would walk over to the blast furnaces with a huge ladle bucket. He'd poke open the taphole in a blast furnace, where the iron was boiling away at 2400 degrees Fahrenheit, and draw off three or four hundred tons of hot iron. Then, scorning the traveling crane, he'd carry the ladle bucket back to Number Seven and dump the hot pig iron into the open hearth with his own hands. He never used the peephole into the furnace door to see how his steel was cooking. Joe had a much simpler way. He would open the furnace door and stick his head inside and watch the iron and the limestone boiling together. Many an old-time steel man will swear that he saw Joe Magarac with his head in Number Seven furnace and the fires from the boiling metal licking around his chin.

Another thing about Joe Magarac that everybody remembers is that he never had much patience with all the tests and new-fangled gadgets the engineers use to tell how a heat of steel is cooking. Once in a while, Joe would make a fracture test if he was working on a very special order, but most of the time he knew exactly what to do without making a test. They say he never spoiled a heat of steel in his life.

Any time that Joe wanted to check the temperature inside Number Seven, he would thrust one of his long, steel arms into the hearth and run his fingers through the bubbling steel. When it began to feel sticky, he knew his steel was cooked, and he tapped the furnace.

It was a beautiful sight to see the steel giant pouring ingots over on the ingot platform. He never splashed a drop of the metal outside the mold.

If his order called for steel rails, Joe did not like to send his ingots over to the rolling mill. As his ingots began to cool from bright yellow to a dull cherry red, Joe would run down to the ingot platform and start squeezing red steel between his fingers. One squeeze between Joe's powerful steel fingers was as good as twenty passes in the rolling mill.

He could squeeze out eight rails at a time, four in each hand, and every rail was as straight and true as any railroad could want.

When the order called for steel pipes, Joe would make them by wrapping hot steel around his little finger and letting it harden there. He made steel cable just for sheer pleasure. One day, when he was amusing himself by making a cat's cradle out of the hot strands of steel wire, he got mixed up and invented barbed wire by accident, or so they say.

Everybody had to admit that Joe Magarac was a one-man steel mill. He made so much steel, and such good steel, that after his first week on the job, the mill superintendent had a big sign made. He hung it on the fence outside the mill where everybody could read it. In big red letters three feet high the sign read:

THIS IS THE HOME OF JOE MAGARAC
THE BEST STEEL MAKER IN THE WORLD

That sign made Joe very happy, and he did his best to live up to it. He worked harder than ever. All day he worked, and all night he worked. He cooked his steel for exactly eight hours, with the same care that Mrs. Horkey took in baking her fluffy seven-layer cakes.

Every week Joe pressed out miles of steel rails between his thick, hard, steel fingers. Within a year he had made enough steel rails to equip every railroad in the United States.

He made rails faster than the steel salesmen could sell them. The rails began to pile up in the stock yard. When the yard was full and Joe kept right on squeezing out rails, the men stacked them along the mill fence. Soon they had twenty acres of steel rails. The place got so crowded with rails that the men in the mill hardly had room to move around. Then the superintendent of the steel works, the melter boss, and the rolling-mill boss held a conference. They decided that they would have to close the mill for a while until they could sell Joe Magarac's rails.

The melter boss went down to Joe's hearth. "Well," he said, "we've so much steel on hand, Joe, we'll have to shut down the mill for a few days until the orders catch up with our supply of rails. We'll shut down operations on Thursday night and not reopen until Monday morning. I'll tell you what you do, Joe; you put Number Seven on slow heat. Go tell the stock man to give you fifty tons of stock. Put your furnace on slow fire so that it will keep warm and be ready to start up again on Monday morning. Then you take a holiday. Rest up. Go to a picnic or a dance. Do anything, Joe, but whatever you do, don't start making any more steel till Monday morning."

Joe Magarac frowned. It looked for a moment as if he were going to say something back to the boss. Then he shut his mouth and did not say a word. The melter boss went on to the next furnace, Number Six, and told Steve Mestrovich the same thing. Then, after the melter boss had shut down the steel plant, he went home for the week end. So did all the workers, except Magarac.

On Monday morning the men came back to work at the furnaces. They were laughing and gay, and they talked about the picnics, the dances, and the boat rides they had had during the holiday. Then they looked over at the hearth at Number Seven and yelled, "Hey, Joe, what did you do with yourself over the week end?"

Nobody answered. Joe Magarac was not standing in front of Number Seven stirring the steel with his bare hands. They looked all over the mill, but they could not find a trace of Joe. Pretty soon the melter boss brought a new furnaceman to Number Seven and told him to take over.

When it was time to tap Number Seven furnace and pour out the steel, the melter boss came to see what kind of steel the slow heat had made. He was standing by the ingot molds when he heard a deep voice say, "Ha, ha, ha! How does the steel look this time?"

The melter boss jumped, for he recognized Joe Magarac's voice. "Well, Joe, where have you been?" he said. "How come you're late for work?"

The melter boss turned around to say something else to Joe, but he could not see him. He looked to the left. He looked to the right. He looked everywhere, but he could not see Joe Magarac.

Then the melter boss heard the deep voice again. "Ha, ha, ha!" the voice laughed. "Look into the ladle, boss. Then you'll see me."

The melter boss climbed up the crane. He looked into the ladle. There was Joe Magarac! The big steel giant was sitting inside the ladle with hot steel boiling up around his neck. The melter boss was badly scared. "What in the world are you doing, Joe Magarac?" he snapped. "How long have you been in there? You'd better crawl out fast, or you'll be a goner. I don't care if you are made out of steel. Even steel melts at that temperature. If you don't get out in a hurry, this time you'll be melted up, for sure."

Joe Magarac grinned at his nervous boss. Then he solemnly closed one eye and winked. "That's fine," said Joe. "That's just what I want. But let me tell you one thing, boss. I don't like the way this steel mill is run. What kind of managing is it to shut down the mill on Thursday and not to start it up again until Monday? What did you expect me to do all the time the mill was shut? You're very lucky I didn't get mad and start all the furnaces and make enough steel to smother the whole city of Pittsburgh.

"Now, Mr. Boss," Joe went on, but he was not laughing now, "listen to me carefully. A few days before you shut down the mill, I heard the superintendent say that he was going to make two or three heats of very good steel to be used in building a new mill that would be the biggest and best mill in Pittsburgh. Is that right?"

"Yes, Joe," answered the melter boss, "that's right."

"Well," said Joe Magarac from inside the ladle, "I got thinking about that new mill. I decided you ought to have the best steel in the world for it. So I jumped into the furnace and let myself get melted up. You know it takes good steel scrap to make a fine heat of steel. So I said to myself, 'What could be better scrap than a man of steel like me?' That's when I jumped into the furnace."

The melter boss made a gesture with his hands, but Joe Magarac kept on talking. "Now, boss," he said, "pretty soon you're going to pour out this ladle of steel that has me in it. Pour it very carefully into the ingot molds. By and by, when the ingot molds cool a bit, shoot them over to the rolling mill. Tell the roller boss to roll them out carefully. Have him make twenty passes at them with the rollers. Then cut the steel into beams and angle pieces for the new mill. You're going to have the finest steel mill anywhere in the world. You'll see."

With that, Joe Magarac grinned again and dipped his head under the boiling steel. That was the last anybody ever saw of Joe Magarac.

Soon the workers poured the steel in the ladle into the ingot molds. Then they rolled the red steel just as Joe Magarac had told them to do. When they cut it into beams and angle pieces, they found that it was absolutely perfect steel, straight and smooth, strong and hard, without a trace of a seam or a flaw.

Then the melter boss, the roller boss, and the mill superintendent called the steelworkers together. "You see that steel?" said the melter boss. "Boys, that is the best steel that was ever made. You've never seen steel like that, and you never will again. Joe Magarac made that steel, and Joe is inside it. Now we're going to take those beams, those channel bars, and those angle pieces and build a new mill with them just like he told us to. It's going to be the greatest steel mill in all the world."

They did just that. When the new steel mill was completed, it was the greatest and the finest steel mill in the world, and every man in

Steeltown considered it an honor to work there. Outside, on the fence of the new steel mill, the melter boss put up a big electric sign. It is brighter even than the glare from the blast furnaces, and it can be seen all over town. It reads:

THIS IS THE HOME OF JOE MAGARAC
WHERE THEY MAKE THE FINEST STEEL
IN THE WORLD

ANANCY[1]

Andrew Salkey

In this story by the Jamaican writer Andrew Salkey, the West African folk tale hero Ananse the Spider (see note page 120) is presented as a strongman rather than a trickster.

I'M GOING TO TELL YOU a story about a spider. The spider's name is Anancy. The story is such a wonder story that not even Anancy himself would want to tell it.[2] And that's the mystery of things, believe me.

Well, now, Anancy was a real big spider, the kind of spider with heaps of shoulder muscles, a black-hair chest and a night-black frighten-children beard on his chin. Anancy was really a frightened-up spectacle of all things powerful and massive. He was a miracle of terror. All the same, though, he had a certain sort of high-class dignity together with all the strong presence that most spiders carry around with them. And this high-class dignity, this sort of big-house pride, was also a form of strength. It was a strength in the way that veins and muscles in the arm are sure signs of stress, strain and strength.

When Anancy walked about the place, he looked like a sort of a war memorial rumbling and tumbling at earthquake time. Anancy was the kind of spider who could do plenty of things, like swim-in-river, climb tall-tall mountains and run long-long races. Anancy was also a great-time trickster and a giant-wrestler, as well. Total everybody called his name and still calling it in a hush-hush voice, "Who, Anancy? Man, Anancy is a giant wrestler! Anancy is a fairground of powers and muscles! Anancy is a spider is a champion is a strangler is a basinful of big-house pride is a real terror is a ocean of magic with him hands and feet!"

"Anancy" by Andrew Salkey from BLACK ORPHEUS, AN ANTHOLOGY OF NEW AFRICAN AND AFRO-AMERICAN STORIES, published by Longmans of Nigeria Ltd., 1964. Reprinted by permission of the author.

1. *Anancy,* (än än′sē). **2.** *not even Anancy . . . to tell it.* Anancy is the greatest of storytellers. A West African folk tale tells how he won all the stories from their former possessor, the sky-god.

Now, one day some fat news reached Anancy and the news said that the ghosts from the far-far country parts were thinking of holding a real serious wrestling match; and because Anancy is all that he is, he decided sudden-like that he would go to the far-far country parts and take part in the match with the ghosts.

Well, when total everybody in Anancy's village heard what Anancy was going to do, some of his wrestler friends felt doubtful and tormented-up, some of his political spider friends started to put bets on him, some decided that they would pray plenty for Anancy, and some just stood shaking their head of worries and sighing heaps of sympathetic sighs.

But Anancy had a mother and a father. And he loved them in a great respectful way. But they didn't like the wrestling match idea, at all, at all. Anancy's mother started to tell Anancy that it is a foolish business for him to wrestle against ghosts because ghosts can read a spider's mind and they can see clear-like total everything that a spider's going to do before he actually does it.

All that Anancy said to that was, "One ghost is a hundred ghosts, and a hundred ghosts is only one ghost. A ghost is only a ghost to me."

But Anancy's mother and father were arguing with plenty love in their hearts for him. They kept reminding him of the days when he couldn't even see straight, of the days when the shadow of a hoe at the slant used to frighten him, of the days when the smallest noise used to make him draw up all his spider legs under himself and shudder. They tried hard to talk protection into him but all he said was, "I'm Anancy."

When his mother and father were pleading, all he was doing was stretching out his arms and yawning a wide tired yawn, and going on like he was bored and frightened about total nothing in the world.

Later on that same day, he went back to his mother and because she was so sad, Anancy whispered some nice-nice words in her ears, and the nice-nice words made her sad face light up with twinkle eyes and merry-merry heart. Then he gave her some corn meal and cassava[3] flour and asked her to make some cassava cakes for him. He rubbed his arms with sweet herbs and he tensed up his muscles. Afterwards, he stepped outside and gave away some juicy mangoes and nuts to the children spiders who were always standing round his hut. He shut his hut door and rested himself for a while. Then he went up to his mother and asked her for the cassava cakes. She was looking pale and mournful as if she saw a funeral standing up in front of her instead of her own son. She cleared her throat and told him that the cassava cakes were not ready. Anancy wrinkled up his eyes and was angry bad-bad. He was puffing and blowing inside himself like a heap of brand-new bellows.

3. *cassava* (kə sä′və), a tropical plant from whose root an edible starch is made.

Well, Anancy didn't wait to hear what his mother was going to explain to him; he just ups and left her and ran down the road to meet his best friend, Brother Tacuma, who always travelled with him wherever he went. Brother Tacuma, was a calm-sea, thoughtful sort of spider, constantly walking by Anancy's side and constantly smiling through dark thinking eyes. This was so much Brother Tacuma's way of behaving that he got the name of "conscience of all spiders."

So now, Anancy and Brother Tacuma started to walk to the far-far country parts where the ghosts were waiting to open the wrestling match. So they were walking in all sorts of darkness in the forest; and different bad sounds and bird noises were making some terrible confusion in both their heads. Trees and leaves and twigs and branches were having some faces of evilness and deadskull laughter. There was no brightfulness in the forest at all. Big lizards and scorpions and cobra-snakes were all over the place; and they were looking ugly and hungry like forty days in the wilderness.

When Brother Tacuma and Anancy got out of the forest they were so tired and full of sleepy eyes and tight muscles that total everything seemed to look like one big blur of confusion and hurricane happenings. Still, now that Anancy actually reached the far-far country of the ghosts, he ran into some good luck. He heard of a new rule that the ghosts had just passed. And this was it: 'When anybody comes to wrestle with a ghost and the ghost beats up that person, the custom is for the conquering ghost to carry that person away and to dash that person's head against a sharp rockstone which is a special river rockstone fixed up for the purpose.'

Now neither Anancy nor Brother Tacuma liked the new rule at all. Stomach turned over flip-flap when they saw what the ghosts were doing to the persons whom they were conquering. After watching those horrible happenings, up comes a small-small ghost to talk to Anancy and Brother Tacuma. Listen to how he's talking to them in a nose voice, "So you two small-time wrestlers come to the match. I recognise you, Anancy. You still among the living, eh? We'll have to see about that."

To that speech Anancy just bowed his head and started to stretch his muscles. That was how Anancy answered the small-small ghost. But the small-small ghost wasn't satisfied. Hear him, "Anancy! You think that pride is a good thing to have, eh? You think that pride is a good mirror for you to see yourself in properly? Up and down this country we break all such mirrors."

After a little foot shifting, clearing of throats, hustling here and there, things really began to look like business. Anancy started to fight, now. Even though it was broad daylight the silence that was surrounding everything and everybody was like the silence of a Sunday morning. The first ghost contestant was a tall-tall ghost with hands and feet like an old-time electric fan, actually going on mad and circular like an old-time electric fan. The first ghost was tough like crocodile skin and stiff like ice; and because he was stiff like ice, he was also slippery out of this world. But Anancy moved up and down like he was a great jack-in-the-box in a trance. He dived into the ghost, twisted him up and twisted him round, and before you could say Jack Mandora, he dropped him like a piece of rolled-up silver paper. After that, he grabbed the ghost and dashed him down on the river rockstone. As soon as the ghost touched the rockstone, he was splintered fine like icing sugar; and just as white as that.

Brother Tacuma started to feel a proud feeling for Anancy. He just looked at Anancy and smiled a lovely-brother-smile at him.

Then another ghost came out and challenged Anancy with plenty hot breathing, insults and wild nose-talking. This ghost had four heads, a big central head with three other heads sitting on it. Anancy looked at him, cute-like. Anancy moved up and down the wrestling ring and began to spin himself like a bright spinning two-and-six piece.[4] When he was doing that the four-headed ghost began to get dizzy and all his eight eyes turned over and became jumbled up like plenty marbles twirling in a circle. After that, Anancy stepped heavy and stepped light and danced round and round until sudden-like the ghost's four heads dropped off. When they touched the ground, they rolled away in four different corners of the ring and the body of the ghost was crumpled up like dry grass.

Well, now, after that pretty victory, another ghost walked into the ring. This ghost had eight heads, and it could think eight times as fast as Anancy. But already Anancy was ready, and quick and brisk he was throwing his hands around the ghost's neck. As Anancy did that, the eight heads dropped off and rolled away like marbles. Then Anancy grabbed the next ghost who had ten heads and beat him up as if nothing happened.

He beat up the twelve-headed one, the fourteen-headed one, the sixteen-headed one, the eighteen-headed one and the twenty-headed one. You won't believe me when I tell you that the heads were rolling all over the place like wild red cabbage, and the eyes were blinking neons turning over and over, showing white, black and red. The whole place was a total of heads and eyes!

By this time, Anancy was really causing the ghosts a lot of worry head. So the ghosts who had promoted the wrestling match decided to hold a Ghosts United Conference. Big meeting of nose accents going on in deep session! After they had talked plenty Summit talking, they found the answer to the Anancy problem. And this was the answer to the problem: Anancy will have one last fight. And this time, Anancy

---

4. *two-and-six piece*, a former British coin worth two shillings and sixpence, or about sixty cents during the first half of this century.

must fight his own spirit. Imagine that, now! Anancy actually fighting Anancy! Yet, that's the mystery of things, believe me. Body against spirit! (Of course, this is one spirit that will have only one head.)

Well, both of them stood up and faced each other, the Anancy's body facing his own spirit. Their eyes made four as they looked at each other. All the total ghosts were holding a long low-breathing silence. Sudden-like, Anancy's spirit looked at Anancy's body, saw right through it and Anancy's body felt all crumpled-up-like.

After all the trembling brain and soul messages between body and spirit, Anancy's spirit made a flash-of-lightning movement and lifted up Anancy's body and dashed it against the rockstone. And Anancy's body was splintered up into small pieces like plenty showers of confetti.

So listen to the ghosts, now, "Ai-ya-ai! At last it's come to pass! At last! Who ever heard of anybody fighting against his own life! Serve him right! Serve him damn right! Proud and stupid spider!"

After that, the chief of the ghosts walked into a thick clump of bush-john, picked some berries off the bush-john tree, and squeezed the juice into the eyes of all the dead ghosts. Quick-like, all of the conquered ghosts jumped up and began to live again and talk in their old-time nose voices.

Brother Tacuma who was watching the chief ghost, decided to do total everything he saw the chief ghost do. So Brother Tacuma went into the thick clump of bush-john, picked some berries off it and squeezed the juice into Anancy's right eye, then, into his left eye. As soon as he did that, quick-like, Anancy came back to life and returned to his normal spider self. Yet, even though Anancy was restored to his living body again, he was feeling very angry and he started to grumble and quarrel with his spirit for being a Judas person to him. He told his spirit that he hated the bad treachery which it did to his body. And the row lasted for a long time.

When the ghosts returned to find Anancy and to pick up his pieces and to eat him for supper, they didn't see him at all. But they heard him far off. They heard him shouting out loud in the distance, quarrelling with his spirit and running away as fast as he could go from the far-far country parts. So the ghosts decided to chase Brother Tacuma and Anancy.

The ghosts were running mad races and Anancy and Brother Tacuma were running even faster. The ghosts started catching up, now. The speed is pure power-house speed between them! But Anancy and Brother Tacuma were getting nearer home, now. The ghosts opened out to a bigger speed and the forest was making plenty celebrating noises like hurricane wind.

Anancy and Brother Tacuma turned the last corner and headed for the door that led into Anancy's mother's hut. The ghosts were coming quicker, now. They were flying low like madness and cursing-hot fever. Then, Anancy, sudden-like, from nowhere, started to feel weak and he felt like all his total courage and power was oozing out of him. As he was having that weak sensation, he gave up the high speeding and he began to slow down. As he was slowing down, quick-like, something burst way deep down inside him. Anancy's spirit, who had been having a big disagreement with Anancy's body, decided to show that he was no Judas person at all. So Anancy's spirit (one-time conqueror and only conqueror of Anancy) shot out of Anancy's sweating body and began to tackle the ghosts. Anancy's spirit performed some terrible wrestling tricks on the ghosts. After about the count of twelve, most of the ghosts who were chasing Anancy cried out in plenty aches and pain and they turned round the other way and ran back to the far-far country parts; all the same, many of them couldn't move because they were too battered and splintered.

As soon as the ghosts were no more, Anancy's spirit made a real flying come-back to Anancy's body. And as that was happening a joyous, heaven-come-down-to-earth smile spread itself all over Anancy's face. Brother Tacuma saw the joyous, heaven-come-down-to-earth smile on Anancy's face and he, too, felt a happy feeling swelling deep down inside himself. And Anancy made Brother Tacuma know that a person is truly strong only after that person's spirit has proved him.

THE
THREE JOURNEYS
OF ILYA OF MUROM

Charles Downing

Ilya of Murom (il yä′ of mü′rom) is the hero of many byliny *(bē lē′nē), Russian folk ballads. The word* bylina *can be translated as "past happenings." The matter of the byliny is both historical and legendary and groups itself into various cycles, concerning different heroes. Ilya of Murom is the greatest hero of the Kiev cycle, which concerns the deeds of Prince Vladimir of Kiev and his companions. Vladimir ruled at the end of the tenth century.*

ILYA OF MUROM'S YOUTH had turned to old age and his old age to the shadow of the tomb, and as he journeyed on across the open plain, he came to a point where three roads met, and there at the cross-roads stood an oaken signpost inscribed thus in letters of gold:

He who takes the first road shall be slain; he who takes the second road shall be wed; and he who takes the third road shall be rich."

"What should it avail an old man like me to be wed?" thought the hero. "And what use are riches to the aged? I shall take the first road, for Death alone befits the old."

Ilya beat his horse on its sloping flanks, and when he had galloped along the first road for the space of three hours and a distance of three hundred versts,[1] he arrived at the foot of a high hill upon which a large white palace stood. Now this palace was the abode of robbers, and they were not less than forty thousand in number. When they spied the old Cossack[2] riding below, they scrambled quickly down the mountain-side and tried to drag him from his horse.

"Ho there, thieves and robbers, rogues and highwaymen!" called out Ilya. "What do you want of an old man like me? I have neither gold nor silver nor the smallest shining pearl. All that I have is my trusty steed, and he is beyond all price. Precious jewels are woven in his mane and shining stones in his tail—not for the sake of grace or beauty, but to

---

"The Three Journeys of Ilya of Murom" From RUSSIAN TALES AND LEGENDS by Charles Downing. Used by permission of Henry Z. Walck, Inc. and Oxford University Press, publishers.

1. *versts*, (vèrstz). A verst is equal to about two-thirds of a mile. **2.** *Cossack*, one of a people living on the plains of southwestern Russia, famous for their horsemanship.

shine in the dark autumn nights that I may see for fifty versts around. But my Circassian[3] saddle is worth five hundred roubles[4] and three hundred roubles my Christian cross!"

"Ho there, thieves and robbers, rogues and highwaymen!" cried the robber ataman[5] in a terrible voice. "Why do you waste time parleying with an old man? Drag him down from his horse and strike off his turbulent head!"

"Ye shall not kill or rob me, old Cossack," cried Ilya, as the robbers rushed upon him, "though I wear a cloak of marten skin with three hundred buttons on it worth fully eight hundred roubles!"

The robbers were angry at his taunts and rose all around the old Cossack, trying to drag him down.

"Ye shall not kill or rob me, old Cossack," cried Ilya. "My trusty steed, which no money can buy, leaps across mountains and bestrides the mighty rivers!"

But still the infuriated robbers strove to kill him.

"Ye shall not kill or rob me, old Cossack," cried Ilya, "for I have a trusty bow and still ten arrows left!"

But still the robbers came on and on.

"Who among ye has little children?" cried Ilya. "Who among ye has a fair young wife? If any there be, let them think now of their widows and orphans, for ye are about to perish all!"

And stretching his mighty bow, the old Cossack shot an arrow into the ground, and so great was the force thereof that the yellow sand flew up in clouds and the damp earth shook.

When they saw this, the robbers stopped in their tracks, and trembling with fear, fell upon their knees.

"Do not slay us, Ilya of Murom!" they cried. "Let us live, and we shall give you golden treasure, flowered garments and herds of fine horses!"

"If I took your golden treasure," replied Ilya, "I should needs dig vaults to hold it. If I took your flowered garments, I should needs hire carts to bear them away. If I took your herds of horses, I should needs become a herdsman, and I still have a long way to go alone."

And rising in his saddle, he brandished his keen steel sabre, and where he slashed, a street appeared, and where he struck, a road. And Ilya of Murom cut off the heads of the robbers like thistles, from the first till the last, till none remained, and riding back to the cross-roads, he wrote thus upon the wooden signpost:

Ilya of Murom, old Cossack, rode this way, and was not slain; and thus is the first road cleared for ever.

---

3. *Circassian,* (sər kash′ən). Circassia is a region in southwestern Russia, on the shore of the Black Sea. 4. *roubles.* (rü′bəlz). A rouble is a Russian coin, formerly of gold. 5. *ataman* (at′ə man), a Cossack chief.

Then Ilya beat his horse on its sloping flanks, and when he had galloped along the second road for the space of three hours and a distance of three hundred versts, he came to a place too large to be a village and too small to be a town, and he halted his horse before a palace of white stone. Now there dwelt therein a fair young maiden, and when she saw the bold Russian knight, she came out of the palace to greet him, and curtsying low before him, she took him by his white hands, kissed him on the lips, and led him into the palace of white stone. She sat him at the oaken table, covered it with a silken cloth, placed upon it all manner of sweet viands, wines, and honeymead, and bade him eat and drink.

And when the old Cossack had eaten and drunk his fill, the maiden took him by his white hands and led him to a soft bed in a warm bedchamber, and bade him rest upon it. But Ilya sensed her perfidy, and lifting her in his strong arms, he dropped her heavily on the soft bed in his place. And straightway the treacherous bed fell open, and the fair maiden, caught in her own trap, fell straight down to the dungeons below. And taking her golden keys, Ilya went down and opened the iron gates of the dungeons and let out the multitude of kings and princes and mighty Russian bogatyrs[6] who had fallen into the treacherous maiden's hands.

"We thank you, Ilya of Murom," they cried, "for you have saved us from our doom."

And leaving the fair maiden in the deep dungeon alone, Ilya rode back to the cross-roads whence he came, and wrote thus upon the wooden signpost:

Ilya of Murom, old Cossack, rode this way, and was not wed; and thus is the second road cleared for ever.

Then Ilya beat his horse on its sloping flanks, and when he had galloped along the third road for the space of three hours and a distance of three hundred versts, he came to a huge rock in the middle of a field. Now the rock weighed thrice times ninety pood,[7] but the old Cossack dismounted from his horse and pushed the stone with his mighty shoulder. The great stone rolled aside, and there in the pit lay gold and silver, precious gems and large round pearls. And taking the treasure, Ilya shared it out among the poor and the widowed and orphaned, and building also a church with many bells, he rode back to the cross-roads whence he came, and wrote thus upon the wooden signpost:

Ilya of Murom, old Cossack, rode this way, and was not made rich; and thus is the third road cleared for ever.

---

6. *bogatyrs* (bō′gä terz), champions. 7. *pood*, (püd). A pood is equal to about thirty-six pounds.

5

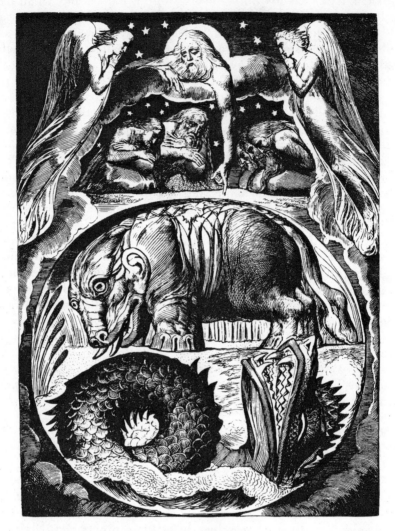

VISIONS
AND
THE
OTHER
WORLD

FRIENDS
IN LIFE
AND DEATH

Stith Thompson

This is a Norwegian folk tale.

ONCE ON A TIME there were two young men who were such great friends that they swore to one another they would never part, either in life or death. One of them died before he was at all old, and a little while after the other wooed a farmer's daughter, and was to be married to her. So when they were bidding guests to the wedding, the bridegroom went himself to the churchyard where his friend lay, and knocked at his grave and called him by name. No! he neither answered nor came. He knocked again, and he called again, but no one came. A third time he knocked louder and called louder to him, to come that he might talk to him. So, after a long, long time, he heard a rustling, and at last the dead man came up out of the grave.

"It was well you came at last," said the bridegroom, "for I have been standing here ever so long, knocking and calling for you."

"I was a long way off," said the dead man, "so that I did not quite hear you till the last time you called."

"All right!" said the bridegroom; "but I am going to stand bridegroom today, and you mind well, I dare say, what we used to talk about, and how we were to stand by each other at our weddings as best man."

"I mind it well," said the dead man, "but you must wait a bit till I have made myself a little smart; and, after all, no one can say I have on a wedding garment."

The lad was hard put to it for time, for he was overdue at home to meet the guests, and it was all but time to go to church; but still he had to wait awhile and let the dead man go into a room by himself, as he begged, so that he might brush himself up a bit, and come smart to church like the rest; for, of course, he was to go with the bridal train to church.

Yes! the dead man went with him both to church and from church, but when they had got so far on with the wedding that they had taken off the bride's crown, he said he must go. So, for old friendship's sake, the bridegroom said he would go with him to the grave again. And as they walked to the churchyard the bridegroom asked his friend if he had seen much that was wonderful, or heard anything that was pleasant to know.

"Yes! that I have," said the dead man. "I have seen much, and heard many strange things."

"That must be fine to see," said the bridegroom. "Do you know, I have a mind to go along with you, and see all that with my own eyes."

"You are quite welcome," said the dead man; "but it may chance that you may be away some time."

"So it might," said the bridegroom; but for all that he would go down into the grave.

But before they went down the dead man took and cut a turf out of the graveyard and put it on the young man's head. Down and down they went, far and far away, through dark, silent wastes, across wood, and moor, and bog, till they came to a great, heavy gate, which opened to them as soon as the dead man touched it. Inside it began to grow lighter, first as though it were moonshine, and the farther they went the lighter it got. At last they got to a spot where there were such green hills, knee-deep in grass, and on them fed a large herd of kine, who grazed as they went; but for all they ate those kine looked poor, and thin, and wretched.

"What's all this?" said the lad who had been bridegroom; "why are they so thin and in such bad case, though they eat, every one of them, as though they were well paid to eat?"

"This is a likeness of those who never can have enough, though they rake and scrape it together ever so much," said the dead man.

So they journeyed on far and farther than far, till they came to some hill pastures, where there was naught but bare rocks and stones, with here and there a blade of grass. Here was grazing another herd of kine, which were so sleek, and fat, and smooth that their coats shone again.

"What are these," asked the bridegroom, "who have so little to live on, and yet are in such good plight? I wonder what they can be."

"This," said the dead man, "is a likeness of those who are content with the little they have, however poor it be."

So they went farther and farther on till they came to a great lake, and it and all about it was so bright and shining that the bridegroom could scarce bear to look at it—it was so dazzling.

"Now, you must sit down here," said the dead man, "till I come back. I shall be away a little while."

With that he set off, and the bridegroom sat down, and as he sat sleep fell on him, and he forgot everything in sweet deep slumber. After a while the dead man came back.

"It was good of you to sit still here, so that I could find you again."

But when the bridegroom tried to get up, he was all overgrown with moss and bushes, so that he found himself sitting in a thicket of thorns and brambles.

So when he had made his way out of it, they journeyed back again, and the dead man led him by the same way to the brink of the grave. There they parted and said farewell, and as soon as the bridegroom got out of the grave he went straight home to the house where the wedding was.

But when he got where he thought the house stood, he could not find his way. Then he looked about on all sides, and asked every one he met, but he could neither hear nor learn anything of the bride, or the wedding, or his kindred, or his father and mother; nay, he could not so much as find any one whom he knew. And all he met wondered at the strange shape, who went about and looked for all the world like a scarecrow.

Well! as he could find no one he knew, he made his way to the priest, and told him of his kinsmen and all that had happened up to the time he stood bridegroom, and how he had gone away in the midst of his wedding. But the priest knew nothing at all about it at first; but when he had hunted in his old registers, he found out that the marriage he spoke of had happened a long, long time ago, and that all the folk he talked of had lived four hundred years before.

In that time there had grown up a great stout oak in the priest's yard, and when he saw it he clambered up into it, that he might look about him. But the greybeard who had sat in heaven and slumbered for four hundred years, and had now at last come back, did not come down from the oak as well as he went up. He was stiff and gouty, as was likely enough; and so when he was coming down he made a false step, fell down, broke his neck, and that was the end of him.

HOW ORPHEUS[1]
THE MINSTREL WENT DOWN TO
THE WORLD OF THE DEAD

Padraic Colum

MANY WERE THE MINSTRELS who, in the early days, went through the world, telling to men the stories of the gods, telling of their wars and their births. Of all these minstrels none was so famous as Orpheus who had gone with the Argonauts;[2] none could tell truer things about the gods, for he himself was half divine.

But a great grief came to Orpheus, a grief that stopped his singing and his playing upon the lyre. His young wife Eurydice[3] was taken from him. One day, walking in the garden, she was bitten on the heel by a serpent, and straightway she went down to the world of the dead.

Then everything in this world was dark and bitter for the minstrel Orpheus; sleep would not come to him, and for him food had no taste. Then Orpheus said: "I will do that which no mortal has ever done before; I will do that which even the immortals might shrink from doing: I will go down into the world of the dead, and I will bring back to the living and to the light my bride Eurydice."

Then Orpheus went on his way to the valley of Acherusia[4] which goes down, down into the world of the dead. He would never have found his way to that valley if the trees had not shown him the way. For as he went along Orpheus played upon his lyre and sang, and the trees heard his song and they were moved by his grief, and with their arms and their heads they showed him the way to the deep, deep valley of Acherusia.

Down, down by winding paths through that deepest and most shadowy of all valleys Orpheus went. He came at last to the great gate that opens upon the world of the dead. And the silent guards who keep watch there for the rulers of the dead were affrighted when they saw a living being, and they would not let Orpheus approach the gate.

But the minstrel, knowing the reason for their fear, said: "I am not Heracles come again to drag up from the world of the dead your

1. *Orpheus*, (ôr′fē əs, ôr′fyüs), 2. *the Argonauts*, the heroes who sailed with Jason on the Ship Argo in search of the Golden Fleece. 3. *Eurydice*, (yü rid′ə sē). 4. *Acherusia*, (ak ə rü′zhə, ak ə rü sē′ə).

three-headed dog Cerberus.[5] I am Orpheus, and all that my hands can do is to make music upon my lyre."

And then he took the lyre in his hands and played upon it. As he played, the silent watchers gathered around him, leaving the gate unguarded. And as he played the rulers of the dead came forth, Aidoneus and Persephone,[6] and listened to the words of the living man.

"The cause of my coming through the dark and fearful ways," sang Orpheus, "is to strive to gain a fairer fate for Eurydice, my bride. All that is above must come down to you at last, O rulers of the most lasting world. But before her time has Eurydice been brought here. I have desired strength to endure her loss, but I cannot endure it. And I come before you, Aidoneus and Persephone, brought here by Love."

When Orpheus said the name of Love, Persephone, the queen of the dead, bowed her young head, and bearded Aidoneus, the king, bowed his head also. Persephone remembered how Demeter, her mother, had sought her all through the world, and she remembered the touch of her mother's tears upon her face. And Aidoneus remembered how his love for Persephone had led him to carry her away from the valley in the upper world where she had been gathering flowers. He and Persephone bowed their heads and stood aside, and Orpheus went through the gate and came amongst the dead.

Still upon his lyre he played. Tantalus[7]—who, for his crimes, had been condemned to stand up to his neck in water and yet never be able to assuage his thirst—Tantalus heard, and for a while did not strive to put his lips toward the water that ever flowed away from him; Sisyphus[8]—who had been condemned to roll up a hill a stone that ever rolled back—Sisyphus heard the music that Orpheus played, and for a while he sat still upon his stone. And even those dread ones who bring to the dead the memories of all their crimes and all their faults, even the Eumenides[9] had their cheeks wet with tears.

In the throng of the newly come dead Orpheus saw Eurydice. She looked upon her husband, but she had not the power to come near

---

5. *Heracles . . . Cerberus.* One of the Twelve Labors which the hero Heracles (her′ə klēz′) performed was to capture Cerberus (ser′bər əs), a three-headed dog that guarded the entrance to the Underworld. **6.** *Aidoneus . . . Persephone.* Aidoneus (i′dō nē′əs), or Hades (see note page 70), was the ruler of the Underworld. He had carried off Persephone, daughter of Demeter, and made her his wife. **7.** *Tantalus,* (tan′tl əs). Tantalus was a son of Zeus and king of Argos. He was on familiar terms with the gods, but for a variety of crimes, including stealing nectar and ambrosia, the foods of the gods which conferred immortality, and inviting the gods to a banquet at which they were served human flesh, he was punished in the Underworld with eternal hunger. **8.** *Sisyphus,* (sis′ə fes). Sisyphus was a trickster. Zeus had commanded Hades to personally escort Sisyphus to the Underworld, but Sisyphus managed to bind the god, and while Hades was a prisoner, no one died. Ares rescued Hades and Sisyphus was led off, but not before he had instructed his wife to leave his body unburied. Once in the Underworld he appealed to Persephone for permission to return to earth to arrange his burial, promising to come back as soon as he had accomplished this. She agreed and he departed, promptly forgetting his promise. This time the cunning Hermes was dispatched to escort him back. **9.** *Eumenides* (yu̇ men′ə dēz), goddesses who punished those guilty of certain crimes, principally those against parents or guests, afflicting the criminals with madness. They were conceived of as hideous women with snakes curling about their faces.

him. But slowly she came when Aidoneus called her. Then with joy Orpheus took her hands.

It would be granted then—no mortal ever gained such privilege before—to leave, both together, the world of the dead, and to abide for another space in the world of the living. One condition there would be—that on their way up through the valley of Acherusia neither Orpheus nor Eurydice should look back. They went through the gate and came amongst the watchers that are around the portals. These showed them the path that went up through the valley of Acherusia. That way they went, Orpheus and Eurydice, he going before her. Up and up through the darkened ways they went, Orpheus knowing that Eurydice was behind him, but never looking back upon her. But as he went, his heart was filled with things to tell—how the trees were blossoming in the garden she had left; how the water was sparkling in the fountain; how the doors of the house stood open, and how they, sitting together, would watch the sunlight on the laurel bushes. All these things were in his heart to tell her, to tell her who came behind him, silent and unseen.

And now they were nearing the place where the valley of Acherusia opened on the world of the living. Orpheus looked on the blue of the sky. A white-winged bird flew by. Orpheus turned around and cried, "O Eurydice, look upon the world that I have won you back to!"

He turned to say this to her. He saw her with her long dark hair and pale face. He held out his arms to clasp her. But in that instant she slipped back into the depths of the valley. And all he heard spoken was a single word, "Farewell!" Long, long had it taken Eurydice to climb so far, but in the moment of his turning around she had fallen back to her place amongst the dead.

Down through the valley of Acherusia Orpheus went again. Again he came before the watchers of the gate. But now he was not looked at nor listened to, and, hopeless, he had to return to the world of the living.

The birds were his friends now, and the trees and the stones. The birds flew around him and mourned with him; the trees and stones often followed him, moved by the music of his lyre. But a savage band slew Orpheus and threw his severed head and his lyre into the River Hebrus. It is said by the poets that while they floated in midstream the lyre gave out some mournful notes and the head of Orpheus answered the notes with song. And now that he was no longer to be counted with the living, Orpheus went down to the world of the dead, not going now by that steep descent through the valley of Acherusia, but going down straightway. The silent watchers let him pass, and he went amongst the dead and saw his Eurydice in the throng. Again they were together, Orpheus and Eurydice, and as they went through the place that King Aidoneus ruled over, they had no fear of looking back, one upon the other.

FORMS
OF THINGS
UNKNOWN

C. S. Lewis

> *. . . that what was myth in one world might*
> *always be fact in some other.*
>
> Perelandra[1]

BEFORE THE CLASS BREAKS UP, gentlemen," said the instructor, "I should like to make some reference to a fact which is known to some of you, but probably not yet to all. High Command, I need not remind you, has asked for a volunteer for yet one more attempt on the Moon. It will be the fourth. You know the history of the previous three. In each case the explorers landed unhurt; or at any rate alive. We got their messages. Every message short, some apparently interrupted. And after that never a word, gentlemen. I think the man who offers to make the fourth voyage has about as much courage as anyone I've heard of. And I can't tell you how proud it makes me that he is one of my own pupils. He is in this room at this moment. We wish him every possible good fortune. Gentlemen, I ask you to give three cheers for Lieutenant John Jenkin."

Then the class became a cheering crowd for two minutes; after that a hurrying, talkative crowd in the corridor. The two biggest cowards exchanged the various family reasons which had deterred them from volunteering themselves. The knowing man said, "There's something behind all this." The vermin said, "He always was a chap who'd do anything to get himself into the limelight." But most just shouted out "Jolly good show, Jenkin," and wished him luck.

Ward and Jenkin got away together into a pub.

"You kept this pretty dark," said Ward. "What's yours?"

"A pint of draught Bass,"[2] said Jenkin.

---

1. *Perelandra* (per ə lan′drə), the title of a novel (1943) by the English writer C. S. Lewis (1898–1963) which tells of a voyage to the planet Venus, called *Perelandra* by its inhabitants. **2.** *draught Bass*, beer.

"Do you want to talk about it?" said Ward rather awkwardly when the drinks had come. "I mean—if you won't think I'm butting in—it's not just because of that girl, is it?"

That girl was a young woman who was thought to have treated Jenkin rather badly.

"Well," said Jenkin. "I don't suppose I'd be going if she had married me. But it's not a spectacular attempt at suicide or any rot of that sort. I'm not depressed. I don't feel anything particular about her. Not much interested in women at all, to tell you the truth. Not now. A bit petrified."

"What is it then?"

"Sheer unbearable curiosity. I've read those three little messages over and over till I know them by heart. I've heard every theory there is about what interrupted them. I've—"

"Is it certain they were all interrupted? I thought one of them was supposed to be complete."

"You mean Traill and Henderson? I think it was as incomplete as the others. First there was Stafford. He went alone, like me."

"Must you? I'll come, if you'll have me."

Jenkin shook his head. "I knew you would," he said. "But you'll see in a moment why I don't want you to. But to go back to the messages. Stafford's was obviously cut short by something. It went: *Stafford from within 50 miles of Point XO308 on the Moon. My landing was excellent. I have*—then silence. Then come Traill and Henderson. *We have landed. We are prefectly well. The ridge M392 is straight ahead of me as I speak. Over.*"

"What do you make of *Over?*"

"Not what you do. You think it means *finis*[3]—the message is over. But who in the world, speaking to Earth from the Moon for the first time in all history, would have so little to say—if he *could* say any more? As if he'd crossed to Calais[4] and sent his grandmother a card to say 'Arrived safely.' The thing's ludicrous."

"Well, what do *you* make of *Over?*"

"Wait a moment. The last lot were Trevor, Woodford, and Fox. It was Fox who sent the message. Remember it?"

"Probably not so accurately as you."

"Well, it was this. *This is Fox speaking. All has gone wonderfully well. A perfect landing. You shot pretty well for I'm on Point XO308 at this moment. Ridge M392 straight ahead. On my left, far away across the crater I see the big peaks. On my right I see the Yerkes cleft.[5] Behind me.* Got it?"

"I don't see the point."

---

3. *finis* (fin′is), "the end." [Latin] 4. *crossed to Calais,* crossed the English Channel to the French port of Calais (ka lā′, kal′ā). 5. *the Yerkes cleft,* an area on the Moon named for the Yerkes (yèr′kēz) Observatory.

"Well Fox was cut off the moment he said *behind me.* Supposing Traill was cut off in the middle of saying "Over my shoulder I can see" or "Over behind me" or something like that?"

"You mean?—"

"All the evidence is consistent with the view that everything went well till the speaker looked behind him. Then something got him."

"What sort of a something?"

"That's what I want to find out. One idea in my head is this. Might there be something on the Moon—or something psychological about the experience of landing on the Moon—which drives men fighting mad?"

"I see. You mean Fox looked round just in time to see Trevor and Woodford preparing to knock him on the head?"

"Exactly. And Traill—for it was Traill—just in time to see Henderson a split second before Henderson murdered him. And that's why I'm not going to risk having a companion; least of all my best friend."

"This doesn't explain Stafford."

"No. That's why one can't rule out the other hypothesis."

"What's it?"

"Oh, that whatever killed them all was something they found there. Something lunar."

"You're surely not going to suggest life on the Moon at this time of day?"

"The word *life* always begs the question. Because, of course, it suggests organization as we know it on Earth—with all the chemistry which organization involves. Of course there could hardly be anything of that sort. But there might—I at any rate can't say there couldn't—be masses of matter capable of movements determined from within, determined, in fact, by intentions."

"Oh Lord, Jenkin, that's nonsense. Animated stones, no doubt! That's mere science fiction or mythology."

"Going to the Moon at all was once science fiction. And as for mythology, haven't they found the Cretan labyrinth?"[6]

"And all it really comes down to," said Ward, "is that no one has ever come back from the Moon, and no one, so far as we know, ever survived there for more than a few minutes. Damn the whole thing." He stared gloomily into his tankard.

"Well," said Jenkin cheerily, "somebody's got to go. The whole human race isn't going to be licked by any blasted satellite."

"I might have known that was your real reason," said Ward.

"Have another pint and don't look so glum," said Jenkin. "Anyway, there's loads of time. I don't suppose they'll get me off for another six months at the earliest."

---

6. *the Cretan labyrinth,* the prison constructed by the craftsman Daedalus for King Minos of Crete to contain the Minotaur, a monster with a bull's head and a human body.

But there was hardly any time. Like any man in the modern world on whom tragedy has descended or who has undertaken a high enterprise, he lived for the next few months a life not unlike that of a hunted animal. The Press, with all their cameras and notebooks were after him. They did not care in the least whether he was allowed to eat or sleep or whether they made a nervous wreck of him before he took off. "Flesh-flies," he called them. When forced to address them, he always said, "I wish I could take you all with me." But he reflected also that a Saturn's ring of dead (and burnt) reporters circling round his space-ship might get on his nerves. They would hardly make "the silence of those eternal spaces"[7] any more homelike.

The take-off when it came was a relief. But the voyage was worse than he had ever anticipated. Not physically—on that side it was nothing worse than uncomfortable—but in the emotional experience. He had dreamed all his life, with mingled terror and longing, of those eternal spaces; of being utterly "outside," in the sky. He had wondered if the agoraphobia[8] of that roofless and bottomless vacuity would overthrow his reason. But the moment he had been shut into his ship there descended upon him the suffocating knowledge that the real danger of space-travel is claustrophobia.[9] You have been put in a little metal container; somewhat like a cupboard, very like a coffin. You can't see out; you can see things only on the screen. Space and the stars are just as remote as they were on the earth. Where you are is always your world. The sky is never where you are. All you have done is to exchange a large world of earth and rock and water and clouds for a tiny world of metal.

This frustration of a lifelong desire bit deeply into his mind as the cramped hours passed. It was not, apparently, so easy to jump out of one's destiny. Then he became conscious of another motive which, unnoticed, had been at work on him when he volunteered. That affair with the girl had indeed frozen him stiff; petrified him, you might say. He wanted to feel again, to be flesh, not stone. To feel anything, even terror. Well, on this trip there would be terrors enough before all was done. He'd be wakened, never fear. That part of his destiny at least he felt he could shake off.

The landing was not without terror, but there were so many gimmicks to look after, so much skill to be exercised, that it did not amount to very much. But his heart was beating a little more noticeably than usual as he put the finishing touches to his spacesuit and climbed out. He was carrying the transmission apparatus with him. It felt, as he had expected, as light as a loaf. But he was not going to send any message in a hurry. That might be where all the others had gone

---

7. *"the silence of those eternal spaces,"* a phrase from the *Pensées* (1670) of Blaise Pascal (1623–1662), French philosopher and mathematician. **8.** *agoraphobia* (ag/ər ə fō/bē ə), an abnormal fear of open spaces. **9.** *claustraphobia* (klô/strə fō/bē ə), an abnormal fear of enclosed places.

wrong. Anyway, the longer he waited the longer those pressmen would be kept out of their beds waiting for their story. Do 'em good.

The first thing that struck him was that his helmet had been too lightly tinted. It was painful to look at all in the direction of the sun. Even the rock—it was, after all, rock not dust (which disposed of one hypothesis)—was dazzling. He put down the apparatus; tried to take in the scene.

The surprising thing was how small it looked. He thought he could account for this. The lack of atmosphere forbade nearly all the effect that distance has on earth. The serrated boundary of the crater was, he knew, about twenty-five miles away. It looked as if you could have touched it. The peaks looked as if they were a few feet high. The black sky, with its inconceivable multitude and ferocity of stars, was like a cap forced down upon the crater; the stars only just out of his reach. The impression of a stageset in a toy theatre, therefore of something arranged, therefore of something waiting for him, was at once disappointing and oppressive. Whatever terrors there might be, here too agoraphobia would not be one of them.

He took his bearings and the result was easy enough. He was, like Fox and his friends, almost exactly on Point XO308. But there was no trace of human remains. If he could find any, he might have some clue as to how they died. He began to hunt. He went in each circle further from the ship. There was no danger of losing it in a place like this.

Then he got his first real shock of fear. Worse still, he could not tell what was frightening him. He only knew that he was engulfed in sickening unreality; seemed neither to be where he was nor to be doing what he did. It was also somehow connected with an experience long ago. It was something that had happened in a cave. Yes; he remembered now. He had been walking along supposing himself alone and then noticed that there was always a sound of other feet following him. Then in a flash he realised what was wrong. This was the exact reverse of the experience in the cave. Then there had been too many footfalls. Now there were too few. He walked on hard rock as silently as a ghost. He swore at himself for a fool—as if every child didn't know that a world without air would be a world without noise. But the silence, though explained, became none the less terrifying.

He had now been alone on the Moon for perhaps thirty-five minutes. It was then that he noticed the three strange things.

The sun's rays were roughly at right angles to his line of sight, so that each of the things had a bright side and a dark side; for each dark side a shadow like Indian ink lay out on the rock. He thought they looked like Belisha beacons.[10] Then he thought they looked like huge apes. They

---

10. *Belisha beacons,* illuminated orange globes mounted on poles to mark pedestrian crossings. They are named for Leslie Hore-Belisha (bə′lē shə), an English politician, who as Minister of Transport introduced their use in 1934.

were about the height of a man. They were indeed like clumsily shaped men. Except—he resisted an impulse to vomit—that they had no heads.

They had something instead. They were (roughly) human up to their shoulders. Then, where the head should have been, there was utter monstrosity—a huge spherical block; opaque, featureless. And every one of them looked as if it had that moment stopped moving or were at that moment to move.

Ward's phrase about "animated stones" darted up hideously from his memory. And hadn't he himself talked of something that we couldn't call life, not in our sense, something that could nevertheless produce locomotion and have intentions? Something which, at any rate, shared with life life's tendency to kill? If there were such creatures—mineral equivalents to organisms—they could probably stand perfectly still for a hundred years without feeling any strain.

Were they aware of him? What had they for senses? The opaque globes on their shoulders gave no hint.

There comes a moment in nightmare, or sometimes in real battle, when fear and courage both dictate the same course: to rush, planless, upon the thing you are afraid of. Jenkin sprang upon the nearest of the three abominations and rapped his gloved knuckles against its globular top.

Ach!—he'd forgotten. No noise. All the bombs in the world might burst here and make no noise. Ears are useless on the Moon.

He recoiled a step and next moment found himself sprawling on the ground. "This is how they all died," he thought.

But he was wrong. The figure above him had not stirred. He was quite undamaged. He got up again and saw what he had tripped over.

It was a purely terrestrial object. It was, in fact, a transmission set. Not exactly like his own, but an earlier and supposedly inferior model—the sort Fox would have had.

As the truth dawned on him an excitement very different from that of terror seized him. He looked at their mis-shaped bodies; then down at his own limbs. Of course; that was what one looked like in a space suit. On his own head there was a similar monstrous globe, but fortunately not an opaque one. He was looking at three statues of spacemen: at statues of Trevor, Woodford, and Fox.

But then the Moon must have inhabitants; and rational inhabitants; more than that, artists.

And what artists! You might quarrel with their taste, for no line anywhere in any of the three statues had any beauty. You could not say a word against their skill. Except for the head and face inside each headpiece, which obviously could not be attempted in such a medium, they were perfect. Photographic accuracy had never reached such a point on earth. And though they were faceless you could see from the set of their shoulders and indeed of their whole bodies, that a momentary pose had been exactly seized. Each was the statue of a man turning to look behind him. Months of work had doubtless gone to the carving of each; it caught that instantaneous gesture like a stone snapshot.

Jenkin's idea was now to send his message at once. Before anything happened to himself, Earth must hear this amazing news. He set off in great strides, and presently in leaps—now first enjoying lunar gravitation—for his ship and his own set. He was happy now. He *had* escaped his destiny. Petrified, eh? No more feelings? Feelings enough to last him forever.

He fixed the set so that he could stand with his back to the sun. He worked the gimmicks. "Jenkin, speaking from the Moon," he began.

His own huge black shadow lay out before him. There is no noise on the Moon. Up from behind the shoulders of his own shadow another shadow pushed its way along the dazzling rock. It was that of a human head. And what a head of hair. It was all rising, writhing—swaying in the wind perhaps. Very thick the hairs looked. Then, as he turned in terror, there flashed through his mind the thought, "But there's no wind. No air. It can't be *blowing* about." His eyes met hers.

THE GIRL WHO WAS SACRIFICED BY HER KIN AND WHOM HER LOVER BROUGHT BACK FROM BELOW

Paul Radin[1]

---

*This tale is told by the Kikuyu (kē kü'yü) people
of Kenya in East Africa.*

THE SUN WAS VERY HOT and there was no rain, so the crops died and
hunger was great. This happened one year; and it happened again a
second, and even a third year, that the rain failed. The people all
gathered together on the great open space on the hilltop, where they
were wont to dance, and they said to each other, "Why does the rain
delay in coming?" And they went to the Medicine-Man and they said
to him, "Tell us why there is no rain, for our crops have died, and we
shall die of hunger."

And he took his gourd and poured out its contents. This he did many
times, and at last he said, "There is a maiden here who must be bought
if rain is to fall, and the maiden is named Wanjiru.[2] The day after
tomorrow let all of you return to this place, and every one of you from
the eldest to the youngest bring with him a goat for the purchase of the
maiden."

On the day after the morrow, old men and young men all gathered
together, and each brought in his hand a goat. Now they all stood in a
circle, and the relations of Wanjiru stood together, and she herself
stood in the middle. As they stood there, the feet of Wanjiru began to
sink into the ground, and she sank in to her knees and cried aloud, "I
am lost!"

1. *Radin*, (rad'ən). 2. *Wanjiru*, (wän ji'rü).

Her father and mother also cried and exclaimed, "We are lost!"

Those who looked on pressed close and placed goats in the keeping of Wanjiru's father and mother. Wanjiru sank lower to her waist, and again she cried aloud, "I am lost, but much rain will come!"

She sank to her breast, but the rain did not come. Then she said again, "Much rain will come."

Now she sank in to her neck, and then the rain came in great drops. Her people would have rushed forward to save her, but those who stood around pressed upon them more goats, and they desisted.

Then Wanjiru said, "My people have undone me," and she sank down to her eyes. As one after another of her family stepped forward to save her, someone in the crowd would give to him or her a goat, and he would fall back. And Wanjiru cried aloud for the last time, "I am undone, and my own people have done this thing." Then she vanished from sight; the earth closed over her, and the rain poured down, not in showers, as it sometimes does, but in a great deluge, and all the people hastened to their own homes.

Now there was a young warrior who loved Wanjiru, and he lamented continually, saying, "Wanjiru is lost, and her own people have done this thing." And he said, "Where has Wanjiru gone? I will go to the same place." So he took his shield and spear. And he wandered over the country day and night until, at last, as the dusk fell, he came to the spot where Wanjiru had vanished. Then he stood where she had stood and, as he stood, his feet began to sink as hers had sunk; and he sank lower and lower until the ground closed over him, and he went by a long road under the earth as Wanjiru had gone and, at length, he saw the maiden. But, indeed, he pitied her sorely, for her state was miserable, and her raiment had perished. He said to her, "You were sacrificed to bring the rain; now the rain has come, and I shall take you back." So he took Wanjiru on his back as if she had been a child and brought her to the road he had traversed, and they rose together to the open air, and their feet stood once more on the ground.

Then the warrior said, "You shall not return to the house of your people, for they have treated you shamefully." And he bade her wait until nightfall. When it was dark he took her to the house of his mother and he asked his mother to leave, saying that he had business, and he allowed no one to enter.

But his mother said, "Why do you hide this thing from me, seeing I am your mother who bore you?" So he suffered his mother to know, but he said, "Tell no one that Wanjiru has returned."

So she abode in the house of his mother. He and his mother slew goats, and Wanjiru ate the fat and grew strong. Then of the skins they made garments for her, so that she was attired most beautifully.

It came to pass that the next day there was a great dance, and her lover went with the throng. But his mother and the girl waited until everyone had assembled at the dance, and all the road was empty. Then they came out of the house and mingled with the crowd. When the relations saw Wanjiru, they said, "Surely, that is Wanjiru whom we had lost."

And they pressed to greet her, but her lover beat them off, for he said, "You sold Wanjiru shamefully."

Then she returned to his mother's house. But on the fourth day her family again came and the warrior repented, for he said, "Surely they are her father and her mother and her brothers."

So he paid them the purchase price, and he wedded Wanjiru who had been lost.

THE
MAN'S WIFE

Theodora Kroeber

THE MAN'S WIFE was a good woman, accomplished in all womanly skills and much beloved by her husband.

One day she died, leaving him bereft and alone, for they were childless. The man had no wish to go on living without his wife. He burned off his hair, smeared his face with mud, and when his wife was buried, refused to leave her grave or to eat or to be in any way consoled. He made a shallow hollow where he lay, his face turned to the grave, and there he stayed crying and blowing tobacco smoke from his pipe over the grave, and repeating from time to time, "I shall wait for you. When you leave, I shall go with you."

For two days and two nights he lay without food or sleep, waiting for his wife. Toward the end of the second night there was a stirring of the loose dirt over her, and she sat up. She did not see her husband, but sat for some time shaking the dirt from her hair, smoothing it with her hands, and tying it back with a narrow band of mink. She cleaned the clinging pieces of dirt from the strands of beads around her neck and over her breasts, then she stood up, straightening her skirt and apron. Clean and neat as in life she stood turning to the north, the south, and the east as if unsure of her directions. Finally she turned to the west, moving slowly away from the grave, westward, without speaking to her husband, still unaware that he was there watching her every motion, and crying.

Following her, the man tried again and again to put his arms around his wife, but he could not hold her; she slipped through his hands. He was, however, able to tie around her slim waist a rope of eagle's down, and clinging to one end of it, he walked a few steps behind her all through the night.

He could see her plainly as long as it was dark, but with daylight she became invisible. He was sure she must be lying across the trail, resting, because the eagledown rope lay there. The old men at home, he remembered, always said that the dead travel only during the dark of the sun. And he felt fairly sure his wife had not escaped him, for the path of the dead was plainly marked, and he could discern his wife's footprints upon it only as far as they had travelled. But as he sat patiently waiting for the sun to set and darkness to come again, keeping his eyes fixed on the trail ahead, he made out there the footprints of many, many others, and among them he was sure he recognized some which belonged to relatives and to old friends dead a long or a short time.

As day darkened to night there was a pull on the eagledown rope, and the wife, once more visible, got to her feet and recommenced her journey along the trail, her husband following after as on the night before. Again darkness gave way to light, the second day passing as had the first, the man's wife invisible to him, unmoving; the man holding to the rope as his clue, keeping his eyes on the trail ahead.

During the whole of the journey he neither slept nor took any food. He smoked his pipe from time to time, blowing the smoke toward his wife while he prayed and cried. So passed one like another, four nights and four days.

They were now close to the land of the dead, and as darkness obscured the day for the fourth time and he could again see his wife, she spoke at last. "Why do you follow me so far, my husband?" she said.

"Because I cannot live without you. Where you go, I shall go."

"But that is not possible." Her voice was gentle and familiar. "Go back to the land of the living while you still can find your way. I must go on, but from here it will be difficult and dangerous for you."

But the man answered her, "I mean to bring you away from that land. Or if I cannot, to stay there with you."

"I believe that that cannot be done," she said, and added coaxingly, "Don't you know—I am nothing now. You cannot by any means get my body back. It went from you when I died."

"Others have said that to me. Nonetheless I believe that I can because I so strongly will it," the man said.

His wife was troubled, but she said no more of his turning back. It would be useless to try to persuade him. It must come out as it would.

On and on they went, the trail ever steeper and narrower and rougher. At one place, it skirted a chasm so deep it appeared to be bottomless, and with only shallow footholds hewn in the rock for a crossing. Here she implored her husband to leave her, greatly fearing that he would slip and be hurled to his death. But, as before, he refused. Slowly, carefully, they made their way across the chasm. Not far beyond, the trail was blocked by two enormous boulders in uneasy balance, sliding apart and clashing together with such violence as to crush a person or animal who chanced to be caught between them. They were no real barrier to the man's wife, because her bones were of course left behind in her grave. She passed between them lightly and quickly, and watched with fear while her husband waited for them to slide apart. Hurling himself between them, repeating a prayer and clinging still to the eagledown rope, the man just made it to his wife's side before the rocks crashed together.

And so at last, on the evening of the sixth day, they came to the banks of the swift river which divides the land of the dead from that of the living—a river spanned only by a narrow, swaying bridge made of strands of grass rope.

The guardian of the bridge talked to them, as is his custom, learning who they were and the village from which they came, and telling them of their relatives who had already crossed over to the other side.

He did not try to dissuade the man from going, sensing his determination and his power. He did, however, warn him that even if his prayers and strength of purpose put him across the bridge, the dead would feel it an intrusion to have a living person amongst them.

He warned them that the bridge was treacherous in its erratic swaying and dipping, and that many fell from it into the river, from which there was no chance of rescue and where monstrous fish devoured them. He reminded them also that demon birds would fly up, trying to frighten them so that they would miss their footing and fall.

The man and his wife said they would go on. It was as the guardian said—demon birds flew before and around them filling the air with their loud cries and making even more hazardous the trip over the slippery, unsteady bridge. But they neither listened to them, nor looked down into the swift waters below. They kept their gaze ahead, the man clung to the rope around his wife's waist, and together they arrived on the far shore and stepped off the bridge into the land of the dead.

The chief of that land met them almost as they stepped from the bridge. To the man's wife he said, "You have come—you bring a companion with you?"

She answered him, "He is my husband. He is a living man."

The chief told her, "I will speak with him. Meanwhile go with my messenger here. He will help you to find your relatives."

When she was gone with the messenger, the chief turned to her husband who was crying, his face distorted and mud-smeared from mourning, and he felt pity for him. He sent him to swim and clean himself; then he had his own daughters bring him food and drink. It had been many days since the man had eaten or drunk, and he accepted the food gratefully. Only after this did the chief question him, asking him how he could have reached this land never before visited by a living person. The man explained how he had come, and the chief said to him, "Tell me, why did you make this dangerous journey?"

"To recover my wife and take her back to the world with me. Or if I cannot do that, to stay here with her."

The chief knew this was a good and strong man, one who, having fasted and prayed, had learned much control and gained much power. He felt he must do for him what he could. He said, speaking carefully, "You should not have come. You are asking for something which we have no power to give you. You must know that we have here only your wife's shadow, that she has left behind in the grave her bones and her body. How can we give these things back to you? You should return to the world and content yourself until it is your time to die.

"Since you are come, and since I believe you to be a good man, you are welcome. But not for long. I must warn you that to the dead the smell of the living is offensive, and there will be a restiveness among them, a feeling of the impropriety of your being here at all. But stay for a little if you will. You will learn how it is with the dead, and that I speak truly. Do not by any means try to steal your wife away. Do not try to sleep with her."

The man sat apart from the dead, quiet, watching. As darkness crept over the land, campfires were lighted one after another until there was a circle of fires all around the open place kept for dancing, and the dead became visible to the man. He recognized his own relatives at one fire, and friends from long ago at another; in the light of still another fire, he saw his wife, surrounded by her own people. He was lonely, but he made no move to join his wife or his relatives, staying where he was and observing the seemingly happy and carefree dead, as they sat by their fires talking or playing the stick game. More and more as the night wore on, they left their fires to dance in the open space the round dance of the dead. He saw that his wife, too, talked, and played the stick game with the women, and that later she also danced. The dancing stopped only with the first dawn, and while the others went off, the man's wife turned back and came to her husband where he sat alone. Because of the daylight he could not see her, but she lay beside him, and they talked together all during the day. When night fell and he could see her, he desired her and tried to fondle her as he was accustomed to do in life, but almost at once he was overcome with sleep. When he wakened, she was gone to play in one of the games and to dance again with the dead.

Again she came to him when dawn began to break, and again she stayed with him, talking to him all day, and he had no thought of sleep. Again he tried to be as a husband to her when it was dark, again he slept, and again she was gone to join the other dead when he wakened.

After all this had happened for the third time, the chief came to the man to tell him that he could stay no longer, that the dead did not feel it to be right to allow a living person to remain among them. But, since he had grieved so deeply and gone through so much to be with his wife, the chief said that she would be allowed to return with him and to her life in the world of the living. He made only one condition: during the trip home, which would take six days and six nights, and until they were home again, the man must not touch his wife.

Joyously the man agreed. The wife, when the chief asked her if she wished to return to her home with her husband, said, "Yes." She knew that this is not how it is between the living and the dead, but she loved her husband, and she could see that he did not know how to live without her.

Together they left the land of the dead, going back across the bridge, between the moving rocks, and over the long trail, on and on until six days and five nights had come and gone and they were once more in country familiar to them. By the next day they would reach their own home.

But as darkness replaced the last of the light from the setting sun at their backs and the man could again see his wife looking quite as she had in life, he could wait no longer. He must and he would have her. She pleaded with him to wait through this one night. He could not. He took her—his love and his longing, his fasting and prayers all given to this moment.

The man's wife vanished, never to return to him.

The sun was high in the sky the next day when hunters from his own village found the man. He was dead, lying face down, arms outstretched, on the trail which leads to the west.

THE FAIRY DWELLING ON SELENA[1] MOOR

Katharine M. Briggs

THE TALE IS ABOUT A MR. NOY, a well-liked farmer, who lived near Selena Moor and who went out to the neighbouring inn one night to order drink for the Harvest Home[2] next day. He left the inn, but never arrived home. They searched for him for three days, and at last, passing within half a mile of his home, they heard dogs howling, and a horse neighing. They went over the treacherous bogland of the moor, and found a great thicket, where Mr. Noy's horse was tethered, with the dogs beside it. The horse had fed well on the rich grass, but the dogs were very thin. The horse led them to a ruined bowjey (or barn) and there they found Mr. Noy fast asleep. He was surprised to see that it was morning already, and was very dazed and bewildered, but at last they got his story from him. He had made a shortcut through the moor, but had lost his way and had wandered, he thought, many miles over country unknown to him, until he saw lights in the distance and heard music. He hurried towards it, thinking that he had come at last to a farmhouse, where they were perhaps holding a Harvest Home supper. His horse and dogs shrank back and would not come with him, so he tied his horse to a thorn, and went on through a most beautiful orchard towards a house, outside which he saw hundreds of people either dancing or sitting drinking at tables. They were all richly dressed, but they looked to him very small, and their benches and tables and cups were small too. Quite close to him stood a girl in white, taller than the rest, and playing a kind of tambourine. The tunes were lively, and the dancers were the nimblest he had ever seen. Soon the girl gave the tambourine to an old fellow near, and went into the house to fetch out a black-jack[3] of ale for the company. Mr. Noy, who loved dancing and

1. *Selena*, (sel/ə nə). 2. *Harvest Home*, a harvest festival. 3. *black-jack*, a large container, originally of tar-coated leather.

would have been glad of a drink, drew near to the corner of the house, but the girl met his eyes, and signed to him to keep back. She spoke a few words to the old fellow with the tambourine, and then came towards him.

"Follow me into the orchard," she said.

She went before him to a sheltered place, and there in the quiet starlight, away from the dazzle of the candles, he recognized her as Grace Hutchens, who had been his sweetheart for a long time, but had died, or was thought to have died, three or four years before.

"Thank the stars, dear William," she said, "that I was on the lookout to stop ye, or ye would this minute be changed into the small people's state, like I am, woe is me!"

He would have kissed her, but she warned him anxiously against touching her, and against eating a fruit or plucking a flower if he wished ever to reach his home again.

"For eating a tempting plum in this enchanted orchard was my undoing," she said. "You may think it strange, but it was all through my love for you that I am come to this. People believed, and so it seemed, that I was found on the moor dead; what was buried for me, however, was only a changeling[4] or a sham body, never mine, I should think, for it seems to me that I feel much the same still as when I lived to be your sweetheart."

As she said this several little voices squeaked, "Grace, Grace, bring us more beer and cider, be quick, be quick!"

"Follow me into the garden, and remain there behind the house; be sure you keep out of sight, and don't for your life touch fruit or flower."

Mr. Noy begged her to bring him a drink of cider too, but she said she would not on his life; and she soon returned, and led him into a bowery walk, where all kinds of flowers were blooming, and told him how she came there. One evening about dusk she was out on Selena Moor looking for a stray sheep, when she heard Mr. Noy hallooing to his dogs, so she took a shortcut towards him, and got lost in a place where the ferns were above her head, and so wandered on for hours until she came to an orchard where music was sounding, but though the music was sometimes quite near she could not get out of the orchard, but wandered round as if she was pixy-led.[5] At length, worn out with hunger and thirst, she plucked a beautiful golden plum from one of the trees, and began to eat it. It dissolved into bitter water in her mouth, and she fell to the ground in a faint. When she revived she found herself surrounded by a crowd of little people, who laughed and rejoiced at getting a neat girl to bake and brew for them and to look after their mortal babies, who were not so strong, they said, as they used to be in the old days.

---

4. *changeling*, a fairy substituted for a human being. 5. *pixy-led*, led astray by fairies.

She said their lives seemed unnatural and a sham. "They have little sense or feeling; what serves them in a way as such, is merely the remembrance of whatever pleased them when they lived as mortals—maybe thousands of years ago. What appear like ruddy apples and other delicious fruit are only sloes, hoggins [haws] and blackberries."

Mr. Noy asked her if any fairy babies were born, and she answered that just occasionally a fairy child was born, and then there was great rejoicing—every little fairy man, however old and wizened, was proud to be thought its father. "For you must remember that they are not of our religion," she said in answer to his surprised look, "but star-worshippers. They don't always live together like Christians and turtledoves; considering their long existence, such constancy would be tiresome for them; anyhow, the small tribe seem to think so."

She told him also that she was now more content with her condition, since she was able to take the form of a small bird and fly about near him.

When she was called away again Mr. Noy thought he might find a way to rescue them both; so he took his hedging gloves out of his pocket, turned them inside out and threw them among the fairies. Immediately all vanished, Grace and all, and he found himself standing alone in the ruined bowjey. Something seemed to hit him on the head, and he fell to the ground.

Like many other visitors to Fairyland, Mr. Noy pined and lost all interest in life after this adventure

from **Black Elk Speaks**
THE GREAT VISION

John G. Neihardt

This account of a visionary experience is from Black Elk Speaks, *the autobiography of a seer or holy man of the Ogalala Sioux, which was dictated to the poet John Neihardt (1881–   ) during the summer of 1931. Black Elk was born in 1863, survived the wars which destroyed the independence of his people, and endured the life of the reservation until his death in 1950.*

WHAT HAPPENED AFTER THAT[1] until the summer I was nine years old is not a story. There were winters and summers, and they were good; for the Wasichus[2] had made their iron road along the Platte[3] and traveled there. This had cut the bison herd in two, but those that stayed in our country with us were more than could be counted, and we wandered without trouble in our land.

Now and then the voices would come back when I was out alone, like someone calling me, but what they wanted me to do I did not know. This did not happen very often, and when it did not happen, I forgot about it; for I was growing taller and was riding horses now and could shoot prairie chickens and rabbits with my bow. The boys of my people began very young to learn the ways of men, and no one taught us; we just learned by doing what we saw, and we were warriors at a time when boys now are like girls.

It was the summer when I was nine years old, and our people were moving slowly towards the Rocky Mountains. We camped one evening in a valley beside a little creek just before it ran into the Greasy Grass,[4] and there was a man by the name of Man Hip who liked me and asked me to eat with him in his tepee.

While I was eating, a voice came and said: "It is time; now they are calling you." The voice was so loud and clear that I believed it, and I thought I would just go where it wanted me to go. So I got right up and started. As I came out of the tepee, both my thighs began to hurt me, and suddenly it was like waking from a dream, and there wasn't any

---

1. *after that,* an earlier vision. **2.** *Wasichus,* a term used to designate white men, but having no reference to the color of their skin. **3.** *iron road along the Platte,* the Union Pacific Railway. **4.** *the Greasy Grass,* the Little Big Horn River.

voice. So I went back into the tepee, but I didn't want to eat. Man Hip looked at me in a strange way and asked me what was wrong. I told him that my legs were hurting me.

The next morning the camp moved again, and I was riding with some boys. We stopped to get a drink from a creek, and when I got off my horse, my legs crumpled under me and I could not walk. So the boys helped me up and put me on my horse; and when we camped again that evening, I was sick. The next day the camp moved on to where the different bands of our people were coming together, and I rode in a pony drag, for I was very sick. Both my legs and both my arms were swollen badly and my face was all puffed up.

When we had camped again, I was lying in our tepee and my mother and father were sitting beside me. I could see out through the opening, and there two men were coming from the clouds, headfirst like arrows slanting down, and I knew they were the same that I had seen before. Each now carried a long spear, and from the points of these a jagged lightning flashed. They came clear down to the ground this time and stood a little way off and looked at me and said: "Hurry! Come! Your Grandfathers are calling you!"

Then they turned and left the ground like arrows slanting upward from the bow. When I got up to follow, my legs did not hurt me any more and I was very light. I went outside the tepee, and yonder where the men with flaming spears were going, a little cloud was coming very fast. It came and stooped and took me and turned back to where it came from, flying fast. And when I looked down I could see my mother and my father yonder, and I felt sorry to be leaving them.

Then there was nothing but the air and the swiftness of the little cloud that bore me and those two men still leading up to where white clouds were piled like mountains on a wide blue plain, and in them thunder beings lived and leaped and flashed.

Now suddenly there was nothing but a world of cloud, and we three were there alone in the middle of a great white plain with snowy hills and mountains staring at us; and it was very still; but there were whispers.

Then the two men spoke together and they said: "Behold him, the being with four legs!"

I looked and saw a bay horse standing there, and he began to speak: "Behold me!" he said, "My life history you shall see." Then he wheeled about to where the sun goes down, and said: "Behold them! Their history you shall know."

I looked, and there were twelve black horses yonder all abreast with necklaces of bison hoofs, and they were beautiful, but I was frightened, because their manes were lightning and there was thunder in their nostrils.

Then the bay horse wheeled to where the great white giant lives (the north) and said: "Behold!" And yonder there were twelve white horses all abreast. Their manes were flowing like a blizzard wind and from their noses came a roaring, and all about them white geese soared and circled.

Then the bay wheeled round to where the sun shines continually (the east) and bade me look; and there twelve sorrel horses, with necklaces of elk's teeth, stood abreast with eyes that glimmered like the day-break star and manes of morning light.

Then the bay wheeled once again to look upon the place where you are always facing (the south), and yonder stood twelve buckskins all abreast with horns upon their heads and manes that lived and grew like trees and grasses.

And when I had seen all these, the bay horse said: "Your Grandfathers are having a council. These shall take you; so have courage."

Then all the horses went into formation, four abreast—the blacks, the whites, the sorrels, and the buckskins—and stood behind the bay, who turned now to the west and neighed; and yonder suddenly the sky was terrible with a storm of plunging horses in all colors that shook the world with thunder, neighing back.

Now turning to the north the bay horse whinnied, and yonder all the sky roared with a mighty wind of running horses in all colors, neighing back. And when he whinnied to the east, there too the sky was filled with glowing clouds of manes and tails of horses in all colors singing back. Then to the south he called, and it was crowded with many colored, happy horses, nickering.

Then the bay horse spoke to me again and said: "See how your horses all come dancing!" I looked, and there were horses, horses everywhere—a whole skyful of horses dancing round me.

"Make haste!" the bay horse said; and we walked together side by side, while the blacks, the whites, the sorrels, and the buckskins followed, marching four by four.

I looked about me once again, and suddenly the dancing horses without number changed into animals of every kind and into all the fowls that are, and these fled back to the four quarters of the world from whence the horses came, and vanished.

Then as we walked, there was a heaped up cloud ahead that changed into a tepee, and a rainbow was the open door of it; and through the door I saw six old men sitting in a row.

The two men with the spears now stood beside me, one on either hand, and the horses took their places in their quarters, looking inward, four by four. And the oldest of the Grandfathers spoke with a kind voice and said: "Come right in and do not fear." And as he spoke, all the horses of the four quarters neighed to cheer me. So I went in and stood before the six, and they looked older than men can ever be—old like hills, like stars.

The oldest spoke again: "Your Grandfathers all over the world are having a council, and they have called you here to teach you." His voice was very kind, but I shook all over with fear now, for I knew that these were not old men, but the Powers of the World. And the first was the Power of the West; the second, of the North; the third, of the East; the fourth, of the South; the fifth, of the Sky; the sixth, of the Earth. I knew this, and was afraid, until the first Grandfather spoke again: "Behold them yonder where the sun goes down, the thunder beings! You shall see, and have from them my power; and they shall take you to the high and lonely center of the earth that you may see; even to the place where the sun continually shines, they shall take you there to understand." And as he spoke of understanding, I looked up and saw the rainbow leap with flames of many colors over me.

Now there was a wooden cup in his hand and it was full of water and in the water was the sky.

"Take this," he said. "It is the power to make live, and it is yours."

Now he had a bow in his hands. "Take this," he said. "It is the power to destroy, and it is yours."

Then he pointed to himself and said: "Look close at him who is your spirit now, for you are his body and his name is Eagle Wing Stretches."

And saying this, he got up very tall and started running toward where the sun goes down; and suddenly he was a black horse that stopped and turned and looked at me, and the horse was very poor and sick; his ribs stood out.

Then the second Grandfather, he of the North, arose with a herb of power in his hand, and said: "Take this and hurry." I took and held it toward the black horse yonder. He fattened and was happy and came prancing to his place again and was the first Grandfather sitting there.

The second Grandfather, he of the North, spoke again: "Take courage, younger brother," he said; "on earth a nation you shall make live, for yours shall be the power of the white giant's wing, the cleansing wind." Then he got up very tall and started running toward the north; and when he turned toward me, it was a white goose wheeling. I looked about me now, and the horses in the west were thunders and the horses of the north were geese. And the second Grandfather sang two songs that were like this:

They are appearing, may you behold!
They are appearing, may you behold!
The thunder nation is appearing, behold!

They are appearing, may you behold!
They are appearing, may you behold!
The white geese nation is appearing, behold!

And now it was the third Grandfather who spoke, he of where the sun shines continually. "Take courage, younger brother," he said, "for across the earth they shall take you!" Then he pointed to where the daybreak star was shining, and beneath the star two men were flying. "From them you shall have power," he said, "from them who have awakened all the beings of the earth with roots and legs and wings." And as he said this, he held in his hand a peace pipe which had a spotted eagle outstretched upon the stem; and this eagle seemed alive, for it was poised there, fluttering, and its eyes were looking at me. "With this pipe," the Grandfather said, "you shall walk upon the earth, and whatever sickens there you shall make well." Then he pointed to a man who was bright red all over, the color of good and of plenty, and as he pointed, the red man lay down and rolled and changed into a bison that got up and galloped toward the sorrel horses of the east, and they too turned to bison, fat and many.

And now the fourth Grandfather spoke, he of the place where you are always facing (the south), whence comes the power to grow. "Younger brother," he said, "with the powers of the four quarters you shall walk, a relative. Behold, the living center of a nation I shall give you, and with it many you shall save." And I saw that he was holding in his hand a bright red stick that was alive, and as I looked it sprouted at the top and sent forth branches, and on the branches many leaves came out and murmured and in the leaves the birds began to sing. And then for just a little while I thought I saw beneath it in the shade the circled villages of people and every living thing with roots or legs or wings, and all were happy. "It shall stand in the center of the nation's circle," said the Grandfather, "a cane to walk with and a people's heart; and by your powers you shall make it blossom."

Then when he had been still a little while to hear the birds sing, he spoke again: "Behold the earth!" So I looked down and saw it lying yonder like a hoop of peoples, and in the center bloomed the holy stick that was a tree, and where it stood there crossed two roads, a red one and a black. "From where the giant lives (the north) to where you always face (the south) the red road goes, the road of good," the Grandfather said, "and on it shall your nation walk. The black road goes from where the thunder beings live (the west) to where the sun continually shines (the east), a fearful road, a road of troubles and of war. On this also you shall walk, and from it you shall have the power to destroy a people's foes. In four ascents you shall walk the earth with power."

I think he meant that I should see four generations, counting me, and now I am seeing the third.

Then he rose very tall and started running toward the south, and was an elk; and as he stood among the buckskins yonder, they too were elks.

Now the fifth Grandfather spoke, the oldest of them all, the Spirit of the Sky. "My boy," he said, "I have sent for you and you have come. My power you shall see!" He stretched his arms and turned into a spotted eagle hovering. "Behold," he said, "all the wings of the air shall come to you, and they and the winds and the stars shall be like relatives. You shall go across the earth with my power." Then the eagle soared above my head and fluttered there; and suddenly the sky was full of friendly wings all coming toward me.

Now I knew the sixth Grandfather was about to speak, he who was the Spirit of the Earth, and I saw that he was very old, but more as men are old. His hair was long and white, his face was all in wrinkles and his eyes were deep and dim. I stared at him, for it seemed I knew him somehow; and as I stared, he slowly changed, for he was growing backwards into youth, and when he had become a boy, I knew that he was myself with all the years that would be mine at last. When he was old again, he said: "My boy, have courage, for my power shall be yours, and you shall need it, for your nation on the earth will have great troubles. Come."

He rose and tottered out through the rainbow door, and as I followed I was riding on the bay horse who had talked to me at first and led me to that place. Then the bay horse stopped and faced the black horses of the west, and a voice said: "They have given you the cup of water to make live the greening day, and also the bow and arrow to destroy." The bay neighed, and the twelve blacks horses came and stood behind me, four abreast.

The bay faced the sorrels of the east, and I saw that they had morning stars upon their foreheads and they were very bright. And the voice said: "They have given you the sacred pipe and the power that is peace, and the good red day." The bay neighed, and the twelve sorrels stood behind me, four abreast.

My horse now faced the buckskins of the south, and a voice said: "They have given you the sacred stick and your nation's hoop, and the yellow day; and in the center of the hoop you shall set the stick and make it grow into a shielding tree, and bloom." The bay neighed, and the twelve buckskins came and stood behind me, four abreast.

Then I knew that there were riders on all the horses there behind me, and a voice said: "Now you shall walk the black road with these; and as you walk, all the nations that have roots or legs or wings shall fear you."

So I started, riding toward the east down the fearful road, and behind me came the horsebacks four abreast—the blacks, the whites, the sorrels, and the buckskins—and far away above the fearful road the daybreak star was rising very dim.

I looked below me where the earth was silent in a sick green light, and saw the hills look up afraid and the grasses on the hills and all the animals; and everywhere about me were the cries of frightened birds and sounds of fleeing wings. I was the chief of all the heavens riding there, and when I looked behind me, all the twelve black horses reared and plunged and thundered and their manes and tails were whirling hail and their nostrils snorted lightning. And when I looked below again, I saw the slant hail falling and the long, sharp rain, and where we passed, the trees bowed low and all the hills were dim.

Now the earth was bright again as we rode. I could see the hills and valleys and the creeks and rivers passing under. We came above a place where three streams made a big one—a source of mighty waters—and something terrible was there. Flames were rising from the waters and in the flames a blue man lived. The dust was floating all about him in the air, the grass was short and withered, the trees were wilting, two-legged and four-legged beings lay there thin and panting, and wings too weak to fly.

Then the black horse riders shouted "Hoka hey!" and charged down upon the blue man, but were driven back. And the white troop shouted, charging, and was beaten; then the red troop and the yellow.

And when each had failed, they all cried together: "Eagle Wing Stretches, hurry!" And all the world was filled with voices of all kinds that cheered me, so I charged. I had the cup of water in one hand and in the other was the bow that turned into a spear as the bay and I swooped down, and the spear's head was sharp lightning. It stabbed the blue man's heart, and as it struck I could hear the thunder rolling and many voices that cried "Un-hee!," meaning I had killed. The flames died. The trees and grasses were not withered any more and murmured happily together, and every living being cried in gladness with whatever voice it had. Then the four troops of horsemen charged down and struck the dead body of the blue man, counting coup;[5] and suddenly it was only a harmless turtle.

You see, I had been riding with the storm clouds, and had come to earth as rain, and it was drouth that I had killed with the power that the Six Grandfathers gave me. So we were riding on the earth now down along the river flowing full from the source of waters, and soon I saw ahead the circled village of a people in the valley. And a Voice said: "Behold a nation; it is yours. Make haste, Eagle Wing Stretches!"

I entered the village, riding, with the four horse troops behind me—the blacks, the whites, the sorrels, and the buckskins; and the place was filled with moaning and with mourning for the dead. The wind was blowing from the south like fever, and when I looked around I saw that in nearly every tepee the women and the children and the men lay dying with the dead.

---

5. *counting coup.* Among some of the Plains Indian peoples, there was a system established by custom which attached varying degrees of merit to certain acts performed in battle or the hunt; for example, striking an enemy in battle with the hand, or with a short stick, called a coup (kü) stick, or being the first person to reach and strike a fallen warrior.

So I rode around the circle of the village, looking in upon the sick and dead, and I felt like crying as I rode. But when I looked behind me, all the women and the children and the men were getting up and coming forth with happy faces.

And a Voice said: "Behold, they have given you the center of the nation's hoop to make it live."

So I rode to the center of the village, with the horse troops in their quarters round about me, and there the people gathered. And the Voice said: "Give them now the flowering stick that they may flourish, and the sacred pipe that they may know the power that is peace, and the wing of the white giant that they may have endurance and face all winds with courage."

So I took the bright red stick and at the center of the nation's hoop I thrust it in the earth. As it touched the earth it leaped mightily in my hand and was a waga chun, the rustling tree,[6] very tall and full of leafy branches and of all birds singing. And beneath it all the animals were mingling with the people like relatives and making happy cries. The women raised their tremolo of joy, and the men shouted all together: "Here we shall raise our children and be as little chickens under the mother sheo's[7] wing." Then I heard the white wind blowing gently through the tree and singing there, and from the east the sacred pipe came flying on its eagle wings, and stopped before me there beneath the tree, spreading deep peace around it.

Then the daybreak star was rising, and a Voice said: "It shall be a relative to them; and who shall see it, shall see much more, for thence comes wisdom; and those who do not see it shall be dark." And all the people raised their faces to the east, and the star's light fell upon them, and all the dogs barked loudly and the horses whinnied.

Then when the many little voices ceased, the great Voice said: "Behold the circle of the nation's hoop, for it is holy, being endless, and thus all powers shall be one power in the people without end. Now they shall break camp and go forth upon the red road, and your Grandfathers shall walk with them." So the people broke camp and took the good road with the white wing on their faces, and the order of their going was like this:

First, the black horse riders with the cup of water; and the white horse riders with the white wing and the sacred herb; and the sorrel riders with the holy pipe; and the buckskins with the flowering stick. And after these the little children and the youths and maidens followed in a band.

Second, came the tribe's four chieftains, and their band was all young men and women.

Third, the nation's four advisers leading men and women neither young nor old.

---

6. *the rustling tree*, the cottonwood. 7. *sheo*, prairie hen.

Fourth, the old men hobbling with their canes and looking to the earth.

Fifth, old women hobbling with their canes and looking to the earth.

Sixth, myself all alone upon the bay with the bow and arrows that the First Grandfather gave me. But I was not the last; for when I looked behind me there were ghosts of people like a trailing fog as far as I could see—grandfathers of grandfathers and grandmothers of grandmothers without number. And over these a great Voice—the Voice that was the South—lived, and I could feel it silent.

And as we went the Voice behind me said: "Behold a good nation walking in a sacred manner in a good land!"

Then I looked up and saw that there were four ascents ahead, and these were generations I should know. Now we were on the first ascent, and all the land was green. And as the long line climbed, all the old men and women raised their hands, palms forward, to the far sky yonder and began to croon a song together, and the sky ahead was filled with clouds of baby faces.

When we came to the end of the first ascent we camped in the sacred circle as before, and in the center stood the holy tree, and still the land about us was all green.

Then we started on the second ascent, marching as before, and still the land was green, but it was getting steeper. And as I looked ahead, the people changed into elks and bison and all four-footed beings and even into fowls, all walking in a sacred manner on the good red road together. And I myself was a spotted eagle soaring over them. But just before we stopped to camp at the end of that ascent, all the marching animals grew restless and afraid that they were not what they had been, and began sending forth voices of trouble, calling to their chiefs. And when they camped at the end of that ascent, I looked down and saw that leaves were falling from the holy tree.

And the Voice said: "Behold your nation, and remember what your Six Grandfathers gave you, for thenceforth your people walk in difficulties."

Then the people broke camp again, and saw the black road before them towards where the sun goes down, and black clouds coming yonder; and they did not want to go but could not stay. And as they walked the third ascent, all the animals and fowls that were the people ran here and there, for each one seemed to have his own little vision that he followed and his own rules; and all over the universe I could hear the winds at war like wild beasts fighting.

And when we reached the summit of the third ascent and camped, the nation's hoop was broken like a ring of smoke that spreads and scatters and the holy tree seemed dying and all its birds were gone. And when I looked ahead I saw that the fourth ascent would be terrible.

Then when the people were getting ready to begin the fourth ascent, the Voice spoke like some one weeping, and it said: "Look there upon your nation." And when I looked down, the people were all changed back to human, and they were thin, their faces sharp, for they were starving. Their ponies were only hide and bones, and the holy tree was gone.

And as I looked and wept, I saw that there stood on the north side of the starving camp a sacred man who was painted red all over his body, and he held a spear as he walked into the center of the people, and there he lay down and rolled. And when he got up, it was a fat bison standing there, and where the bison stood a sacred herb sprang up right where the tree had been in the center of the nation's hoop. The herb grew and bore four blossoms on a single stem while I was looking—a blue, a white, a scarlet, and a yellow—and the bright rays of these flashed to the heavens.

I know now what this meant, that the bison were the gift of a good spirit and were our strength, but we should lose them, and from the same good spirit we must find another strength. For the people all seemed better when the herb had grown and bloomed, and the horses raised their tails and neighed and pranced around, and I could see a light breeze going from the north among the people like a ghost; and suddenly the flowering tree was there again at the center of the nation's hoop where the four-rayed herb had blossomed.

I was still the spotted eagle floating, and I could see that I was already in the fourth ascent and the people were camping yonder at the top of the third long rise. It was dark and terrible about me, for all the winds of the world were fighting. It was like rapid gunfire and like whirling smoke, and like women and children wailing and like horses screaming all over the world.

I could see my people yonder running about, setting the smoke-flap poles and fastening down their tepees against the wind, for the storm cloud was coming on them very fast and black, and there were frightened swallows without number fleeing before the cloud.

Then a song of power came to me and I sang it there in the midst of that terrible place where I was. It went like this:

A good nation I will make live.
This the nation above has said.
They have given me the power to make over.

And when I had sung this, a Voice said: "To the four quarters you shall run for help, and nothing shall be strong before you. Behold him!"

Now I was on my bay horse again, because the horse is of the earth, and it was there my power would be used. And as I obeyed the Voice and looked, there was a horse all skin and bones yonder in the west, a faded brownish black. And a Voice there said: "Take this and make him over; and it was the four-rayed herb that I was holding in my hand. So I rode above the poor horse in a circle, and as I did this I could hear the people yonder calling for spirit power, "A-hey! a-hey! a-hey! a-hey!" Then the poor horse neighed and rolled and got up, and he was a big, shiny, black stallion with dapples all over him and his mane about him like a cloud. He was the chief of all the horses; and when he snorted, it was a flash of lightning and his eyes were like the sunset star. He dashed to the west and neighed, and the west was filled with a dust of hoofs, and horses without number, shiny black, came plunging from the dust. Then he dashed toward the north and neighed, and to the east and to the south, and the dust clouds answered, giving forth their plunging horses without number—whites and sorrels and buckskins, fat, shiny, rejoicing in their fleetness and their strength. It was beautiful, but it was also terrible.

Then they all stopped short, rearing, and were standing in a great hoop about their black chief at the center, and were still. And as they stood, four virgins, more beautiful than women of the earth can be, came through the circle, dressed in scarlet, one from each of the four quarters, and stood about the great black stallion in their places; and one held the wooden cup of water, and one the white wing, and one the pipe, and one the nation's hoop. All the universe was silent, listening; and then the great black stallion raised his voice and sang. The song he sang was this:

My horses, prancing they are coming.
My horses, neighing they are coming;
Prancing, they are coming.

All over the universe they come.
They will dance; may you behold them. (4 times)
A horse nation, they will dance. May you behold them. (4 times)

His voice was not loud, but it went all over the universe and filled it. There was nothing that did not hear, and it was more beautiful than anything can be. It was so beautiful that nothing anywhere could keep from dancing. The virgins danced, and all the circled horses. The leaves on the trees, the grasses on the hills and in the valleys, the waters in the creeks and in the rivers and the lakes, the four-legged and the two-legged and the wings of the air—all danced together to the music of the stallion's song.

And when I looked down upon my people yonder, the cloud passed over, blessing them with friendly rain, and stood in the east with a flaming rainbow over it.

Then all the horses went singing back to their places beyond the summit of the fourth ascent, and all things sang along with them as they walked.

And a Voice said: "All over the universe they have finished a day of happiness." And looking down I saw that the whole wide circle of the day was beautiful and green, with all fruits growing and all things kind and happy.

Then a Voice said: "Behold this day, for it is yours to make. Now you shall stand upon the center of the earth to see, for there they are taking you."

I was still on my bay horse, and once more I felt the riders of the west, the north, the east, the south, behind me in formation, as before, and we were going east. I looked ahead and saw the mountains there with rocks and forests on them, and from the mountains flashed all colors upward to the heavens. Then I was standing on the highest mountain of them all, and round about beneath me was the whole hoop of the world. And while I stood there I saw more than I can tell and I understood more than I saw; for I was seeing in a sacred manner the shapes of all things in the spirit, and the shape of all shapes as they must live together like one being. And I saw that the sacred hoop of my people was one of many hoops that made one circle, wide as daylight and as starlight, and in the center grew one mighty flowering tree to shelter all the children of one mother and one father. And I saw that it was holy.

Then as I stood there, two men were coming from the east, head first like arrows flying, and between them rose the daybreak star. They came and gave a herb to me and said: "With this on earth you shall undertake anything and do it." It was the daybreak-star herb, the herb of understanding, and they told me to drop it on the earth. I saw it falling far, and when it struck the earth it rooted and grew and flowered, four blossoms on one stem, a blue, a white, a scarlet, and a yellow; and the rays from these streamed upward to the heavens so that all creatures saw it and in no place was there darkness.

Then the Voice said: "Your Six Grandfathers—now you shall go back to them."

I had not noticed how I was dressed until now, and I saw that I was painted red all over, and my joints were painted black, with white stripes between the joints. My bay had lightning stripes all over him, and his mane was cloud. And when I breathed, my breath was lightning.

Now two men were leading me, head first like arrows slanting upward—the two that brought me from the earth. And as I followed on the bay, they turned into four flocks of geese that flew in circles, one above each quarter, sending forth a sacred voice as they flew: Br-r-r-p, br-r-r-p, br-r-r-p, br-r-r-p!

Then I saw ahead the rainbow flaming above the tepee of the Six

Grandfathers, built and roofed with cloud and sewed with thongs of lightning; and underneath it were all the wings of the air and under them the animals and men. All these were rejoicing, and thunder was like happy laughter.

As I rode in through the rainbow door, there were cheering voices from all over the universe, and I saw the Six Grandfathers sitting in a row, with their arms held toward me and their hands, palms out; and behind them in the cloud were faces thronging, without number, of the people yet to be.

"He has triumphed!" cried the six together, making thunder. And as I passed before them there, each gave again the gift that he had given me before—the cup of water and the bow and arrows, the power to make live and to destroy; the white wing of cleansing and the healing herb; the sacred pipe; the flowering stick. And each one spoke in turn from west to south, explaining what he gave as he had done before, and as each one spoke he melted down into the earth and rose again; and as each did this, I felt nearer to the earth.

Then the oldest of them all said: "Grandson, all over the universe you have seen. Now you shall go back with power to the place from whence you came, and it shall happen yonder that hundreds shall be sacred, hundreds shall be flames! Behold!"

I looked below and saw my people there, and all were well and happy except one, and he was lying like the dead—and that one was myself. Then the oldest Grandfather sang, and his song was like this:

There is someone lying on earth in a sacred manner.
There is someone—on earth he lies.
In a sacred manner I have made him to walk.

Now the tepee, built and roofed with cloud, began to sway back and forth as in a wind, and the flaming rainbow door was growing dimmer. I could hear voices of all kinds crying from outside: "Eagle Wing Stretches is coming forth! Behold him!"

When I went through the door, the face of the day of earth was appearing with the daybreak star upon its forehead; and the sun leaped up and looked upon me, and I was going forth alone.

And as I walked alone, I heard the sun singing as it arose, and it sang like this:

"With visible face I am appearing.
In a sacred manner I appear.
For the greening earth a pleasantness I make.
The center of the nation's hoop I have made pleasant.
With visible face, behold me!
The four-leggeds and two-leggeds, I have made them to walk;

The wings of the air, I have made them to fly.
With visible face I appear.
My day, I have made it holy."

When the singing stopped, I was feeling lost and very lonely. Then a Voice above me said: "Look back!" It was a spotted eagle that was hovering over me and spoke. I looked, and where the flaming rainbow tepee, built and roofed with cloud, had been, I saw only the tall rock mountain at the center of the world.

I was all alone on a broad plain now with my feet upon the earth, alone but for the spotted eagle guarding me. I could see my people's village far ahead, and I walked very fast, for I was homesick now. Then I saw my own tepee, and inside I saw my mother and my father bending over a sick boy that was myself. And as I entered the tepee, some one was saying: "The boy is coming to; you had better give him some water."

Then I was sitting up; and I was sad because my mother and my father didn't seem to know I had been so far away.

AMERICAN INDIAN RELIGION / THE POWER VISION

The experience of the universe as mysterious and powerful is basic to the psychology of all human religion. The human awareness that in this mystery and power is the source of birth and sterility, strength and blight, food and want, life and death, has led all peoples to try to engage the more-than-human, the supernatural, to their benefit through religious practice. In American Indian cultures the supernatural was the object of a great deal of activity. The effort was not to organize a consistent body of beliefs, but rather through liturgy and ordeal to come to some direct experience of the supernatural, and from this experience to obtain guidance for life and protection from danger.

Among the small, semi-nomadic groups which formed the nations of the Great Plains the emphasis was on ordeal and vision. The individual males sought for visions which would enable them to be successful hunters and warriors. The ordeal involved isolation from the tribe, prolonged fasting, and sometimes self-inflicted injury to encourage visions when they did not come. The visions took a variety of forms but had a standard outline. The supernatural would manifest itself as a being combining animal and human natures, a figure like Coyote (see selection page 30). The hunter would accompany this being and when they arrived at its dwelling, which might be deep in the forest or above the clouds or under the sea, he would receive the "spirit power" which he sought, usually consisting of a song to be used when power was needed and some sort of fetish or talisman, the hunter's "medicine," which the being would give him or which he must find or make, and which involved a special ritual for its proper use. However the procedure involved in gaining the power vision need not be so strenuous. A vision might even arrive unsought, coming as a dream in sleep, or accompanying a fever.

RITE
OF ENCOUNTER

Russell L. Bates

IN THE THIRD WEEK of his fasting, Singing-owl found the white men.

The young Kiowa[1] awakened that morning to lilting daybreak calls of birds. Rain had fallen in the night; his buffalo robe was soaked and smelly; his buckskin shirt and leggings were clammy wet. He was miserable. A chill wind blew in under the overhanging rocks. Singing-owl shivered, almost forgetting the receding hunger pangs. Almost . . .

At last the sun warmed the rocks around him. Singing-owl sat up wearily, hoping that this new day would finally bring him the vision. He dried his long black hair and braided it loosely on the left side. Then he stared for a long while downward from the rocky cleft. The hillside was unchanging: scattered clumps of scrub oaks, moss-grown boulders, thick yellow-green grass and black soil. Hillsides beyond bore the same colors and shapes.

Singing-owl had dreamed sometime before dawn. Of deer and clouds and fishes and snow . . . But the dream had not been the vision he was seeking. When that came, he would speak with spirits and come away with pieces of their wisdom. The wisdom, in songs and chants and riddles, would be his power as a warrior and as a man.

At least that was what the medicine man promised to him. But how much longer did he have to wait? The moon had been just past full when Singing-owl started his fast; soon, it would be full once again.

Singing-owl thought of the medicine man who slept warm at the camp and had no want of food or clothing.

That toothless, half-blind old man! I hope he got bloated on the meat I gave him!

1. *Kiowa* (kiʹō wä), a Plains Indian people.

The hunger pangs increased at the mention of food. Singing-owl leaned over and pulled a small deerskin parcel from a crack in the rocks. Wrapped inside was a handful of pounded dried meat mixed with suet. He smelled it for a long time, then closed his eyes and tried to swallow. He put the meat away again, feeling very guilty.

At length he forced himself to leave the cleft. When he stood, dizziness and nausea made him stagger. He leaned back against the rocks, momentarily unable to see. His arms and legs tingled and a cramp twisted the muscles in his side. Then the white sparkles faded from before his eyes.

Water. Must get water.

Singing-owl made his way carefully down the hill; the going was harder than the day before. He could no longer jump from boulder to boulder and instead squeezed between them. Sharp rocks hurt his feet through wet moccasins.

The slope leveled off, and Singing-owl sat on the ground to catch his breath. He glanced up the hill; it didn't seem any higher than he remembered. But now he regretted having passed by other, more gentle slopes.

I chose my suffering spot well. But will I be able to climb it again?

He followed a deer trail and walked listlessly among the trees. Twice he stumbled over tree roots. Another time he brushed against a tree and grabbed it desperately to keep from falling. He stopped and looked around.

Is this the right trail to the river? It's so long. I'm lost!

Singing-owl left the trail and headed away across the clearing. The thick grass slowed him to a stumbling pace. Then he smelled water and knew the river was close.

When he reached its muddy bank, he fell to his knees and threw himself forward to drink. The river was cool and slightly muddied. But the water made him feel better. He washed his face, then stripped off his buckskins to wash the many bruised cuts on his arms, chest and back. His frenzied thrashing against the rocks the evening before had gained him nothing but exhausted sleep; the self-tortures had not made him worthy of the vision. At last, Singing-owl slipped into the water and washed himself vigorously. Some of the fatigue, muscle aches, and light-headedness flowed away with the sandy mud he used for scrubbing.

Then he lay against a log at the water's edge; the river current soothed his body. It was a struggle to stay awake.

A dog barked. Singing-owl sat up and listened. Again. Close by. Upstream.

He crawled out of the water, grabbed his buckskins, and listened again. The barking broke into howls. He scrambled up the bank into bushes and made his way toward the sound, at once curious and afraid.

In this isolated land, no other tribes roamed. A dog meant white men.

Singing-owl paused to put on his buckskins. Then he crept ahead through the bushes: cautious, patient, silent. A few moments later, he reached the edge of a clearing and could see the camp, the dog, and the white men.

The dog was tied to a tree. One white man lay beside a long-dead fire. Another sat against a tree, his arms limp, his head fallen forward to his chest. A third lay sprawled on the riverbank, his head and one arm in the water. All were dressed in dirty gray and brown clothes, with boots scuffed and mud-caked.

A breeze fluttered the leaves of cottonwoods around the clearing; it also brought Singing-owl a whiff of decay. The men were dead.

The dog sensed Singing-owl and barked louder, leaping to the limit of the rope. Singing-owl stood up slowly, then walked into the camp. The dog retreated a little but kept up its barking. Singing-owl noticed a broken rope between two trees; horses had long since pulled free and wandered off.

He stopped at the body lying beside the ashes. The dead man lay face-down, a blanket across his legs. Singing-owl bent down, picked up a fine pistol; it was fully loaded, with light, circular tracings along the barrel. Perhaps there were other weapons.

Singing-owl turned to the dog. It was brown and white spotted; its fur was matted and the mouth was dirty. Starving and dying of thirst, it had been eating mud.

Singing-owl put the gun in his shirt and hunted through the men's packs. He found hardtack biscuits and dried meat. He also found metal cans but discarded them because their markings were meaningless. He looked with longing at the food. But another nudge of guilt made him throw it to the dog.

It sniffed the morsels suspiciously, then began to eat in great gulps.

Singing-owl sighed, then picked up a small pot to get water. He shivered as he passed the man by the tree. At the riverbank he noticed something strange as he bent to fill the pot. The dead man lying there was covered with sores.

He looked closer. The hand that lay out of the water was almost raw; crusted yellow ooze edged what little skin remained on its back. He looked at the face. The sores there had ragged white strings that waved in the flowing water. Singing-owl filled the pot quickly and stepped away.

The dog drank the water and wagged its tail. Then it looked up at him, expectant. Singing-owl reached out carefully, untied the rope. The dog brushed against him, happy.

"What killed your people, dog?" Singing-owl said, not truly breaking the ban against speaking to anyone.

The dog shook its head and barked. Its tail slapped against Singing-owl's legs.

"That was a bad way to meet death. Maybe I'd better not stay here any longer." He skirted wide of the man sitting at the tree. Yes, the sores were there. He didn't bother turning over the man under the blanket.

Singing-owl rememberd the pistol; he took it out with a trembling hand and dropped it. The dog walked with him away from the camp, then stopped.

Singing-owl looked back. "Going to stay here, yes? I wouldn't be able to keep you anyway. Hope you find something to eat . . ." He brushed away the obvious and horrible thought, heading back into the hills.

When evening came, Singing-owl made a small fire and began his chanting prayers. The wind blew warm over the rocky cleft; stars were glistening in the dying film of twilight. Surely the strange events of the day were signs that the vision was coming. The robes that hid things to come would be lifted and . . .

Singing-owl found himself repeating the words of the medicine man and was disgusted. He waited. Nothing. The air turned cool and the fire slowly fell away.

Where is it? The medicine man is a liar! But what of all the other warriors who claim power from a vision?

He sat quietly, then decided to fast for only a few more days. If no vision came, he would go back to the Kiowas. He'd have to tell them something; exactly what, he did not know.

But he would repay the medicine man for many days of discomfort. Singing-owl's brow wrinkled as he half frowned, half smiled. His reputation for playing pranks and outwitting his tribesmen was to gain yet another distinction. He would do nothing harmful, to be sure, just a few tricks to upset the old man. Such as: giving him skunk bones if he asked for weasel, hawk meat if he asked for prairie bird, or putting green sticks in his firewood. Singing-owl wanted to laugh, but he couldn't.

He noticed the fire and started to add more wood. But he felt warm enough; in fact, he felt almost too warm. He touched his face: hot.

Perhaps I'm tired. All right. I am tired.

He lay down to sleep. He remembered the white men and their sores, though he really didn't want to. Something had killed them. Quickly. Quietly. He tried to think of other things. The vision. The many tricks he had played. Gray Bear's daughters. A running hunt through trees after a deer.

But nothing forced the image of the dead men from the edge of his sight. Finally, he fell asleep, feeling warmer than before.

Singing-owl opened his eyes. The sun was high above the hills. He lay quietly and listened to his body. All was well, apparently. Relieved, he sat up, yawned and stretched. He pushed the buffalo robe away and started to get up.

The thing sat a short distance away, watching him. Singing-owl stared, unable to move further. It was shaped like a man. But it wasn't a man.

It was a mass of raw flesh. With a body, and arms and legs, and a head. No skin or hair; just endless running sores. It appeared to be looking at him, but its face was featureless, red, open flesh. Yellow fluids trickled from over its entire body; wet streams ran down the rock on which it sat.

Singing-owl crawled backward, pressed himself against the rocks, eyes wide.

A ghost? Is it a white man's ghost? Or is . . . is that the vision?

He choked on the words: "Are you one of the spirits? Have . . . have you come because I am worthy?"

It moved, raised an arm, touched its chest. In a thick watery voice, it said, "I am Black Smallpox. And I wish to walk with you."

Singing-owl almost fainted. He stared at it, tried to speak.

But the creature spoke first. "Do not be afraid. I will not harm you. I only wish to go with you to the Kiowas." It stood, and the yellow streams ran down its legs. "Yes, we will walk together to your people."

Singing-owl thought quickly, blinking. It surely was not the vision. Or was it perhaps the vision after all, somehow spoiled by white man's evil? Yes, the white men. Their sores. *Death.*

"No!" he said, feeling for a loose rock. "You came with the white men! You killed them! And now you want to kill . . ." He found a rock and threw it. Smallpox wavered like a reflection in water, then suddenly was standing a short distance further away. The rock clattered harmlessly to the ground.

Smallpox stepped closer. "Come. Let us go."

Singing-owl sprang away suddenly and clambered down the hillside. He ran, stumbled, fell, crawled, slid over boulders, ran again. When he reached flatter ground, he broke into a run and didn't look back. He staggered and almost tripped several times. He ran past trees, over hills, down gullies, into grass and bare ground.

At last he ran, stumbled, ran into a narrow valley. He fell, gasping and crying. He landed on his face and hands at the edge of a rain water pool. He lay beside a boulder and a small bush. He tried to crawl, but fell back. His body shook and shivered, though sweat coated him. Then his breathing slowed and he raised himself on one arm.

Singing-owl heard wailing and moaning, but very faint. Then he saw people reflected in the pool. They were Kiowas; ragged, wet sores covered their arms and faces. The wailing reflections reached for him, crying louder.

Singing-owl jerked himself backward and pushed dirt into the pool with his feet. Something stood at the limit of his side vision; he turned and saw Smallpox standing beside the bush.

It stepped toward him. "Why did you stop? We are going to the Kiowas, are we not? The sooner we get there, the better it will please me."

Singing-owl scrambled up, backed away in a low crouch. "No! I won't take you! You have no place here! Go away!"

It raised a hand. "We must go. The day grows long."

Singing-owl turned and ran again.

He climbed a cliff. Smallpox walked to the edge above him before he reached the top.

He ran over the plateau and dove from more than treetop height into a lake. Smallpox stood atop the beaver lodge when Singing-owl swam toward the dam.

He hid in a box canyon. Smallpox was standing behind him near the sheer rock face. Singing-owl quickly set a grass fire by striking stones together. The flames swept into the canyon, swirling with smoke, trapping Smallpox. But when Singing-owl ran into a forest, Smallpox stepped from behind a tree to meet him.

Through the rest of the day Singing-owl ran, set traps, ran again. But he could neither outrun nor outwit Smallpox; it was always there when he stopped. Night fell and Singing-owl found he could run no more.

He sat on the top of a grassy hill and watched as Smallpox walked slowly toward him. Light from a nearly full moon flashed in white sparks from the dripping liquids.

I have lost. I have no more tricks. Yet . . .

Singing-owl thought hurriedly, formed a plan, then hung his head as Smallpox stopped beside him. "All right," he said. "We will go to the Kiowas."

Somewhere, Singing-owl felt a flicker of hope.

The lodges were quiet; moonlight revealed a score or more of them built at the base of a tree-lined hill. The main campfire was low. Camp dogs roamed in the spaces between the lodges. Sentries stood unmoving at long intervals around the village.

At a distance, Singing-owl circled the camp quietly. Smallpox walked with him.

At the far end of the camp, a woman came out of a lodge and threw bones on the ground. The dogs ran toward her and began fighting over the meal.

Singing-owl saw his chance and boldly walked in among the lodges where there was no sentry. Then he stopped and abruptly turned to Smallpox. "We are here. Now will you let me go? I am ashamed."

It stepped forward and regarded the circle of lodges. "Not just yet. There is still something you must do. Come."

He followed it, glancing from side to side, nervous. Smallpox led him to a large deerskin bag that was supported by crossed poles.

"This water," it said, standing very close to him and pointing. "Spit into it."

Singing-owl only stared, not understanding.

"I said, spit into this water."

He stepped to the bag, opened a flap near the top, and spat.

"Again. That will do it. You are free."

Singing-owl moved back. "Free?"

Smallpox turned away. "Your usefulness is at an end." It sat down, still with its back to him; the open flesh gleamed wetly in the moonlight. "You will not understand, but I will tell you anyway. There are but a few I cannot kill. You are one. But I still lived inside you and thus was my purpose served. Leave me."

Singing-owl pretended to walk toward a lodge near large shade trees. "Yes," he said, looking back. "I must go to my lodge. My family will be glad to see me."

But when Smallpox was no longer in sight, Singing-owl ran for the trees. Two dogs ran after him, barking. A sentry shouted and more dogs ran after him. Singing-owl reached the shadows and ran out of the camp. He lost his pursuers quickly.

I'm free. I'm free! And the Pawnees[2] are no friends to the Kiowas! They deserve Smallpox!

Dawn found Singing-owl far away from the Pawnee camp. When he was sure no one followed, he trapped a rabbit and ate his first meal in twenty days. His stomach ached a little when he set out again. But he was still happy at finally outwitting Smallpox.

He laughed. What a tale he would tell of his vision when he reached the Kiowas!

He was almost there when he heard wailing. He stopped and looked around frantically. Nothing else could be seen on the rolling plains except grasses moving in the wind. Then the wailing faded to be replaced by a laughing taunt. It was the voice of Smallpox.

"Where are you?" Singing-owl said, turning in circles. "You cannot be here! I outwitted you!"

"I told you, but you did not understand. We still walk together. I am

---

2. *Pawnees,* (pô nēz′).

a part of you. I will be with you always. You cannot get rid of me!" And the laughing began again.

Then Singing-owl knew the laughing came from inside him. He clutched at himself, tore at his own flesh, and screamed.

The laugh rolled on, unstopping.

The cleft of rocks offered little protection from the raging thunderstorm. Singing-owl huddled under his buffalo robe and watched the storm. Lightning split trees on far hills and flashed the night away for brief moments. Thunder snapped down from the clouds and shook the ground. Rain splashed on Singing-owl's face and ran in pools under him.

He prayed, asked the mercy of the spirits. Small things came back to him: a boy's game with a willow hoop; his mother and stories and songs and gentle scoldings; the self-tortures that had declared him a man; the smiling, teasing daughter of Gray Bear; how fat quail sizzled when roasted . . .

For days, Singing-owl had considered exile or suicide. But he knew the one would be spent in temptation to see loved ones again. And there was no honor in the other.

Now Smallpox was to be finally outwitted. Singing-owl was fasting once more. But this time the fasting would go on, until there was nothing left.

He smiled faintly and pulled the buffalo robe tighter around him. At least, he thought, the laughing has stopped.

6

THE
END
OF THINGS

THE BATTLE
OF GAVRA

Rosemary Sutcliff

---

*One of the three cycles of Irish heroic literature deals with the adventures of
Finn Mac Cool (fin mak cül) and his companions the Fianna (fē'ən ə). The Irish
word* fian *means warrior band, and the Fianna formed a kind of militia in the
service of the kings of Ireland. The greatest of the Fian chiefs was Finn, who
served Cormac Mac Art (kôr'mak mak ärt), the High King of Ireland.
According to the Irish annals, Cormac ruled in the third century* A.D. *Ireland at
that time was divided into five small kingdoms—Ulster (ul'stər) in the north,
Munster (mun'stər) and Leinster (len'stər) in the south, Connacht (kon'ôt) in
the west, and Meath (mēth) in the center. Over them all ruled the High King
from his court at Tara (tar'ə) in Meath.*

CORMAC MAC ART the High King died.

And Cairbri[1] of the Liffey, his son, set his foot on the Crowning
Stone in the midst of the High Court at Tara, and standing so, with one
foot on the Stone and the other on a red bull's hide, he was crowned
High King of Erin in his father's place. And Finn with the Fian chiefs
and champions stood by, on one side, facing the warriors of the King's
household standing on the other, and raised three great shouts of
triumph and of greeting for the new High King.

But Finn's heart was heavy under his bronze breast-armour, and a
shadow lay on his mind, for he knew Cairbri had always hated him and
the Clan Bascna.[2]

Now Cairbri had a daughter called Sgeimh Solais,[3] which means
Light of Beauty. And indeed she was well named, for though scarcely
yet out of her childhood, she was already the fairest thing in all Erin,
more fair even than Grania[4] had been at her age. And many great chiefs
and nobles and even kings from across the seas came seeking her in
marriage. And at last, after many others had failed—for this princess
too was hard to please—a marriage was arranged between her and the
King's son of the Decies, and a great wedding feast was made ready.

---

1. *Cairbri,* (kar'brə). **2.** *Clan Bascna* (klan bask'nə), the family of Finn. **3.** *Sgeimh Solais,* (sāv sōl'əs). **4.**
Grania, (gran'yə). In his old age Finn decided to marry a young woman, Grania. On the eve of the
marriage she eloped with Dearmid (dér'mid), one of Finn's companions. Finn pursued them and finally,
after Dearmid was killed while hunting a wild boar, Grania returned to Finn and became his wife. There
was much ill will toward Finn among the Fianna after the death of Dearmid.

It was the custom that when any princess of the royal house of Tara went to her wedding, the High King should give the Fianna a tribute of twenty ingots of gold. And the way of it was this: that when the nine days' wedding feast was about to begin, the chiefs of the Fianna sent their youngest and most newly-joined warrior into the High King's hall to claim the tribute, and themselves waited for his return in their encampment on the broad green before the palace.

But Cairbri of the Liffey hated not only Finn and the Clan Bascna, for Dearmid's sake, but he hated the whole Fianna, for under Finn's captaincy they had grown to be a great power in the land; and Cairbri was afraid that the time might come when they would be stronger than the High King. He had long been looking for a chance to break them, and now it seemed to him that the chance was come . . .

The Fianna in their encampment waited long and long for the return of young Ferdia[5] with the royal slaves bearing the gold. He came at last, but not out through the gates with the gold-bearers behind him. He came alone and over the ramparts, falling all arms and legs, heavy as a dead man falls. And when they ran forward and stood about him they saw the spear wound over his heart. And the voice of Cairbri's herald called down to them from the ramparts, "Hear the words of the High King of Erin, 'There have been overmany demands from the Fianna in my father's time; take now from me the answer that I make to all such, now that I, Cairbri, am the High King.'"

They brought the boy's body to Finn and told him the words of Cairbri Mac Cormac.

And Finn stood up and swore a mighty and terrible oath. "The High King's answer is received and laid to heart. I, Finn Mac Cool the Lord of the Fianna, have laid it *close* to heart. And now I swear on my father's head, that never again while I am its Captain, shall there be peace between the High King and the Fianna of Erin!"

Then the Fianna of Clan Bascna shouted their wrath and beat with their spears upon their shields. And many shouted to Finn to lead them at once in storming the Royal Hill of Tara. But Fer-tai, the Fian Chief of Tara and the Meath men, who was marriage-kin to Goll Mac Morna,[6] rose and stood over against him with the Clan Morna at his back, and called on them to hold by the High King and not by Finn Mac Cool. So fighting broke out between Clan Bascna and Clan Morna, and the old feud that had slept so long woke and raged forth like a forest fire.

But Cairbri, seeing from the walls of Tara the fighting in the Fian camp, knew that the two clans were too nearly matched; and he had need of the Clan Morna chieftains. So he sent his swiftest messenger running to them with word to break off the fight and fall back within

---

5. *Ferdia*, (fer'dyə). 6. *Fer-tai . . . Goll Mac Morna.* Goll Mac Morna (gul mak mōr'nə), Fian chief of Connaught, had killed Finn's father in battle. Fer-tai (fer ti) was Goll's son-in-law.

the walls of the Royal Hill. Then the Clan Morna chiefs under Fer-tai broke off the fight, and fell back, while the King's own household warriors manned the ramparts to cover their retreat with a hailstorm of spears.

Then, seeing that to push after them would be to run upon disaster, Finn sounded his horn to recall his own men. And that sunset, without pausing even to break the camp, Finn ordered the standard of the Fianna to be raised, and they marched South to join themselves to Fercob, King of Munster, who was marriage-kin to Finn Mac Cool, even as was Cairbri, but a friend and sworn comrade beside.

They sent runners ahead to warn Fercob, and as they went, they called on the main body of the Fianna to gather to the Munster hosting-plain.

And in like manner, Cairbri sent out his runners, summoning them, and the kings of all the Provinces, to muster to him at Tara. And the Clan Morna and the kings of Ulster and Connacht and even Finn's own Leinster mustered to Tara. But Fercob of Munster gathered his spears to fight beside Finn, and the Clan Bascna were with them there.

The sound of armourers' hammers on anvils rang from shore to shore of Erin, and the *whitt-whitt-whitt* of weapons on weapon-stones in the forecourts of chief and captain; and the very ground trembled under the tramp of feet as the warriors gathered to Cairbri or to Finn.

Then the fighting began, and the ding of hammer on anvil became the clash of blade on blade where the war-bands met in small fierce weapon-flurries, trying each other's strength. Then, as streamlets flow into a stream and the streams flow at last into the Shannon or the slow strong Boyne, the small fights became greater ones, and at last the two war hosts came to face each other on the bare sunny moors of Gavra for the last battle that must settle all things between them.

On the night before the battle the watchfires of the hosts were as though the stars had fallen from the sky in two great scattered swathes of light, and between them the moor was an emptiness of dark. When the morning came, the two war hosts took up their battle array, and between them the moor stretched empty to the wind and sunlight, and murmurous with bees.

On the one side, Cairbri the High King stood beneath his silken standard, and behind him and on either side stretched the war host of Tara, company by company under their chieftains. Fer-tai and Fer-li[7] his son captained the Clan Morna and all of the Fianna that stood with them, and the kings of the provinces each with their warriors, and close around the High King the five sons of Urgriu[8] of the ancient tribes of Tara, each leading one of the "Pillars" of the High King's own household troops.

---

7. *Fer-li*, (fer lē). **8.** *Urgriu*, (ür′gryü).

And on the other side the war host was drawing up in three parts, and in the centre the King of Munster commanded all the fighting-strength of his province, while the Fianna of Clan Bascna and such as had joined them were drawn up on the wings. Osca[9] commanded the left wing, and the leader of the right (the post which in all battles carries the most of honour and of danger) was Finn Mac Cool himself.

The Fian Captain had put on his whole splendour of war gear; a silk shirt next his skin, and over it a battle shirt of many layers of linen waxed together, and over that his tunic of fine-meshed ringmail, and over that his gold-bordered belly-armour. Round his waist, a belt clasped with golden dragon heads; his sword hung at his side, his blue-bladed Lochlan[10] war spear was in his hand; on his shoulder his round shield covered with green leather, its boss enriched with flowers of gold and silver and bronze. On his head, his war-cap of gilded bronze set about the brow with mountain gems that sparked back yellow-tawny light in the early rays of the sun. And around him the Clan Bascna stood close—shoulder to shoulder and shield to shield under their bright-tipped spears.

The war horns sounded, and the two war hosts rushed upon each other. As they drew close together, the throwing-spears began to hum to and fro, and the moor of Gavra shook beneath their running feet, and from both sides the war cries and the Dord-Fian[11] rose like the surf of a mighty sea. And when they came together, the crash of their meeting rang through the Five Provinces of Erin and echoed back from the cold outer circle of the sky.

Then many a spear was broken, and many a bright blade shattered into crimsoned shards, and many a shield and war-cap hacked in two, and many a champion cut down into his own blood, and many a dead face turned towards the sky. And the young heather grew purple-red as though it were in flower a month before its time.

Osca was the spearhead of the attack that day, and wherever he turned his spear it seemed that a hundred warriors fell before him, opening a broad path for his following, into the boiling heart of the battle.

And so he came at last, with his wounds blazing red upon him, to where Cairbri fought at the head of his household warriors. Cairbri leapt to meet him, and there among all the turmoil of the battle, they fought as though they had been alone in all the sunny uplands of Gavra. Again and again they wounded each other sore, but neither felt the sting of wounds that would have slain lesser men three times over, until at last Osca got in a blow that entered Cairbri's body where the upper and lower plates of his belly armour came together, and drove out again through the small of his back. But as the High King fell, his

---

9. *Osca* (ōsʹcə), Finn's grandson. 10. *Lochlan* (loнʹlən), Scandinavia. 11. *Dord-Fian* (dôrd fēʹən), the war cry of the Fianna. The Irish word *dord* means "humming" or "muttering."

falling twisted the spear from Osca's grasp, and from the ground he thrust up at him, so that the spear entered below his guard and pierced upward from his belly into his breast. The blood came into his mouth, and he pitched forward across the High King's body, with the pains of death already upon him.

Then Cairbri's household warriors charged forward to get possession of their lord's body, and the champion's who had slain him. But those who followed Osca did the same, and after a sharp and bitter struggle they brought the young champion off, with still a breath of life in him, and bore him back to where Finn stood on a little hillock, ordering the battle, and laid him at the Fian Captain's feet.

And Osca opened his eyes one last time, and said, "I have slain Cairbri for you."

"I would that you had left him for my slaying, and for me to get my death from him, instead of you," said Finn, and for the second time in his life,[12] he wept.

"Do not be doing that for me," Osca said, "for if it were you lying there, and I standing over you, do you think it's one tear I'd be weeping for you?"

"I know well enough that you would not, for Dearmid O'Dyna stands between us even now," said Finn. "But as for me, I will weep for whom I choose to weep for!"

And with the thing part in jest and part in sorrow between them, Osca died. And there was not a palm's breadth of his body without a wound on it.

"That was a hero's death," said Finn.

And the battle frenzy woke in him—the battle fury that all men, himself among them, had thought that he was too old to know again—and he plunged forward into the boil of battle, with his closest sword companions storming at his heels. And his sword was a two-edged lightning clearing a path for him wherever he turned his face, and the hero light blazed upon his brow, so that no warrior could withstand him, and the dead fell in tangled heaps about him; and he thrust over them and through them like a young bull through standing barley. But as he went, one after another of the men behind him fell, Dering and Keelta and Coil Croda and Finvel and Ligan Lumina until he was raging alone through the enemy war host. And Fer-li the son of Fer-tai, saw him with no friend to guard his back, and made at him with drawn sword, for both their spears were gone long since; and so they fought until both were sore wounded. But at the last Finn swung up his sword for a mighty blow, and struck Fer-li's head from his shoulders so that it went rolling and bouncing away under the feet of the battle, and Finn Mac Cool had the victory in *that* fight.

---

12. *the second time . . . he wept.* The first time Finn wept was for the death of his great wolfhound, Bran.

But after, Fer-tai came hurling himself upon him to avenge his son. "Great deeds, Finn!" he shouted. "Great deeds to be slaying a boy!"

"Not so much a boy. And if you felt him so young and helpless, why did you not come before?" Finn mocked him.

"I had hoped that he would finish the slaying. I had rather that he had the pride and the honour of it!"

So they fought across Fer-li's headless body, knee to knee and shield to shield, and over their shields and under their armour, the blood ran down. And at last Finn slew the father as he had slain the son.

And as he stood over their bodies, panting and far spent, and half blind with blood, the five sons of Urgriu came upon him in a circle, and Finn turned about and saw them all round him, closing in with spears raised to strike; and he knew that the end was come. He let his shield that could not face five ways at once drop to his feet, and stood straight and unmoving as a pillar-stone.

And the five spears came at him, making five great wounds that put out the light of the sun . . .

THE
WONDER-WORKER
OF THE PLAINS

Paul Radin

This tale is told by the Baronga (bä rong'gə)
people of Mozambique.

ONCE THERE WAS a man and a woman to whom were born first a boy
and then a girl. When the bride-price had been paid for the girl and she
was married, the parents said to the son, "We have a herd for you to
dispose of. It is now time for you to take a wife. We will choose you a
pretty wife, one whose parents are honest people."

The son, however, firmly refused. "No," he said, "do not bother. I do
not like any of the girls who are here. If I absolutely have to marry, I
shall choose for myself what I want."

"Do as you will," said the parents, "but if you are unhappy later on,
it will not be our fault."

Then the boy set out, left the country, and travelled far, very far, into
an unknown region. Finally, he came to a village where he saw some
young girls, some of them crushing corn and others cooking. Secretly
he made his choice, and said to himself, "That one there is the one I
like." Then he went to the men of the village and said, "Good day,
fathers!"

"Good day, young man!" they answered. "What is it that you wish?"

"I want to look at your daughters, for I want to take a wife."

"Well, well," they said, "we shall show them to you, and then you
can choose."

So they led all of their daughters past him and he indicated the one
he wanted. She gave her consent right away.

"Your parents, we expect, will pay us a visit and bring us the
bride-price, is that right?" asked the young girl's parents.

"No, not at all," answered the young man, "I have my bride-price with me. Take it; here it is!"

"Then," they added, "they will, we trust, come later in order to conduct your wife to you?"

"No, no, I fear they would only pain you with the hard admonitions they would give the girl. Let me, myself, take her along right away."

The parents of the young girl gave their consent to this request, but they took her aside in the hut once more to give her advice on how to conduct herself. "Be good to your parents-in-law and take diligent care of your husband!" Then they offered the young couple a younger daughter who could help with the housework. But the woman refused. Two, ten, twenty were then offered for her to choose from. All the girls were first examined before being offered to her.

"No," she insisted, "I do not want them. Give me instead the buffalo of the country, our buffalo, the Wonder-Worker of the Plains. Let him serve me."

"How can you ask for him?" they said. "You know that our life depends on him. Here he is well taken care of, but what would you do with him in a strange country? He will starve, die, and then all of us will die with him."

Before she left her parents, she took with her a pot containing a package of medicinal roots, a horn for bleeding, a little knife for making incisions, and a gourd full of fat.

Then she set out with her husband. The buffalo followed them, but he was visible to her alone. The man did not see him. He did not suspect that the Wonder-Worker of the Plains was the servant accompanying his wife.

As soon as they had come to the husband's village, they were received with joyful cries: *"Hoyo, hoyo!"*

"Now look at him!" said the old ones. "So you have found a wife after all! You did not want one of those whom we suggested to you, but that makes no difference. It is well as it is. You have acted according to your own will. If, however, at some time, you have enemies, you will have no right to complain."

The man then took his wife into the fields and showed her which were his and which were his mother's. The girl noted everything carefully and returned with him to the village. On the way she said, "I have lost my pearls in the field; I must return to look for them at once." In reality, however, she wanted to see the buffalo. She said to him, "Here is the boundary of the fields. Stay here! And there, too, is the forest in which you can hide."

"You are right," he replied.

Now whenever the wife wanted any water, she merely went to the cultivated fields and set the pitcher down in front of the buffalo. He ran with it to the lake, filled it, and brought the vessel back to his mistress.

Whenever she wanted wood, he would go into the brush, break trees with his horns, and bring her as much as she needed.

The people in the village were surprised at all these things. "What strength she has!" they said. "She is always back from the well right away; in the twinkling of an eye she has gathered a bundle of dry wood." But no one suspected that a buffalo assisted her as a servant.

The wife did not, however, bring the buffalo anything to eat, for she had only one plate for herself and her husband. At home, of course, they had had a separate plate for the Wonder-Worker and fed him carefully. Here, therefore, the buffalo was hungry. She would bring him her pitcher and send him to fetch water. This he did willingly, but he felt great pangs of hunger.

One day she showed him a corner in the brush which he was to clear. During the night the buffalo took a hoe and prepared a vast acreage. Everyone commented, "How clever she is! And how fast she has done her work!"

One evening the buffalo said to his mistress, "I am hungry and you give me nothing to eat. Soon I shall not be able to work any more!"

"*Aie,*" said she, "what shall I do? We have only one plate at the house. The people at home were right when they said that you would have to start stealing. So, steal! Go into my field and take a bean here and there. Then, again, go farther. Do not however, take them all from the same spot, thus the owners may not be too much aware of it and will not fall over in terror right away."

That night, accordingly, the buffalo went to the field. He devoured a bean here and a bean there, jumped from one corner to the other, and finally fled back to his hiding place. When the women came into the fields the next morning, they could not believe their eyes. "Hey, hey, what is going on here? We have never seen anything like this! A wild beast has destroyed our plants! One can even follow his spoor. Ho, the poor land!" So they ran back and told the story in the village.

In the evening, the young woman said to the buffalo, "To be sure, they were very much terrified, but not too much, nevertheless. They did not fall on their backs. So keep on stealing tonight!" And so it continued. The owners of the devastated fields cried out loud and then turned to the men and asked them to summon the watchmen with their guns.

Now, the husband of the young woman was a very good marksman. He, therefore, hid in an ambush in his field and waited. The buffalo, however, thought that someone might be lying in wait for him where he had stolen the night before, so he went to his mistress's beans, the place where he had pastured the first time.

"Say," cried the man, "this is a buffalo! One has never seen any like him here. This is a strange animal, indeed." He fired. The bullet entered the temple of the buffalo, close to the ear, and came out exactly opposite on the other side. The Wonder-Worker of the Plains turned one somersault and fell dead.

"That was a good shot!" exclaimed the hunter and announced it to the village.

But the woman now began to cry out in pain and writhe. "Oh, I have stomach-aches, oh, oh!"

"Calm yourself," she was told. She seemed sick, but in reality she only wanted to explain why she was crying thus, and why she was so terrified when she heard of the buffalo's death. She was given medicine, but she poured it out when nobody else saw her.

Now everyone set out, women with baskets, and men with weapons, in order to cut up the buffalo. The young wife alone remained in the village. Soon, however, she followed them, holding her belly, whimpering and crying.

"What is wrong with you, that you come here," said her husband. "If you are sick, stay at home!"

"No, I did not want to stay in the village all by myself."

Her mother-in-law scolded her, saying that she could not understand what she was doing and that she would kill herself by this. When they had filled the baskets with meat, she said, "Let me carry the head!"

"But no, you are sick, it is much too heavy for you."

"No," said she, "let me do it!" So she shouldered it and carried it.

After they had arrived at the village, however, instead of stepping into the house, she went into the shed where the cooking-pots were kept and set down the buffalo's head. Obstinately, she refused to move. Her husband looked for her in order to bring her into the hut. He said she would be much better off there, but she only replied to him harshly, "Do not disturb me!"

Then her mother-in-law came and admonished her gently. "Why do you torture yourself?"

And she replied crossly, "Will you not let me sleep even a little?"

Then they brought her some food, but she pushed it away. Night came. Her husband went to rest. He did not sleep, however, but listened.

The woman now fetched fire, cooked some water in her little pot, and poured into it the package of medicine which she had brought with her from her home. Then she took the buffalo's head and, with the knife, made incisions in front of the ear, at the temple, where the bullet had struck the animal. There she set the bleeding horn and sucked, sucked with all the force of her body, and succeeded in drawing first a few lumps of clotted blood, and then liquid blood. Thereupon she exposed the place to the steam which rose from the cooking-pot, after having, however, smeared it completely with the fat that she had saved in the gourd. That soothed the spot. Then she sang as follows:

Ah, my father, Wonder-Worker of the Plains,
They told me: You would go through the deep darkness; that in all
    directions you would stumble through the night,
    Wonder-Worker of the Plains;
You are the young wonder-tree plant, grown out of ruins, which dies
    before its time, consumed by a gnawing worm. . . .
You made flowers and fruit fall upon your road, Wonder-Worker of
    the Plains!

When she had finished her invocation formula, the head moved, the
limbs grew again, the buffalo came to life once more, shook his ears
and horns, rose up, and stretched his limbs. . . .

But at this point the man, who could not sleep in the hut, stepped out
and said, "Why does my wife have to cry so long? I must see why she
pours out all these sighs!" He entered the shed and called for her, but
in great anger she replied, "Leave me alone!" Thereupon, however, the
buffalo's head fell to the ground again, dead, pierced as before.

The man returned to the hut; he had understood nothing of all this
and had seen nothing. Once again the woman took the pot, cooked the
medicine, made the incisions, placed the bleeding horn in the proper
spot, exposed the wound to the steam, and sang as before:

Ah, my father, Wonder-Worker of the Plains,
Indeed they have told me: You would go through the deep darkness;
    that in all directions you would stumble through the night,
    Wonder-Worker of the Plains;
You are the young wonder-tree plant, grown out of ruins, which dies
    before its time, consumed by a gnawing worm. . . .
You made flowers and fruit fall upon your road, Wonder-Worker of
    the Plains!

Once again, the buffalo rose up, his limbs grew together again, he
felt himself coming to life, shook his ears and horns, stretched
himself—but then again came the man, disquieted, in order to see what
his wife was doing. Then she became very angry with him, but he
settled down in the shed in order to watch what was going on. Now she
took her fire, her cooking pot and all the other things and went out. She
pulled up grass to kindle the embers and began for the third time to
resuscitate the buffalo.

Morning had already broken when her mother-in-law came—and
once more the head fell to the ground. Day came, and the buffalo's
wound began to grow worse.

Finally, she said to all of them, "I would like to go bathing in the
lake all alone."

They answered her, "But how will you get there since you are sick?"

She went on her way anyhow and then came back and said, "On my way I came upon someone from home. He told me that my mother is very, very sick. I told him to come here to the village but he refused and said, 'They would offer me food and that would only delay me.' He went on right away and added that I should hurry lest my mother die before my arrival. Therefore, good-bye, I am going away!"

Of course, all this was a lie. She had thought of the idea of going to the lake so that she could invent this story and have a reason for carrying the news of the buffalo's death to her people.

She went off, carrying the basket on her head and singing all along the road the end of the song about the Wonder-Worker of the Plains. Wherever she passed, the people would band together behind her to accompany her into her village. Arrived there, she announced to them that the buffalo no longer lived.

Then they sent out messengers in all directions in order to gather together the inhabitants of the country. They reproached the young woman earnestly, saying, "Do you see now? We told you so. But you refused all the young girls and wanted absolutely to have the buffalo. Now you have killed all of us!"

Things had advanced thus far when the man, who had followed his wife into the village, also arrived. He rested his gun against a tree trunk and sat down. They greeted him by shouting, "Be saluted, criminal, be saluted! You have killed us all!" He did not understand this and wondered how one could call him a murderer and a criminal.

"To be sure, I have killed a buffalo," said he, "but that is all."

"Yes, but this buffalo was your wife's assistant. He drew water for her, cut wood, worked in the field."

Completely stunned, the man said, "Why did you not let me know that? I would not have killed him then."

"That is how it is," they added. "The lives of all of us depended on him."

Thereupon all of the people began to cut their own throats. First, the young woman, who, as she did it, called out:

"Ah, my father, Wonder-Worker of the Plains!"

Then came her parents, brothers, sisters, one after the other.

The first one said:

"You shall go through darkness!"

The next:

"You shall stumble through the night in all directions!"

The next:

"You are the young wonder-tree plant which dies before its time."

The next:

"You made flowers and fruit fall upon your road!"

All cut their throats and they even slew the little children who were still being carried in skins upon the back. "Why should we let them live," they said, "since they would only lose their minds!"

The man returned home and told his people how, by shooting the buffalo, he had killed them all. His parents said to him, "Do you see now? Did we not tell you that misfortune would come to you? When we offered a fitting and wise woman for you, you wanted to act according to your own desire. Now you have lost your fortune. Who will give it back to you, since they are all dead, all of your wife's relatives, to whom you have given your money!"

This is the end.

THE END OF THE WORLD

Archibald MacLeish

Quite unexpectedly as Vasserot
The armless ambidextrian was lighting
A match between his great and second toe
And Ralph the lion was engaged in biting
5   The neck of Madame Sossman while the drum
Pointed, and Teeny was about to cough
In waltz-time swinging Jocko by the thumb—
Quite unexpectedly the top blew off:

And there, there overhead, there, there, hung over
10 Those thousands of white faces, those dazed eyes,
There in the starless dark, the poise, the hover,
There with vast wings across the canceled skies,
There in the sudden blackness, the black pall
Of nothing, nothing, nothing—nothing at all.

CHARON

Lord Dunsany

Charon (kar′ən) was the boatman who ferried the souls of the dead across the river Styx (stiks) to Hades (hā′dēz), or Dis (dis), the Underworld of classical mythology.

Charon LEANED FORWARD and rowed. All things were one with his weariness.

It was not with him a matter of years or of centuries, but of wide floods of time, and an old heaviness and a pain in the arms that had become for him part of the scheme that the gods had made and was of a piece with Eternity.

If the gods had even sent him a contrary wind it would have divided all time in his memory into two equal slabs.

So grey were all things always where he was that if any radiance lingered a moment among the dead, on the face of such a queen perhaps as Cleopatra, his eyes could not have perceived it.

It was strange that the dead nowadays were coming in such numbers. They were coming in thousands where they used to come in fifties. It was neither Charon's duty nor his wont to ponder in his grey soul why these things might be. Charon leaned forward and rowed.

Then no one came for a while. It was not usual for the gods to send no one down from Earth for such a space. But the gods knew best.

Then one man came alone. And the little shade sat shivering on a lonely bench and the great boat pushed off. Only one passenger; the gods knew best. And great and weary Charon rowed on and on beside the little, silent, shivering ghost.

And the sound of the river was like a mighty sigh that Grief in the beginning had sighed among her sisters, and that could not die like the echoes of human sorrow failing on earthly hills, but was as old as time and the pain in Charon's arms.

Then the boat from the slow, grey river loomed up to the coast of Dis and the little, silent shade still shivering stepped ashore, and Charon turned the boat to go wearily back to the world. Then the little shadow spoke, that had been a man.

"I am the last," he said.

No one had ever made Charon smile before, no one before had ever made him weep.

NIGHTFALL

Isaac Asimov

If the stars should appear one night in a thousand years, how would men believe and adore, and preserve for many generations the remembrance of the city of God?

Emerson[1]

ATON 77, DIRECTOR of Saro University, thrust out a belligerent lower lip and glared at the young newspaperman in a hot fury.

Theremon 762 took that fury in his stride. In his earlier days, when his now widely syndicated column was only a mad idea in a cub reporter's mind, he had specialized in "impossible" interviews. It had cost him bruises, black eyes, and broken bones; but it had given him an ample supply of coolness and self-confidence.

So he lowered the outthrust hand that had been so pointedly ignored and calmly waited for the aged director to get over the worst. Astronomers were queer ducks, anyway, and if Aton's actions of the last two months meant anything, this same Aton was the queer-duckiest of the lot.

Aton 77 found his voice, and though it trembled with restrained emotion, the careful, somewhat pedantic phraseology, for which the famous astronomer was noted, did not abandon him.

"Sir," he said, "you display an infernal gall in coming to me with that impudent proposition of yours."

The husky telephotographer of the Observatory, Beenay 25, thrust a tongue's tip across dry lips and interposed nervously, "Now, sir, after all—"

The director turned to him and lifted a white eyebrow. "Do not interfere, Beenay. I will credit you with good intentions in bringing this man here; but I will tolerate no insubordination now."

Theremon decided it was time to take a part. "Director Aton, if you'll let me finish what I started saying, I think—"

---

1. *Emerson.* Ralph Waldo Emerson (1803–1882) was an American essayist, poet, and philosopher.

"I don't believe, young man," retorted Aton, "that anything you could say now would count much as compared with your daily columns of these last two months. You have led a vast newspaper campaign against the efforts of myself and my colleagues to organize the world against the menace which it is now too late to avert. You have done your best with your highly personal attacks to make the staff of this Observatory objects of ridicule."

The director lifted a copy of the Saro City *Chronicle* from the table and shook it at Theremon furiously. "Even a person of your well-known impudence should have hesitated before coming to me with a request that he be allowed to cover today's events for his paper. Of all newsmen, you!"

Aton dashed the newspaper to the floor, strode to the window, and clasped his arms behind his back.

"You may leave," he snapped over his shoulder. He stared moodily out at the skyline where Gamma, the brightest of the planet's six suns, was setting. It had already faded and yellowed into the horizon mists, and Aton knew he would never see it again as a sane man.

He whirled. "No, wait, come here!" He gestured peremptorily. "I'll give you your story."

The newsman had made no motion to leave, and now he approached the old man slowly. Aton gestured outward. "Of the six suns, only Beta is left in the sky. Do you see it?"

The question was rather unnecessary. Beta was almost at zenith, its ruddy light flooding the landscape to an unusual orange as the brilliant rays of setting Gamma died. Beta was at aphelion. It was small; smaller than Theremon had ever seen it before, and for the moment it was undisputed ruler of Lagash's sky.

Lagash's own sun, Alpha, the one about which it revolved, was at the antipodes, as were the two distant companion pairs. The red dwarf Beta—Alpha's immediate companion—was alone, grimly alone.

Aton's upturned face flushed redly in the sunlight. "In just under four hours," he said, "civilization, as we know it, comes to an end. It will do so because, as you see, Beta is the only sun in the sky." He smiled grimly. "Print that! There'll be no one to read it."

"But if it turns out that four hours pass—and another four—and nothing happens?" asked Theremon softly.

"Don't let that worry you. Enough will happen."

"Granted! And *still*—if nothing happens?"

For a second time, Beenay 25 spoke. "Sir, I think you ought to listen to him."

Theremon said, "Put it to a vote, Director Aton."

There was a stir among the remaining five members of the Observatory staff, who till now had maintained an attitude of wary neutrality.

"That," stated Aton flatly, "is not necessary." He drew out his pocket watch. "Since your good friend, Beenay, insists so urgently, I will give you five minutes. Talk away."

"Good! Now, just what difference would it make if you allowed me to take down an eyewitness account of what's to come? If your prediction comes true, my presence won't hurt; for in that case my column would never be written. On the other hand, if nothing comes of it, you will just have to expect ridicule or worse. It would be wise to leave that ridicule to friendly hands."

Aton snorted. "Do you mean yours when you speak of friendly hands?"

"Certainly!" Theremon sat down and crossed his legs. "My columns may have been a little rough, but I gave you people the benefit of the doubt every time. After all, this is not the century to preach 'The end of the world is at hand' to Lagash. You have to understand that people don't believe the *Book of Revelations* anymore, and it annoys them to have scientists turn about-face and tell us the Cultists are right after all—"

"No such thing, young man," interrupted Aton. "While a great deal of our data has been supplied us by the Cult, our results contain none of the Cult's mysticism. Facts are facts, and the Cult's so-called mythology *has* certain facts behind it. We've exposed them and ripped away their mystery. I assure you that the Cult hates us now worse than you do."

"I don't hate you. I'm just trying to tell you that the public is in an ugly humor. They're angry."

Aton twisted his mouth in derision. "Let them be angry."

"Yes, but what about tomorrow?"

"There'll be no tomorrow!"

"But if there is. Say that there is—just to see what happens. That anger might take shape into something serious. After all, you know business has taken a nosedive these last two months. Investors don't really believe the world is coming to an end, but just the same they're being cagy with their money until it's all over. Johnny Public doesn't believe you, either, but the new spring furniture might just as well wait a few months—just to make sure.

"You see the point. Just as soon as this is all over, the business interests will be after your hide. They'll say that if crackpots—begging your pardon—can upset the country's prosperity any time they want, simply by making some cockeyed prediction—it's up to the planet to prevent them. The sparks will fly, sir."

The director regarded the columnist sternly. "And just what were you proposing to do to help the situation?"

"Well"—Theremon grinned—"I was proposing to take charge of the publicity. I can handle things so that only the ridiculous side will show. It would be hard to stand, I admit, because I'd have to make you all out to be a bunch of gibbering idiots, but if I can get people laughing at you, they might forget to be angry. In return for that, all my publisher asks is an exclusive story."

Beenay nodded and burst out, "Sir, the rest of us think he's right. These last two months we've considered everything but the million-to-one chance that there is an error somewhere in our theory or in our calculations. We ought to take care of that too."

There was a murmur of agreement from the men grouped about the table, and Aton's expression became that of one who found his mouth full of something bitter and couldn't get rid of it.

"You may stay if you wish, then. You will kindly refrain, however, from hampering us in our duties in any way. You will also remember that I am in charge of all activities here, and in spite of your opinions as expressed in your columns, I will expect full cooperation and full respect—" His hands were behind his back, and his wrinkled face thrust forward determinedly as he spoke. He might have continued indefinitely but for the intrusion of a new voice.

"Hello, hello, hello!" It came in a high tenor, and the plump cheeks of the newcomer expanded in a pleased smile. "What's this morgue-like atmosphere about here? No one's losing his nerve, I hope."

Aton started in consternation and said peevishly, "Now what the devil are you doing here, Sheerin? I thought you were going to stay behind in the Hideout."

Sheerin laughed and dropped his tubby figure into a chair. "Hideout be blowed! The place bored me. I wanted to be here, where things are getting hot. Don't you suppose I have my share of curiosity? I want to see these Stars the Cultists are forever speaking about." He rubbed his hands and added in a soberer tone, "It's freezing outside. The wind's enough to hang icicles on your nose. Beta doesn't seem to give any heat at all, at the distance it is."

The white-haired director ground his teeth in sudden exasperation. "Why do you go out of your way to do crazy things, Sheerin? What kind of good are you around here?"

"What kind of good am I around there?" Sheerin spread his palms in comical resignation. "A psychologist isn't worth his salt in the Hideout. They need men of action and strong, healthy women that can breed children. Me? I'm a hundred pounds too heavy for a man of action, and I wouldn't be a success at breeding children. So why bother them with an extra mouth to feed? I feel better over here."

Theremon spoke briskly. "Just what is the Hideout, sir?"

Sheerin seemed to see the columnist for the first time. He frowned and blew his ample cheeks out. "And just who in Lagash are you, redhead?"

Aton compressed his lips and then muttered sullenly, "That's Theremon 762, the newspaper fellow. I suppose you've heard of him."

The columnist offered his hand. "And, of course, you're Sheerin 501 of Saro University. I've heard of you." Then he repeated, "What is this Hideout, sir?"

"Well," said Sheerin, "we have managed to convince a few people of the validity of our prophecy of—er—doom, to be spectacular about it, and those few have taken proper measures. They consist mainly of the immediate members of the families of the Observatory staff, certain of the faculty of Saro University, and a few outsiders. Altogether, they number about three hundred, but three quarters are women and children."

"I see! They're supposed to hide where the Darkness and the—er—Stars can't get at them, and then hold out when the rest of the world goes poof."

"If they can. It won't be easy. With all of mankind insane, with the great cities going up in flames—environment will not be conducive to survival. But they have food, water, shelter, and weapons—"

"They've got more," said Aton. "They've got all our records, except for what we will collect today. Those records will mean everything to the next cycle, and *that's* what must survive. The rest can go hang."

Theremon uttered a long, low whistle and sat brooding for several minutes. The men about the table had brought out a multi-chess board and started a six-member game. Moves were made rapidly and in silence. All eyes bent in furious concentration on the board. Theremon watched them intently and then rose and approached Aton, who sat apart in whispered conversation with Sheerin.

"Listen," he said, "let's go somewhere where we won't bother the rest of the fellows. I want to ask some questions."

The aged astronomer frowned sourly at him, but Sheerin chirped up, "Certainly. It will do me good to talk. It always does. Aton was telling me about your ideas concerning world reaction to a failure of the prediction—and I agree with you. I read your column pretty regularly, by the way, and as a general thing I like your views."

"Please, Sheerin," growled Aton.

"Eh? Oh, all right. We'll go into the next room. It has softer chairs, anyway."

There were softer chairs in the next room. There were also thick red curtains on the windows and a maroon carpet on the floor. With the bricky light of Beta pouring in, the general effect was one of dried blood.

Theremon shuddered. "Say, I'd give ten credits for a decent dose of white light for just a second. I wish Gamma or Delta were in the sky."

"What are your questions?" asked Aton. "Please remember that our time is limited. In a little over an hour and a quarter we're going upstairs, and after that there will be no time for talk."

"Well, here it is." Theremon leaned back and folded his hands on his chest. "You people seem so all-fired serious about this that I'm beginning to believe you. Would you mind explaining what it's all about?"

Aton exploded, "Do you mean to sit there and tell me that you've been bombarding us with ridicule without even finding out what we've been trying to say?"

The columnist grinned sheepishly. "It's not that bad, sir. I've got the general idea. You say there is going to be a worldwide Darkness in a few hours and that all mankind will go violently insane. What I want now is the science behind it."

"No, you don't. No, you don't," broke in Sheerin. "If you ask Aton for that—supposing him to be in the mood to answer at all—he'll trot out pages of figures and volumes of graphs. You won't make head or tail of it. Now if you were to ask me, I could give you the layman's standpoint."

"All right; I ask you."

"Then first I'd like a drink." He rubbed his hands and looked at Aton.

"Water?" grunted Aton.

"Don't be silly!"

"Don't you be silly. No alcohol today. It would be too easy to get my men drunk. I can't afford to tempt them."

The psychologist grumbled wordlessly. He turned to Theremon, impaled him with his sharp eyes, and began.

"You realize, of course, that the history of civilization on Lagash displays a cyclic character—but I mean, *cyclic!*"

"I know," replied Theremon cautiously, "that that is the current archaeological theory. Has it been accepted as a fact?"

"Just about. In this last century it's been generally agreed upon. This cyclic character is—or rather, was—one of the great mysteries. We've located series of civilizations, nine of them definitely, and indications of others as well, all of which have reached heights comparable to our own, and all of which, without exception, were destroyed by fire at the very height of their culture.

"And no one could tell why. All centers of culture were thoroughly gutted by fire, with nothing left behind to give a hint as to the cause."

Theremon was following closely. "Wasn't there a Stone Age too?"

"Probably, but as yet practically nothing is known of it, except that men of that age were little more than rather intelligent apes. We can forget about that."

"I see. Go on!"

"There have been explanations of these recurrent catastrophes, all of a more or less fantastic nature. Some say that there are periodic rains of fire; some that Lagash passes through a sun every so often; some even wilder things. But there is one theory, quite different from all of these, that has been handed down over a period of centuries."

"I know. You mean this myth of the 'Stars' that the Cultists have in their *Book of Revelations.*"

"Exactly," rejoined Sheerin with satisfaction. "The Cultists said that every two thousand and fifty years Lagash entered a huge cave, so that all the suns disappeared, and there came *total darkness all over the world!* And then, they say, things called Stars appeared, which robbed men of their souls and left them unreasoning brutes, so that they destroyed the civilization they themselves had built up. Of course they mix all this up with a lot of religio-mystic notions, but that's the central idea."

There was a short pause in which Sheerin drew a long breath. "And now we come to the Theory of Universal Gravitation." He pronounced the phrase so that the capital letters sounded—and at that point Aton turned from the window, snorted loudly, and stalked out of the room.

The two stared after him, and Theremon said, "What's wrong?"

"Nothing in particular," replied Sheerin. "Two of the men were due several hours ago and haven't shown up yet. He's terrifically short-handed, of course, because all but the really essential men have gone to the Hideout."

"You don't think the two deserted, do you?"

"Who? Faro and Yimot? Of course not. Still, if they're not back within the hour, things would be a little sticky." He got to his feet suddenly, and his eyes twinkled. "Anyway, as long as Aton is gone—"

Tiptoeing to the nearest window, he squatted, and from the low window box beneath withdrew a bottle of red liquid that gurgled suggestively when he shook it.

"I *thought* Aton didn't know about this," he remarked as he trotted back to the table. "Here! We've only got one glass so, as the guest, you can have it. I'll keep the bottle." And he filled the tiny cup with judicious care.

Theremon rose to protest, but Sheerin eyed him sternly. "Respect your elders, young man."

The newsman seated himself with a look of anguish on his face. "Go ahead, then, you old villain."

The psychologist's Adam's apple wobbled as the bottle upended, and then, with a satisfied grunt and a smack of the lips, he began again. "But what do you know about gravitation?"

"Nothing, except that it is a very recent development, not too well established, and that the math is so hard that only twelve men in Lagash are supposed to understand it."

"*Tcha!* Nonsense! Baloney! I can give you all the essential math in a sentence. The Law of Universal Gravitation states that there exists a cohesive force among all bodies of the universe, such that the amount of this force between any two given bodies is proportional to the product of their masses divided by the square of the distance between them."

"Is that all?"

"That's enough! It took four hundred years to develop it."

"Why that long? It sounded simple enough, the way you said it."

"Because great laws are not divined by flashes of inspiration, whatever you may think. It usually takes the combined work of a world full of scientists over a period of centuries. After Genovi 41 discovered that Lagash rotated about the sun Alpha rather than vice versa—and that was four hundred years ago—astronomers have been working. The complex motions of the six suns were recorded and analyzed and unwoven. Theory after theory was advanced and checked and counter-checked and modified and abandoned and revived and converted to something else. It was a devil of a job."

Theremon nodded thoughtfully and held out his glass for more liquor. Sheerin grudgingly allowed a few ruby drops to leave the bottle.

"It was twenty years ago," he continued after remoistening his own throat, "that it was finally demonstrated that the Law of Universal Gravitation accounted exactly for the orbital motions of the six suns. It was a great triumph."

Sheerin stood up and walked to the window, still clutching his bottle. "And now we're getting to the point. In the last decade, the motions of Lagash about Alpha were computed according to gravity, and *it did not account for the orbit observed;* not even when all perturbations due to the other suns were included. Either the law was invalid, or there was another, as yet unknown, factor involved."

Theremon joined Sheerin at the window and gazed out past the wooded slopes to where the spires of Saro City gleamed bloodily on the horizon. The newsman felt the tension of uncertainty grow within him as he cast a short glance at Beta. It glowered redly at zenith, dwarfed and evil.

"Go ahead, sir," he said softly.

Sheerin replied, "Astronomers stumbled about for years, each proposed theory more untenable than the one before—until Aton had the inspiration of calling in the Cult. The head of the Cult, Sor 5, had access to certain data that simplified the problem considerably. Aton set to work on a new track.

"What if there were another nonluminous planetary body such as Lagash? If there were, you know, it would shine only by reflected light, and if it were composed of bluish rock, as Lagash itself largely is, then, in the redness of the sky, the eternal blaze of the suns would make it invisible—drown it out completely."

Theremon whistled. "What a screwy idea!"

"You think *that's* screwy? Listen to this: Suppose this body rotated about Lagash at such a distance and in such an orbit and had such a mass that its attraction would exactly account for the deviations of Lagash's orbit from theory—do you know what would happen?"

The columnist shook his head.

"Well, sometimes this body would get in the way of a sun." And Sheerin emptied what remained in the bottle at a draft.

"And it does, I suppose," said Theremon flatly.

"Yes! But only one sun lies in its plane of revolution." He jerked a thumb at the shrunken sun above. "Beta! And it has been shown that the eclipse will occur only when the arrangement of the suns is such that Beta is alone in its hemisphere and at maximum distance, at which time the moon is invariably at minimum distance. The eclipse that results, with the moon seven times the apparent diameter of Beta, covers all of Lagash and lasts well over half a day, so that no spot on the planet escapes the effects. *That eclipse comes once every two thousand and forty-nine years."*

Theremon's face was drawn into an expressionless mask. "And that's my story?"

The psychologist nodded. "That's all of it. First the eclipse—which will start in three quarters of an hour—then universal Darkness and, maybe, these mysterious Stars—then madness, and end of the cycle."

He brooded. "We had two months' leeway—we at the Observatory—and that wasn't enough time to persuade Lagash of the danger. Two centuries might not have been enough. But our records are at the Hideout, and today we photograph the eclipse. The next cycle will *start off* with the truth, and when the *next* eclipse comes, mankind will at last be ready for it. Come to think of it, that's part of your story too."

A thin wind ruffled the curtains at the window as Theremon opened it and leaned out. It played coldly with his hair as he stared at the crimson sunlight on his hand. Then he turned in sudden rebellion.

"What is there in Darkness to drive *me* mad?"

Sheerin smiled to himself as he spun the empty liquor bottle with abstracted motions of his hand. "Have you ever experienced Darkness, young man?"

The newsman leaned against the wall and considered. "No. Can't say I have. But I know what it is. Just—uh—" He made vague motions with his fingers and then brightened. "Just no light. Like in caves."

"Have you ever been in a cave?"

"In a *cave!* Of course not!"

"I thought not. *I* tried last week—just to see—but I got out in a hurry. I went in until the mouth of the cave was just visible as a blur of light, with black everywhere else. I never thought a person my weight could run that fast."

Theremon's lip curled. "Well, if it comes to that, I guess I wouldn't have run if I had been there."

The psychologist studied the young man with an annoyed frown.

"My, don't you talk big! I dare you to draw the curtain."

Theremon looked his surprise and said, "What for? If we had four or five suns out there, we might want to cut the light down a bit for comfort, but now we haven't enough light as it is."

"That's the point. Just draw the curtain; then come here and sit down!"

"All right." Theremon reached for the tasseled string and jerked. The red curtain slid across the wide window, the brass rings hissing their way along the crossbar, and a dusk-red shadow clamped down on the room.

Theremon's footsteps sounded hollowly in the silence as he made his way to the table, and then they stopped halfway. "I can't see you, sir," he whispered.

"Feel your way," ordered Sheerin in a strained voice.

"But I can't see you, sir." The newsman was breathing harshly. "I can't see anything."

"What did you expect?" came the grim reply. "Come here and sit down."

The footsteps sounded again, waveringly, approaching slowly. There was the sound of someone fumbling with a chair. Theremon's voice came thinly, "Here I am. I feel . . . *ulp* . . . all right."

"You like it, do you?"

"N—no. It's pretty awful. The walls seem to be—" He paused. "They seem to be closing in on me. I keep wanting to push them away. But I'm not going *mad!* In fact, the feeling isn't as bad as it was."

"All right. Draw the curtain back again."

There were cautious footsteps through the dark, the rustle of Theremon's body against the curtain as he felt for the tassel, and then the triumphant *ro-o-osh* of the curtain slithering back. Red light flooded the room, and with a cry of joy Theremon looked up at the sun.

Sheerin wiped the moisture off his forehead with the back of a hand and said shakily, "And that was just a dark room."

"It can be stood," said Theremon lightly.

"Yes, a dark room can. But were you at the Jonglor Centennial Exposition two years ago?"

"No, it so happens I never got around to it. Six thousand miles was just a bit too much to travel, even for the exposition."

"Well, I was there. You remember hearing about the 'Tunnel of Mystery' that broke all records in the amusement area—for the first month or so, anyway?"

"Yes. Wasn't there some fuss about it?"

"Very little. It was hushed up. You see, that Tunnel of Mystery was just a mile-long tunnel—with no lights. You got into a little open car and jolted along through Darkness for fifteen minutes. It was very popular—while it lasted."

"Popular?"

"Certainly. There's a fascination in being frightened *when it's part of a game.* A baby is born with three instinctive fears: of loud noises, of falling, and of the absence of light. That's why it's considered so funny to jump at someone and shout 'Boo!' That's why it's such fun to ride a roller coaster. And that's why that Tunnel of Mystery started cleaning up. People came out of that Darkness shaking, breathless, half dead with fear, but they kept on paying to get in."

"Wait a while, I remember now. Some people came out dead, didn't they? There were rumors of that after it shut down."

The psychologist snorted. "Bah! Two or three died. That was nothing! They paid off the families of the dead ones and argued the Jonglor City Council into forgetting it. After all, they said, if people with weak hearts want to go through the tunnel, it was at their own risk—and besides, it wouldn't happen again. So they put a doctor in the front office and had every customer go through a physical examination before getting into the car. That actually *boosted* ticket sales."

"Well, then?"

"But you see, there was something else. People sometimes came out in perfect order, except that they refused to go into buildings—any buildings; including palaces, mansions, apartment houses, tenements, cottages, huts, shacks, lean-tos, and tents."

Theremon looked shocked. "You mean they refused to come in out of the open? Where'd they sleep?"

"In the open."

"They should have *forced* them inside."

"Oh, they did, they did. Whereupon these people went into violent hysterics and did their best to bat their brains out against the nearest wall. Once you got them inside, you couldn't keep them there without a strait jacket or a heavy dose of tranquilizer."

"They must have been crazy."

"Which is exactly what they were. One person out of every ten who went into that tunnel came out that way. They called in the psychologists, and we did the only thing possible. We closed down the exhibit." He spread his hands.

"What was the matter with these people?" asked Theremon finally.

"Essentially the same thing that was the matter with you when you thought the walls of the room were crushing in on you in the dark. There is a psychological term for mankind's instinctive fear of the absence of light. We call it 'claustrophobia,' because the lack of light is always tied up with enclosed places, so that fear of one is fear of the other. You see?"

"And those people of the tunnel?"

"Those people of the tunnel consisted of those unfortunates whose mentality did not quite possess the resiliency to overcome the claustrophobia that overtook them in the Darkness. Fifteen minutes without light is a long time; you only had two or three minutes, and I believe you were fairly upset.

"The people of the tunnel had what is called a 'claustrophobic fixation.' Their latent fear of Darkness and enclosed places had crystalized and become active, and, as far as we can tell, permanent. That's what fifteen minutes in the dark will do."

There was a long silence, and Theremon's forehead wrinkled slowly into a frown. "I don't believe it's that bad."

"You mean you don't want to believe," snapped Sheerin. "You're afraid to believe. Look out the window!"

Theremon did so, and the psychologist continued without pausing. "Imagine Darkness—everywhere. No light, as far as you can see. The houses, the trees, the fields, the earth, the sky—black! And Stars thrown in, for all I know—whatever *they* are. Can you conceive it?"

"Yes, I can," declared Theremon truculently.

And Sheerin slammed his fist down upon the table in sudden passion. "You lie! You can't conceive that. You brain wasn't built for the conception any more than it was built for the conception of infinity or of eternity. You can only talk about it. A fraction of the reality upsets you, and when the real thing comes, your brain is going to be presented with the phenomenon outside its limits of comprehension. You will go mad, completely and permanently! There is no question of it!"

He added sadly, "And another couple of millennia of painful struggle comes to nothing. Tomorrow there won't be a city standing unharmed in all Lagash."

Theremon recovered part of his mental equilibrium. "That doesn't follow. I still don't see that I can go loony just because there isn't a sun in the sky—but even if I did, and everyone else did, how does that harm the cities? Are we going to blow them down?"

But Sheerin was angry, too. "If you were in Darkness, what would you want more than anything else; what would it be that every instinct would call for? Light, damn you, *light!*"

"Well?"

"And how would you get light?"

"I don't know," said Theremon flatly.

"What's the *only* way to get light, short of a sun?"

"How should I know?"

They were standing face to face and nose to nose.

Sheerin said, "You burn something, mister. Ever see a forest fire? Ever go camping and cook a stew over a wood fire? Heat isn't the only thing burning wood gives off, you know. It gives off light, and people know that. And when it's dark they want light, and they're going to *get* it."

"So they burn wood?"

"So they burn whatever they can get. They've got to have light. They've got to burn something, and wood isn't handy—so they'll burn whatever is nearest. They'll have their light—and every center of habitation goes up in flames!"

Eyes held each other as though the whole matter were a personal affair of respective will powers, and then Theremon broke away wordlessly. His breathing was harsh and ragged, and he scarcely noted the sudden hubbub that came from the adjoining room behind the closed door.

Sheerin spoke, and it was with an effort that he made it sound matter-of-fact. "I think I heard Yimot's voice. He and Faro are probably back. Let's go in and see what kept them."

"Might as well!" muttered Theremon. He drew a long breath and seemed to shake himself. The tension was broken.

The room was in an uproar, with members of the staff clustering about two young men who were removing outer garments even as they parried the miscellany of questions being thrown at them.

Aton bustled through the crowd and faced the newcomers angrily. "Do you realize that it's less than half an hour before deadline? Where have you two been?"

Faro 24 seated himself and rubbed his hands. His cheeks were red with the outdoor chill. "Yimot and I have just finished carrying through a little crazy experiment of our own. We've been trying to see if we couldn't construct an arrangement by which we could simulate the appearance of Darkness and Stars so as to get an advance notion as to how it looked."

There was a confused murmur from the listeners, and a sudden look of interest entered Aton's eyes. "There wasn't anything said of this before. How did you go about it?"

"Well," said Faro, "the idea came to Yimot and myself long ago, and we've been working it out in our spare time. Yimot knew of a low one-story house down in the city with a domed roof—it had once been used as a museum, I think. Anyway, we bought it—"

"Where did you get the money?" interrupted Aton peremptorily.

"Our bank accounts," grunted Yimot 70. "It cost two thousand credits." Then, defensively, "Well, what of it? Tomorrow, two thousand credits will be two thousand pieces of paper. That's all."

"Sure," agreed Faro. "We bought the place and rigged it up with black velvet from top to bottom so as to get as perfect a Darkness as possible. Then we punched tiny holes in the ceiling and through the roof and covered them with little metal caps, all of which could be shoved aside simultaneously at the close of a switch. At least we didn't do that part ourselves; we got a carpenter and an electrician and some others—money didn't count. The point was that we could get the light to shine through those holes in the roof, so that we could get a starlike effect."

Not a breath was drawn during the pause that followed. Aton said stiffly, "You had no right to make a private—"

Faro seemed abashed. "I know sir—but frankly, Yimot and I thought the experiment was a little dangerous. If the effect really worked, we half expected to go mad—from what Sheerin says about all this, we thought that would be rather likely. We wanted to take the risk ourselves. Of course if we found we could retain sanity, it occurred to us that we might develop immunity to the real thing, and then expose the rest of you the same way. But things didn't work out at all—"

"Why, what happened?"

It was Yimot who answered. "We shut ourselves in and allowed our eyes to get accustomed to the dark. It's an extremely creepy feeling because the total Darkness makes you feel as if the walls and ceiling are crushing in on you. But we got over that and pulled the switch. The caps fell away and the roof glittered all over with little dots of light—"

"Well?"

"Well—nothing. That was the whacky part of it. Nothing happened. It was just a roof with holes in it, and that's just what it looked like. We tried it over and over again—that's what kept us so late—but there just isn't any effect at all."

There followed a shocked silence, and all eyes turned to Sheerin, who sat motionless, mouth open.

Theremon was the first to speak. "You know what this does to this whole theory you've built up, Sheerin, don't you?" He was grinning with relief.

But Sheerin raised his hand. "Now wait a while. Just let me think this through." And then he snapped his fingers, and when he lifted his head there was neither surprise nor uncertainty in his eyes. "Of course—"

He never finished. From somewhere up above there sounded a sharp clang, and Beenay, starting to his feet, dashed up the stairs with a "What the devil!"

The rest followed after.

Things happened quickly. Once up in the dome, Beenay cast one horrified glance at the shattered photographic plates and at the man bending over them; and then hurled himself fiercely at the intruder, getting a death grip on his throat. There was a wild threshing, and as others of the staff joined in, the stranger was swallowed up and smothered under the weight of half a dozen angry men.

Aton came up last, breathing heavily. "Let him up!"

There was a reluctant unscrambling and the stranger, panting harshly, with his clothes torn and his forehead bruised, was hauled to his feet. He had a short yellow beard curled elaborately in the style affected by the Cultists.

Beenay shifted his hold to a collar grip and shook the man savagely. "All right, rat, what's the idea? These plates—"

"I wasn't after *them,*" retorted the Cultist coldly. "That was an accident."

Beenay followed his glowering stare and snarled, "I see. You were after the cameras themselves. The accident with the plates was a stroke of luck for you, then. If you had touched Snapping Bertha or any of the others, you would have died by slow torture. As it is—" He drew his fist back.

Aton grabbed his sleeve. "Stop that! Let him go!"

The young technician wavered, and his arm dropped reluctantly. Aton pushed him aside and confronted the Cultist. "You're Latimer, aren't you?"

The Cultist bowed stiffly and indicated the symbol upon his hip. "I am Latimer 25, adjutant of the third class to his serenity, Sor 5."

"And"—Aton's white eyebrows lifted—"you were with his serenity when he visited me last week, weren't you?"

Latimer bowed a second time.

"Now, then, what do you want?"

"Nothing that you would give me of your own free will."

"Sor 5 sent you, I suppose—or is this your own idea?"

"I won't answer that question."

"Will there be any further visitors?"

"I won't answer that, either."

Aton glanced at his timepiece and scowled. "Now, man, what is it your master wants of me? I have fulfilled my end of the bargain."

Latimer smiled faintly, but said nothing.

"I asked him," continued Aton angrily, "for data only the Cult could supply, and it was given to me. For that, thank you. In return I promised to prove the essential truth of the creed of the Cult."

"There was no need to prove that," came the proud retort. "It stands proven by the *Book of Revelations.*"

"For the handful that constitute the Cult, yes. Don't pretend to mistake my meaning. I offered to present scientific backing for your beliefs. And I did!"

The Cultist's eyes narrowed bitterly. "Yes, you did—with a fox's subtlety, for your pretended explanation backed our beliefs, and at the same time removed all necessity for them. You made of the Darkness and of the Stars a natural phenomenon and removed all its real significance. That was blasphemy."

"If so, the fault isn't mine. The facts exist. What can I do but state them?"

"Your 'facts' are a fraud and a delusion."

Aton stamped angrily. "How do you know?"

And the answer came with the certainty of absolute faith. "I know!"

The director purpled and Beenay whispered urgently. Aton waved him silent. "And what does Sor 5 want us to do? He still thinks, I suppose, that in trying to warn the world to take measures against the menace of madness, we are placing innumerable souls in jeopardy. We aren't succeeding, if that means anything to him."

"The attempt itself has done harm enough, and your vicious effort to gain information by means of your devilish instruments must be stopped. We obey the will of the Stars, and I only regret that my clumsiness prevented me from wrecking your infernal devices."

"It wouldn't have done you too much good," returned Aton. "All our data, except for the direct evidence we intend collecting right now, is already safely cached and well beyond possibility of harm." He smiled grimly. "But that does not affect your present status as an attempted burglar and criminal."

He turned to the men behind him. "Someone call the police at Saro City."

There was a cry of distaste from Sheerin. "Damn it, Aton, what's wrong with you? There's no time for that. Here"—he bustled his way forward—"let me handle this."

Aton stared down his nose at the psychologist. "This is not the time for your monkeyshines, Sheerin. Will you please let me handle this my own way? Right now you are a complete outsider here, and don't forget it."

Sheerin's mouth twisted eloquently. "Now why should we go to the impossible trouble of calling the police—with Beta's eclipse a matter of minutes from now—when this young man here is perfectly willing to pledge his word of honor to remain and cause no trouble whatsoever?"

The Cultist answered promptly, "I will do no such thing. You're free to do what you want, but it's only fair to warn you that just as soon as I get my chance I'm going to finish what I came out here to do. If it's my word of honor you're relying on, you'd better call the police."

Sheerin smiled in a friendly fashion. "You're a determined cuss, aren't you? Well, I'll explain something. Do you see that young man at the window? He's a strong, husky fellow, quite handy with his fists, and he's an outsider besides. Once the eclipse starts there will be nothing for him to do except keep an eye on you. Besides him, there will be myself—a little too stout for active fisticuffs, but still able to help."

"Well, what of it?" demanded Latimer frozenly.

"Listen and I'll tell you," was the reply. "Just as soon as the eclipse starts, we're going to take you, Theremon and I, and deposit you in a little closet with one door, to which is attached one giant lock and no windows. You will remain there for the duration."

"And afterward," breathed Latimer fiercely, "there'll be no one to let me out. I know as well as you do what the coming of the Stars means—I know it far better than you. With all your minds gone, you are not likely to free me. Suffocation or slow starvation, is it? About what I might have expected from a group of scientists. But I don't give my word. It's a matter of principle, and I won't discuss it further."

Aton seemed perturbed. His faded eyes were troubled. "Really, Sheerin, locking him—"

"Please!" Sheerin motioned him impatiently to silence. "I don't think for a moment things will go that far. Latimer has just tried a clever little bluff, but I'm not a psychologist just because I like the sound of the word." He grinned at the Cultist. "Come now, you don't really think I'm trying anything as crude as slow starvation. My dear Latimer, if I lock you in the closet, you are not going to see the Darkness, and you are not going to see the Stars. It does not take much knowledge of the fundamental creed of the Cult to realize that for you to be hidden from the Stars when they appear means the loss of your immortal soul. Now, I believe you to be an honorable man. I'll accept your word of honor to make no further effort to disrupt proceedings, if you'll offer it."

A vein throbbed in Latimer's temple, and he seemed to shrink within himself as he said thickly, "You have it!" And then he added with swift fury, "But it is my consolation that you will all be damned for your deeds of today." He turned on his heel and stalked to the high three-legged stool by the door.

Sheerin nodded to the columnist. "Take a seat next to him, Theremon—just as a formality. Hey, Theremon!"

But the newspaperman didn't move. He had gone pale to the lips. "Look at that!" The finger he pointed toward the sky shook, and his voice was dry and cracked.

There was one simultaneous gasp as every eye followed the pointing finger and, for one breathless moment, stared frozenly.

Beta was chipped on one side! The tiny bit of encroaching blackness was perhaps the width of a fingernail, but to the staring watchers it magnified itself into the crack of doom.

Only for a moment they watched, and after that there was a shrieking confusion that was even shorter of duration and which gave way to an orderly scurry of activity—each man at his prescribed job. At the crucial moment there was no time for emotion. The men were merely scientists with work to do. Even Aton had melted away.

Sheerin said prosaically, "First contact must have been made fifteen minutes ago. A little early, but pretty good considering the uncertainties involved in the calculation." He looked about him and then tiptoed to Theremon, who still remained staring out the window, and dragged him away gently.

"Aton is furious," he whispered, "so stay away. He missed first contact on account of this fuss with Latimer, and if you get in his way he'll have you thrown out the window."

Theremon nodded shortly and sat down. Sheerin stared in surprise at him.

"The devil, man," he exclaimed, "you're shaking."

"Eh?" Theremon licked dry lips and then tried to smile. "I don't feel very well, and that's a fact."

The psychologist's eyes hardened. "You're not losing your nerve?"

"No!" cried Theremon in a flash of indignation. "Give me a chance, will you? I haven't really believed this rigmarole—not way down beneath, anyway—till just this minute. Give me a chance to get used to the idea. You've been preparing yourself for two months or more."

"You're right, at that," replied Sheerin thoughtfully. "Listen! Have you got a family—parents, wife, children?"

Theremon shook his head. "You mean the Hideout, I suppose. No, you don't have to worry about that. I have a sister, but she's two thousand miles away. I don't even know her exact address."

"Well, then, what about yourself? You've got time to get there, and they're one short anyway, since I left. After all, you're not needed here, and you'd make a darned fine addition—"

Theremon looked at the other wearily. "You think I'm scared stiff, don't you? Well, get this, mister, I'm a newspaperman and I've been assigned to cover a story. I intend covering it."

There was a faint smile on the psychologist's face. "I see. Professional honor, is that it?"

"You might call it that. But, man, I'd give my right arm for another bottle of that sockeroo juice even half the size of the one you hogged. If ever a fellow needed a drink, I do."

He broke off. Sheerin was nudging him violently. "Do you hear that? Listen!"

Theremon followed the motion of the other's chin and stared at the Cultist, who, oblivious to all about him, faced the window, a look of wild elation on his face, droning to himself the while in singsong fashion.

"What's he saying?" whispered the columnist.

"He's quoting Book of Revelations, fifth chapter," replied Sheerin. Then, urgently, "Keep quiet and listen, I tell you."

The Cultist's voice had risen in a sudden increase of fervor: " 'And it came to pass that in those days the Sun, Beta, held lone vigil in the sky for ever longer periods as the revolutions passed; until such time as for full half a revolution, it alone, shrunken and cold, shone down upon Lagash.

"'And men did assemble in the public squares and in the highways, there to debate and to marvel at the sight, for a strange depression had seized them. Their minds were troubled and their speech confused, for the souls of men awaited the coming of the Stars.

"'And in the city of Trigon, at high noon, Vendret 2 came forth and said unto the men of Trigon, "Lo, ye sinners! Though ye scorn the ways of righteousness, yet will the time of reckoning come. Even now the Cave approaches to swallow Lagash; yea, and all it contains."

"'And even as he spoke the lip of the Cave of Darkness passed the edge of Beta so that to all Lagash it was hidden from sight. Loud were the cries of men as it vanished, and great the fear of soul that fell upon them.

"'It came to pass that the Darkness of the Cave fell upon Lagash, and there was no light on all the surface of Lagash. Men were even as blinded, nor could one man see his neighbor, though he felt his breath upon his face.

"'And in this blackness there appeared the Stars, in countless numbers, and to the strains of music of such beauty that the very leaves of the trees cried out in wonder.

"'And in that moment the souls of men departed from them, and their abandoned bodies became even as beasts; yea, even as brutes of the wild; so that through the blackened streets of the cities of Lagash they prowled with wild cries.

"'From the Stars there then reached down the Heavenly Flame, and where it touched, the cities of Lagash flamed to utter destruction, so that of man and of the works of man nought remained.

"'Even then—'"

There was a subtle change in Latimer's tone. His eyes had not shifted, but somehow he had become aware of the absorbed attention of the other two. Easily, without pausing for breath, the timbre of his voice shifted and the syllables became more liquid.

. Theremon, caught by surprise, stared. The words seemed on the border of familiarity. There was an elusive shift in the accent, a tiny change in the vowel stress; nothing more—yet Latimer had become thoroughly unintelligible.

Sheerin smiled slyly. "He shifted to some old-cycle tongue, probably their traditional second cycle. That was the language in which the *Book of Revelations* was originally written, you know."

"It doesn't matter; I've heard enough." Theremon shoved his chair back and brushed his hair back with hands that no longer shook. "I feel much better now."

"You do?" Sheerin seemed mildly surprised.

"I'll say I do. I had a bad case of jitters just a while back. Listening to you and your gravitation and seeing that eclipse start almost finished me. But this"—he jerked a contemptuous thumb at the yellow-bearded Cultist—"*this* is the sort of thing my nurse used to tell me. I've been laughing at that sort of thing all my life. I'm not going to let it scare me *now.*"

He drew a deep breath and said with a hectic gaiety, "But if I expect to keep on the good side of myself, I'm going to turn my chair away from the window."

Sheerin said, "Yes, but you'd better talk lower. Aton just lifted his head out of that box he's got it stuck into and gave you a look that should have killed you."

Theremon made a mouth. "I forgot about the old fellow." With elaborate care he turned the chair from the window, cast one distasteful look over his shoulder, and said, "It has occurred to me that there must be considerable immunity against this Star madness."

The psychologist did not answer immediately. Beta was past its zenith now, and the square of bloody sunlight that outlined the window upon the floor had lifted into Sheerin's lap. He stared at its dusky color thoughtfully and then bent and squinted into the sun itself.

The chip in its side had grown to a black encroachment that covered a third of Beta. He shuddered, and when straightened once more his florid cheeks did not contain quite as much color as they had had previously.

With a smile that was almost apologetic, he reversed his chair also. "There are probably two million people in Saro City that are all trying to join the Cult at once in one gigantic revival." Then, ironically, "The Cult is in for an hour of unexampled prosperity. I trust they'll make the most of it. Now, what was it you said?"

"Just this. How did the Cultists manage to keep the *Book of Revelations* going from cycle to cycle, and how on Lagash did it get written in the first place? There must have been some sort of immunity, for if everyone had gone mad, who would be left to write the book?"

Sheerin stared at his questioner ruefully. "Well, now, young man, there isn't any eyewitness answer to that, but we've got a few damned good notions as to what happened. You see, there are three kinds of people who might remain relatively unaffected. First, the very few who don't see the Stars at all: the seriously retarded or those who drink themselves into a stupor at the beginning of the eclipse and remain so to the end. We leave them out—because they aren't really witnesses.

"Then there are children below six, to whom the world as a whole is too new and strange for them to be too frightened at Stars and Darkness. They would be just another item in an already surprising world. You see that, don't you?"

The other nodded doubtfully. "I suppose so."

"Lastly, there are those whose minds are too coarsely grained to be entirely toppled. The very insensitive would be scarcely affected—oh, such people as some of our older, work-broken peasants. Well, the children would have fugitive memories, and that, combined with the confused, incoherent babblings of the half-mad morons, formed the basis for the *Book of Revelations.*

"Naturally, the book was based, in the first place, on the testimony of those least qualified to serve as historians; that is, children and morons; and was probably edited and reedited through the cycles."

"Do you suppose," broke in Theremon, "that they carried the book through the cycles the way we're planning on handing on the secret of gravitation?"

Sheerin shrugged. "Perhaps, but their exact method is unimportant. They do it, somehow. The point I was getting at was that the book can't help but be a mass of distortion, even if it is based on fact. For instance, do you remember the experiment with the holes in the roof that Faro and Yimot tried—the one that didn't work?"

"Yes."

"You know why it didn't w—" He stopped and rose in alarm, for Aton was approaching, his face a twisted mask of consternation. *"What's happened?"*

Aton drew him aside and Sheerin could feel the fingers on his elbow twitching.

"Not so loud!" Aton's voice was low and tortured. "I've just gotten word from the Hideout on the private line."

Sheerin broke in anxiously. "They are in trouble?"

"Not *they.*" Aton stressed the pronoun significantly. "They sealed themselves off just a while ago, and they're going to stay buried till day after tomorrow. They're safe. But the *city,* Sheerin—it's a shambles. You have no idea—" He was having difficulty in speaking.

"Well?" snapped Sheerin impatiently. "What of it? It will get worse. What are you shaking about?" Then, suspiciously, "How do you feel?"

Aton's eyes sparked angrily at the insinuation, and then faded to anxiety once more. "You don't understand. The Cultists are active. They're rousing the people to storm the Observatory—promising them immediate entrance into grace, promising them salvation, promising them anything. What are we to do, Sheerin?"

Sheerin's head bent, and he stared in long abstraction at his toes. He tapped his chin with one knuckle, then looked up and said crisply, "Do? What is there to do? Nothing at all. Do the men know of this?"

"No, of course not!"

"Good! Keep it that way. How long till totality?"

"Not quite an hour."

"There's nothing to do but gamble. It will take time to organize any really formidable mob, and it will take more time to get them out here. We're a good five miles from the city—"

He glared out the window, down the slopes to where the farmed patches gave way to clumps of white houses in the suburbs; down to where the metropolis itself was a blur on the horizon—a mist in the waning blaze of Beta.

He repeated without turning, "It will take time. Keep on working and pray that totality comes first."

Beta was cut in half, the line of division pushing a slight concavity into the still-bright portion of the Sun. It was like a gigantic eyelid shutting slantwise over the light of a world.

The faint clatter of the room in which he stood faded into oblivion, and he sensed only the thick silence of the fields outside. The very insects seemed frightened mute. And things were dim.

He jumped at the voice in his ear. Theremon said, "Is something wrong?"

"Eh? Er—no. Get back to the chair. We're in the way." They slipped back to their corner, but the psychologist did not speak for a time. He lifted a finger and loosened his collar. He twisted his neck back and forth but found no relief. He looked up suddenly.

"Are you having any difficulty in breathing?"

The newspaperman opened his eyes wide and drew two or three long breaths. "No. Why?"

"I looked out the window too long, I suppose. The dimness got me. Difficulty in breathing is one of the first symptoms of a claustrophobic attack."

Theremon drew another long breath. "Well, it hasn't got me yet. Say, here's another of the fellows."

Beenay had interposed his bulk between the light and the pair in the corner, and Sheerin squinted up at him anxiously. "Hello, Beenay."

The astronomer shifted his weight to the other foot and smiled feebly. "You won't mind if I sit down awhile and join in the talk? My cameras are set, and there's nothing to do till totality." He paused and eyed the Cultist, who fifteen minutes earlier had drawn a small, skin-bound book from his sleeve and had been poring intently over it ever since. "That rat hasn't been making trouble, has he?"

Sheerin shook his head. His shoulders were thrown back and he frowned his concentration as he forced himself to breathe regularly. He said, "Have you had any trouble breathing, Beenay?"

Beenay sniffed the air in his turn. "It doesn't seem stuffy to me."

"A touch of claustrophobia," explained Sheerin apologetically.

"Ohhh! It worked itself differently with me. I get the impression that my eyes are going back on me. Things seem to blur and—well, nothing is clear. And it's cold too."

"Oh, it's cold all right. That's no illusion." Theremon grimaced.

"My toes feel as if I've been shipping them cross-country in a refrigerating car."

"What we need," put in Sheerin, "is to keep our minds busy with extraneous affairs. I was telling you a while ago, Theremon, why Faro's experiments with the holes in the roof came to nothing."

"You were just beginning," replied Theremon. He encircled a knee with both arms and nuzzled his chin against it.

"Well, as I started to say, they were misled by taking the *Book of Revelations* literally. There probably wasn't any sense in attaching any physical significance to the Stars. It might be, you know, that in the presence of total Darkness, the mind finds it absolutely necessary to create light. This illusion of light might be all the Stars there really are."

"In other words," interposed Theremon, "you mean the Stars are the results of the madness and not one of the causes. Then, what good will Beenay's photographs be?"

"To prove that it is an illusion, maybe; or to prove the opposite; for all I know. Then again—"

But Beenay had drawn his chair closer, and there was an expression of sudden enthusiasm on his face. "Say, I'm glad you two got onto this subject." His eyes narrowed and he lifted one finger. "I've been thinking about these Stars and I've got a really cute notion. Of course it's strictly ocean foam, and I'm not trying to advance it seriously, but I think it's interesting. Do you want to hear it?"

He seemed half reluctant, but Sheerin leaned back and said, "Go ahead! I'm listening."

"Well, then, supposing there were other suns in the universe." He broke off a little bashfully. "I mean suns that are so far away that they're too dim to see. It sounds as it I've been reading some of that fantastic fiction, I suppose."

"Not necessarily. Still, isn't that possibility eliminated by the fact that, according to the Law of Gravitation, they would make themselves evident by their attractive forces?"

"Not if they were far enough off," rejoined Beenay, "really far off—maybe as much as four light years, or even more. We'd never be able to detect perturbations then, because they'd be too small. Say that there were a lot of suns that far off; a dozen or two, maybe."

Theremon whistled melodiously. "What an idea for a good Sunday supplement article. Two dozen suns in a universe eight light years across. Wow! That would shrink our world into insignificance. The readers would eat it up."

"Only an idea," said Beenay with a grin, "but you see the point. During an eclipse, these dozen suns would become visible because there'd be no *real* sunlight to drown them out. Since they're so far off, they'd appear small, like so many little marbles. Of course the Cultists talk of millions of Stars, but that's probably exaggeration. There just isn't any place in the universe you could put a million suns—unless they touch one another."

Sheerin had listened with gradually increasing interest. "You've hit something there, Beenay. And exaggeration is just exactly what would happen. Our minds, as you probably know, can't grasp directly any number higher than five; above that there is only the concept of 'many.' A dozen would become a million just like that. A damn good idea!"

"And I've got another cute little notion," Beenay said. "Have you ever thought what a simple problem gravitation would be if only you had a sufficiently simple system? Supposing you had a universe in which there was a planet with only one sun. The plant would travel in a perfect ellipse and the exact nature of the gravitational force would be so evident it could be accepted as an axiom. Astronomers on such a world would start off with gravity probably before they even invented the telescope. Naked-eye observation would be enough."

"But would such a system be dynamically stable?" questioned Sheerin doubtfully.

"Sure! They call it the 'one-and-one' case. It's been worked out mathematically, but it's the philosophical implications that interest me."

"It's nice to think about," admitted Sheerin, "as a pretty abstraction—like a perfect gas, or absolute zero."

"Of course," continued Beenay, "there's the catch that life would be impossible on such a planet. It wouldn't get enough heat and light, and if it rotated there would be total Darkness half of each day. You couldn't expect life—which is fundamentally dependent upon light—to develop under those conditions. Besides—"

Sheerin's chair went over backward as he sprang to his feet in a rude interruption. "Aton's brought out the lights."

Beenay said, "Huh," turned to stare, and then grinned halfway around his head in open relief.

There were half a dozen foot-long, inch-thick rods cradled in Aton's arms. He glared over them at the assembled staff members.

"Get back to work, all of you. Sheerin, come here and help me!"

Sheerin trotted to the older man's side and, one by one, in utter silence, the two adjusted the rods in makeshift metal holders suspended from the walls.

With the air of one carrying through the most sacred item of a religious ritual, Sheerin scraped a large, clumsy match into spluttering life and passed it to Aton, who carried the flame to the upper end of one of the rods.

It hesitated there awhile, playing futilely about the tip, until a sudden, crackling flare cast Aton's lined face into yellow highlights. He withdrew the match and a spontaneous cheer rattled the window.

The rod was topped by six inches of wavering flame! Methodically, the other rods were lighted, until six independent fires turned the rear of the room yellow.

The light was dim, dimmer even than the tenuous sunlight. The flames reeled crazily, giving birth to drunken, swaying shadows. The torches smoked devilishly and smelled like a bad day in the kitchen. But they emitted yellow light.

There was something about yellow light, after four hours of somber, dimming Beta. Even Latimer had lifted his eyes from his book and stared in wonder.

Sheerin warmed his hands at the nearest, regardless of the soot that gathered upon them in a fine, gray powder, and muttered ecstatically to himself. "Beautiful! Beautiful! I never realized before what a wonderful color yellow is."

But Theremon regarded the torches suspiciously. He wrinkled his nose at the rancid odor and said, "What are those things?"

"Wood," said Sheerin shortly.

"Oh, no, they're not. They aren't burning. The top inch is charred and the flame just keeps shooting up out of nothing."

"That's the beauty of it. This is a really efficient artificial-light mechanism. We made a few hundred of them, but most went to the Hideout, of course. You see"—he turned and wiped his blackened hands upon his handerchief—"you take the pithy core of coarse water reeds, dry them thoroughly, and soak them in animal grease. Then you set fire to it and the grease burns, little by little. These torches will burn for almost half an hour without stopping. Ingenious, isn't it? It was developed by one of our own young men at Saro University."

After the momentary sensation, the dome had quieted. Latimer had carried his chair directly beneath a torch and continued reading, lips moving in the monotonous recital of invocations to the Stars. Beenay had drifted away to his cameras once more, and Theremon seized the opportunity to add to his notes on the article he was going to write for the Saro City *Chronicle* the next day—a procedure he had been following for the last two hours in a perfectly methodical, perfectly conscientious and, as he was well aware, perfectly meaningless fashion.

But, as the gleam of amusement in Sheerin's eyes indicated, careful note-taking occupied his mind with something other than the fact that the sky was gradually turning a horrible deep purple-red, as if it were one gigantic, freshly peeled beet; and so it fulfilled its purpose.

The air grew, somehow, denser. Dusk, like a palpable entity, entered the room, and the dancing circle of yellow light about the torches etched itself into ever-sharper distinction against the gathering grayness beyond. There was the odor of smoke and the presence of little chuckling sounds that the torches made as they burned; the soft pad of one of the men circling the table at which he worked, on hesitant tiptoes; the occasional indrawn breath of someone trying to retain composure in a world that was retreating into the shadow.

It was Theremon who first heard the extraneous noise. It was a vague, unorganized *impression* of sound that would have gone unnoticed but for the dead silence that prevailed within the dome.

The newsman sat upright and replaced his notebook. He held his breath and listened; then, with considerable reluctance, threaded his way between the solarscope and one of Beenay's cameras and stood before the window.

The silence ripped to fragments at his startled shout: *"Sheerin!"*

Work stopped! The psychologist was at his side in a moment. Aton joined him. Even Yimot 70, high in his little lean-back seat at the eyepiece of the gigantic solarscope, paused and looked downward.

Outside, Beta was a mere smoldering splinter, taking one last desperate look at Lagash. The eastern horizon, in the direction of the city, was lost in Darkness, and the road from Saro to the Observatory was a dull-red line bordered on both sides by wooded tracts, the trees of which had somehow lost individuality and merged into a continuous shadowy mass.

But it was the highway itself that held attention, for along it there surged another, and infinitely menacing, shadowy mass.

Aton cried in a cracked voice, "The madmen from the city! They've come!"

"How long to totality?" demanded Sheerin.

"Fifteen minutes, but . . . but they'll be here in five."

"Never mind, keep the men working. We'll hold them off. This place is built like a fortress. Aton, keep an eye on our young Cultist just for luck. Theremon, come with me."

Sheerin was out the door, and Theremon was at his heels. The stairs stretched below them in tight, circular sweeps about the central shaft, fading into a dank and dreary grayness.

The first momentum of their rush had carried them fifty feet down, so that the dim, flickering yellow from the open door of the dome had disappeared and both above and below the same dusky shadow crushed in upon them.

Sheerin paused, and his pudgy hand clutched at his chest. His eyes bulged and his voice was a dry cough. "I can't . . . breathe. . . . Go down . . . yourself. Close all doors—"

Theremon took a few downward steps, then turned. "Wait! Can you hold out a minute?" He was panting himself. The air passed in and out his lungs like so much molasses, and there was a little germ of screeching panic in his mind at the thought of making his way into the mysterious Darkness below by himself.

Theremon, after all, was afraid of the dark!

"Stay here," he said. "I'll be back in a second." He dashed upward two steps at a time, heart pounding—not altogether from the exertion—tumbled into the dome and snatched a torch from its holder. It was foul-smelling, and the smoke smarted his eyes almost blind, but he clutched that torch as if he wanted to kiss it for joy, and its flame streamed backward as he hurtled down the stair again.

Sheerin opened his eyes and moaned as Theremon bent over him. Theremon shook him roughly. "All right, get a hold on yourself. We've got light."

He held the torch at tiptoe height and, propping the tottering psychologist by an elbow, made his way downward in the middle of the protecting circle of illumination.

The offices on the ground floor still possessed what light there was, and Theremon felt the horror about him relax.

"Here," he said brusquely, and passed the torch to Sheerin. "You can hear *them* outside."

And they could. Little scraps of hoarse, wordless shouts.

But Sheerin was right; the Observatory was built like a fortress. Erected in the last century, when the neo-Gavottian style of architecture was at its ugly height, it had been designed for stability and durability rather than for beauty.

The windows were protected by the grillwork of inch-thick iron bars sunk deep into the concrete sills. The walls were solid masonry that an earthquake couldn't have touched, and the main door was a huge oaken slab reinforced with iron. Theremon shot the bolts and they slid shut with a dull clang.

At the other end of the corridor, Sheerin cursed weakly. He pointed to the lock of the back door which had been neatly jimmied into uselessness.

"That must be how Latimer got in," he said.

"Well, don't stand there," cried Theremon impatiently. "Help drag up the furniture—and keep that torch out of my eyes. The smoke's killing me."

He slammed the heavy table up against the door as he spoke, and in two minutes had built a barricade which made up for what it lacked in beauty and symmetry by the sheer inertia of its massiveness.

Somewhere, dimly, far off, they could hear the battering of naked fists upon the door; and the screams and yells from outside had a sort of half reality.

That mob had set off from Saro City with only two things in mind: the attainment of Cultist salvation by the destruction of the Observatory, and a maddening fear that all but paralyzed them. There was no time to think of ground cars, or of weapons, or of leadership, or even of organization. They made for the Observatory on foot and assaulted it with bare hands.

And now that they were there, the last flash of Beta, the last ruby-red drop of flame, flickered feebly over a humanity that had left only stark, universal fear!

Theremon groaned, "Let's get back to the dome!"

In the dome, only Yimot, at the solarscope, had kept his place. The rest were clustered about the cameras, and Beenay was giving his instructions in a hoarse, strained voice.

"Get it straight, all of you. I'm snapping Beta just before totality and changing the plate. That will leave one of you to each camera. You all know about . . . about times of exposure—"

There was a breathless murmur of agreement.

Beenay passed a hand over his eyes. "Are the torches still burning? Never mind, I see them!" He was leaning hard against the back of a chair. "Now remember, don't . . . don't try to look for good shots. Don't waste time trying to get t-two stars at a time in the scope field. One is enough. And . . . and if you feel yourself going, *get away from the camera.*"

At the door, Sheerin whispered to Theremon, "Take me to Aton. I don't see him."

The newsman did not answer immediately. The vague forms of the astronomers wavered and blurred, and the torches overhead had become only yellow splotches.

"It's dark," he whimpered.

Sheerin held out his hand. "Aton." He stumbled forward. "Aton!"

Theremon stepped after and seized his arm. "Wait, I'll take you." Somehow he made his way across the room. He closed his eyes against the Darkness and his mind against the chaos within it.

No one heard them or paid attention to them. Sheerin stumbled against the wall. "Aton!"

The psychologist felt shaking hands touching him, then withdrawing, and a voice muttering, "Is that you, Sheerin?"

"Aton!" He strove to breathe normally. "Don't worry about the mob. The place will hold them off."

Latimer, the Cultist, rose to his feet, and his face twisted in desperation. His word was pledged, and to break it would mean placing his soul in mortal peril. Yet that word had been forced from him and had not been given freely. The Stars would come soon! He could not stand by and allow—And yet his word was pledged.

Beenay's face was dimly flushed as it looked upward at Beta's last ray, and Latimer, seeing him bend over his camera, made his decision. His nails cut the flesh of his palms as he tensed himself.

He staggered crazily as he started his rush. There was nothing before him but shadows; the very floor beneath his feet lacked substance. And then someone was upon him and he went down with clutching fingers at his throat.

He doubled his knee and drove it hard into his assailant. "Let me up or I'll kill you."

Theremon cried out sharply and muttered through a blinding haze of pain. "You double-crossing rat!"

The newsman seemed conscious of everything at once. He heard Beenay croak, "I've got it. At your cameras, men!" and then there was the strange awareness that the last thread of sunlight had thinned out and snapped.

Simultaneously he heard one last choking gasp from Beenay, and a queer little cry from Sheerin, a hysterical giggle that cut off in a rasp—and a sudden silence, a strange, deadly silence from outside.

And Latimer had gone limp in his loosening grasp. Theremon peered into the Cultist's eyes and saw the blankness of them, staring upward, mirroring the feeble yellow of the torches. He saw the bubble of froth upon Latimer's lips and heard the low animal whimper in Latimer's throat.

With the slow fascination of fear, he lifted himself on one arm and turned his eyes toward the bloodcurdling blackness of the window.

Through it shone the Stars!

Not Earth's feeble thirty-six hundred Stars visible to the eye; Lagash was in the center of a giant cluster. Thirty thousand mighty suns shone down in a soul-searing splendor that was more frighteningly cold in its awful indifference than the bitter wind that shivered across the cold, horribly bleak world.

Theremon staggered to his feet, his throat constricting him to breathlessness, all the muscles of his body writhing in an intensity of terror and sheer fear beyond bearing. He was going mad and knew it, and somewhere deep inside a bit of sanity was screaming, struggling to fight off the hopeless flood of black terror. It was very horrible to go mad and know that you were going mad—to know that in a little minute you would be here physically and yet all the real essence would be dead and drowned in the black madness. For this was the Dark—the Dark and the Cold and the Doom. The bright walls of the universe were shattered and their awful black fragments were falling down to crush and squeeze and obliterate him.

He jostled someone crawling on hands and knees, but stumbled somehow over him. Hands groping at his tortured throat, he limped toward the flame of the torches that filled all his mad vision.

"Light!" he screamed.

Aton, somewhere, was crying, whimpering horribly like a terribly frightened child. "Stars—all the Stars—we didn't know at all. We didn't know anything. We thought six stars in a universe is something the Stars didn't notice is Darkness forever and ever and ever and the walls are breaking in and we didn't know we couldn't know and anything—"

Someone clawed at the torch, and it fell and snuffed out. In the instant, the awful splendor of the indifferent Stars leaped nearer to them.

On the horizon outside the window, in the direction of Saro City, a crimson glow began growing, strengthening in brightness, that was not the glow of a sun.

The long night had come again.

RAGNAROK

Roger Lancelyn Green

The origin of the word Ragnarok *(rag′nə rok) is in the phrase first used by the early Icelandic poets to describe the last battle between the Norse gods and their enemies. They spoke simply of "the end of the gods." Later writers substituted for the word meaning "fate" or "end" a similar one meaning "obscurity" or "twilight," producing the phrase which has become traditional, "the twilight of the gods." For some background in Norse myth and the pronunciation of names see the notes on pages 32 and 333.*

EVEN FROM THE MORNING of time Odin had known, the Aesir soon knew, and even the dwellers in Midgard learnt to know also, that the whole world would perish on a day—the Day of Ragnarok, the Twilight of the Gods—the Day of the Last Great Battle.

Baldur was dead and Hodur was dead also. Loki was bound, and Valhalla was growing full of the Einheriar. There were shadows over Asgard, and in Jotunheim the Giants stirred and muttered threateningly. In Midgard men turned towards the evil Loki had taught them, treachery grew and greed and pride also.

Odin knew much of what was to happen when Ragnarok came: but there was much he did not know, for even he could not see the future. If the Norns[1] knew, they would not speak: their task was to weave the web of each man's life, but not the life of the whole world.

But here and there a strange woman was born or died who could see into the future, some a little way and concerning little things; but one or two with powers of sight beyond that of any other creature. Such a one was the dead Volva[2] whom Odin had raised from her grave to tell him of the death of Baldur. Such another was born and lived her life in Midgard. Her name was Haid[3] and she was famed among men for her prophecies.

Seated in Lidskialf,[4] whence he could see all that happened in the Nine Worlds, Odin saw Haid, the wise sibyl, passing from house to

1. *Norns* (nôrnz), the three goddesses who determined the fates of gods and men. 2. *Volva*, (vōl′vä). 3. *Haid*, (hīd). 4. *Lidskialf* (lid′skyälf), Odin's cloud throne.

house among men. And suddenly he knew that here was one wiser even than Volva, one who could answer what he desired most to know.

So he went down to Midgard wearing his usual disguise of wide-brimmed hat, blue cloak, and tall staff. Before he went in search of Haid, the Valkyries[5] had visited her, bringing such gifts as the high ones of Asgard could give: cunning treasure-spells, rune sticks,[6] and rods of divination.

Odin came to her as she sat alone before a cave overlooking the broad land of the Danes and the blue waters of the Sound.[7] He came as a man, bringing her presents of rings and necklaces, and begging her to read the future for him. But she knew him at once and spoke to him in the deep, thrilling tones of a prophetess:

"What ask you of me? Why would you tempt me? I know all, Odin; yes, I know where you have hidden your eye in the holy well of Mimir. I can see all things; both the world's beginning and the world's ending. I can see Ginnungagap as it was before the Sons of Borr raised the earth out of it: the Giant Ymir I know, and the Cow Audumla[8]. . . . I can see the shaft of death, the mistletoe that Loki cut from the oak; the dart that flew into Baldur's heart, and Frigga weeping in Fensalir."

"You know of the past, and that I know also," said Odin. "But, since the gift is yours and yours alone, look into the future, wise Haid—you whom we in Asgard call Vola,[9] the Sibyl—look and tell me of the World's Ending: tell me of Ragnarok and the Great Battle on the Plain of Vigrid."[10]

Then he took his stand behind Haid the Vola, placing his hands above her head and murmuring the runes of wisdom so that his knowledge should be mingled with hers.

And now her eyes grew wide and vacant as she gazed out across the land and over the water, seeing neither; seeing things unseen.

"There shall come the Fimbul Winter," she cried, "after man's evil has reached its height. For brother shall slay brother, and son shall not spare father, and honour shall be dead among men.

"In that awful Winter snow shall drive from all quarters, frost shall not break, the winds shall be keen, and the sun give no heat. And for three years shall that Fimbul Winter last.

"Eastward in Iron Wood an aged witch is sitting, breeding the brood of Fenris and the wolf that shall swallow the Sun. He shall feed on the lives of death-doomed mortals, spattering the heavens with their red blood.

5. *Valkyries* (val kir′ēz), "the choosers of the slain," goddesses sent by Odin to battlefields, where they selected the heroes who would die, and afterward led them to Odin's mead-hall Valhalla where they feasted and fought and awaited Ragnarok. **6.** *rune sticks*, sticks inscribed with the characters of the runic (rü′nic) alphabet of the Teutonic peoples, used for magical purposes. **7.** *the Sound*, the strait between Denmark and Sweden. **8.** *the Sons of Borr . . . the Cow Audumla.* The Sons of Borr were the gods Odin, Vili, and Ve. They killed the Giant Ymir (im′r) who fed on the milk of the Cow Audumla (ou düm′lə) and created the world from his body. **9.** *Vola* (vō′lä), "prophetess." **10.** *Vigrid,* (vig′rid).

"Ragnarok comes; I see it far in the days to be. Yet to me, the far-seer, it is as if that day were now, and all that I see in the future is happening before me now. I see it, and I tell you what I see and hear as it rises about me until Future and Present seem as one.

"For I see the Wolf Skoll[11] who in that far day swallows the Sun, and the Moon is swallowed also, while the stars are quenched with blood. Now the earth shakes, the trees and the rocks are torn up and all things fall to ruin.

"Away in Jotunheim the red cock Fialar[12] crows loudly; and another cock with golden crest crows over Asgard. Then all bonds are loosened: the Fenris Wolf breaks free; the sea gushes over the land as Jormungand the Midgard Serpent swims ashore. Then the ship Naglfar[13] is loosened; it is made of dead men's nails—therefore when a man dies, shear his nails close so that Naglfar may be long in the building. But now I see it moving over the flood, and the Giant Hymir[14] steers it. Fenris advances with open mouth, and Jormungand blows venom over sea and air: terrible is he as he takes his place beside the Wolf Fenris.

"Then the sky splits open and the Sons of Muspell come in fire: Surtur leads them with his flaming sword, and when they ride over Bifrost the bridge breaks behind them and falls in pieces to the earth. Loki also is set free and comes to the Field of Vigrid; he and Hymir lead the Frost Giants to the battle. But all Hela's champions follow Loki; Garm the Hell Hound bays fiercely before the Gnipa[15] Cave, and his jaws slobber with blood.

"Now I hear Heimdall in the Gate of Asgard blowing upon the Giallar Horn. Its notes sound clear and shrill throughout all worlds: it is the Day of Ragnarok. The Aesir meet together; Odin rides to Mimir's Well for the last time. Yggdrasill the World Tree trembles, and nothing shall be without fear in heaven or in earth.

"Now I see the Aesir put on their armour and ride to the field of battle. Odin rides first in his golden helmet and his fair armour; Sleipnir is beneath him and he holds the spear Gungnir[16] in his hand. He rides against the Fenris Wolf, and Thor stands at his side, shaking Miolnir; yet he cannot help Odin, for all his strength is needed in his own battle with Jormungand.

"Now Frey fights against Surtur; the struggle is long, but Frey falls at the last. Ah, he would not have died had he his sword in his hand: But that sword he gave to Skirnir.[17] Oh, how loudly Garm bays in the Gnipa Cave! Now he has broken loose and fights against Tyr: had Tyr two hands it would go hard with Garm, but now they slay and are slain the one by the other.

"Thor slays the Midgard Serpent, and no greater deed was ever done.

---

11. *Skoll*, (skol). 12. *Fialar*, (fyäl′är). 13. *Naglfar*, (nä′gəl fär). 14. *Hymir*, (hü′mir). 15. *Gnipa*, (nē′pə). 16. *Gungnir*, (güng′nir). 17. *Skirnir*, (skèr′nir).

He strides away from the spot; nine paces only, and then he falls to the earth and dies, so deadly is the venom which Jormungand has poured upon him.

"Odin and Fenris still fight together: but in the end the Wolf has the victory and devours Odin. But Vidar strides forward to avenge his father, and sets his foot on the lower jaw of Fenris. On that foot is the shoe made of the scraps of leather which men cut from their toes or heels: therefore should men cut often and fling away if they desire to help the Aesir. Vidar takes the Wolf by the upper jaw and tears him apart, and that is the end of Fenris.

"Loki battles with Heimdall, and in their last struggle each slays the other and both fall.

"Now Surtur spreads fire over the whole earth and all things perish. Darkness descends, and I can see no more."

The voice of Haid the Vola faded away into silence. But still she sat rigid and still gazing beyond the distance, gazing into the future with wide, unseeing eyes.

Very slowly, as he stood behind her, it seemed to Odin that her power was creeping into him. His own eye grew misty—grew dark—and then on a sudden he was looking out with two eyes, with her eyes and not his own. At first he saw only a great waste of water, tossing and tumbling over all the world. But as he watched, a new earth rose out of the sea, green and fruitful, with unfading forests and pleasant meadows smiling in the light of a new sun. Then the waters fell away, making wide rivers, and sparkling falls and a new blue sea about the land.

Then, on Ida's[18] Plain where Asgard had stood before, he saw Vidar and Vali, the two of the Aesir who had survived through Ragnarok. Thor's two sons, Magni and Modi,[19] came to join them, bearing Miolnir in their hands. After this the earth opened and back from Helheim came Baldur the Beautiful, holding his brother Hodur by the hand.

They sat down and spoke together concerning all that had happened, of the passing of Fenris and Jormungand, and other evils. Then, shining among the grass and flowers, they saw the ancient golden chessmen of the Aesir, and collecting them began to play once more on the board of life.

Presently Honir came to them out of Vanaheim, bringing great wisdom to the new Aesir. At his bidding new halls rose on Ida's Plain, glittering palaces waiting for the souls of dead men and women from Midgard.

For in Midgard also life came again. In the deep place called Hoddminir's Holt[20] a man and a woman had escaped from Surtur's

---

18. *Ida's,* (ē′dəz). **19.** *Magni and Modi,* (mäg′nē *and* mō′dē). **20.** *Hoddminir's Holt,* (hod′min irz hōlt).

fire. Now they awoke from sleep, Lif and Lifthrasir;[21] and for food they found the morning dew was all they needed. From them were born many children so that Midgard was peopled anew. And there were children also in the new Asgard which was called Gimli[22] the Gem Lea, where the halls were thatched with gold. There the blessed among men mingled with the new race of the Aesir, and the new Sun shone brightly, and the new world was filled with light and song.

Then Odin wept with joy, and as the tears coursed down his face, the vision faded into the greyness of the cold Northern world where Ragnarok is yet to come. The wind moaned over the chill plains, the wolves howled in the lonely mountains, and across the sea stole forth a longship hung with shields in which Viking men went out to harry and slay and burn.

The old sibyl sat alone by her cave, chanting the words of the *Volo-spa,* the poem of prophecy, the finest of all the old Northern poems which are still known among men.

But Odin threaded his way quietly across Midgard to Bifrost Bridge, up its gleaming arch where Hiemdall stood on guard, and so brought his good news to the Aesir.

For now he knew the meaning of the mysterious word which he had whispered into Baldur's ear as his dead son lay upon the funeral ship: the word "Rebirth" which was to bring comfort and hope to the Men of Midgard as well as to the Gods of Asgard.

---

21. *Lif and Lifthrasir,* (lef *and* lef⁄thrä sir). **22.** *Gimli,* (gim⁄lē).

NORSE MYTHOLOGY / THE NINE WORLDS

The mythology of the Teutonic peoples of Northern Europe told of the great ash tree Yggdrasil (īg′drə sil), whose roots and branches spread throughout the universe and supported the Nine Worlds. The first of these was Asgard (as′gärd, az′gärd), the home of the Aesir (ā′sir, ē′sir), the principal Norse gods. Connected to Asgard by the rainbow bridge, Bifrost (bēf′rōst), was Midgard (mid′gärd), or Middle-Earth, the human world, so called because it was halfway between the frozen world of Nifelheim (niv′əl hām), far to the North, and the fiery world of Muspellheim (müs′pəl hām), to the far South. These worlds were inhabited by monsters of fire and ice, the enemies of gods and men.

Below Midgard was Helheim (hel′hām), the cold, gloomy Underworld inhabited by the souls of the dead, except for those who died in battle. These, the Einherjar (ān′hėr yär), go to join the gods in Asgard, and dwell in the great mead-hall Valhalla (val hal′ə), feasting and fighting until the Day of Ragnarok (rag′nə rok), when they and the Aesir will fight the last great battle against their enemies (see selection page 328). Foremost of these are the Giants from Jotunheim (yô′tün-hām), against whom they have fought an ages-long war (see selections pages 32 and 154).

The remaining three worlds are Vanaheim (vä′nä hām), the home of the Vanir (vä′nir), god-like beings who are allies of the Aesir; and the Elvish worlds of Alfheim (älf′hām) and Svartalfheim (swärt äl′fə-hām), the first the home of the Light Elves, the second of the Dark Elves. The following is a list of the principal Aesir, Vanir, and Giants, with some others:

Baldur (bôl′dər), god ′of light and goodness, a son of Odin, killed through Loki's treachery
Bragi (brä′gē), god of poetry
Fenris (fen′rəs), a monstrous wolf, one of Loki's children
Forseti (fôr′se tē), god of justice, a son of Baldur
Frey (frā), a god of fertility, one of the Vanir
Freya (frā′ə), goddess of love and beauty, the sister of Frey
Frigga (frig′ə), goddess of the sky, the wife of Odin
Garm (gärm), the great dog who guarded Helheim
Gerda (gėr′də), a goddess, the wife of Frey

Heimdall (hām′däl), the watchman of Asgard, who will blow the *Giallar* (gyäl′lər) Horn on the Day of Ragnarok

Hela (hel′ə), the goddess who rules the dead, one of Loki's children

Hodur (hōd′ər), the blind god, Baldur's brother, who killed the god of light

Honir (hōn′ər), a god, Odin's brother.

Iduna (ē dün′ə), a goddess who kept the golden apples by which the Aesir renewed their youth

Jormungand (yôr′mü gänd), the Midgard Serpent, a sea-monster, one of Loki's children

Loki (lō′kē), a Giant who dwelt with the Aesir, full of malice and cunning

Mimir (mē′mir), a Giant who guarded the well whose waters gave knowledge of the past, present, and future

Nanna (nän′nə), a goddess, the wife of Baldur

Njord (nyôrd), god of wealth, the father of Frey and Freya

Odin (ōd′n), god of wisdom and war, chief of the Aesir

Sage (sä′gə), a goddess, one of the Aesir

Sif (sif), goddess of the home, the wife of Thor

Skadi (skä′dē), a Giantess, the wife of Njord

Sleipnir (slāp′nər), Odin's eight-legged horse

Surtur (sürt′ər), a fire demon, the ruler of Muspellheim

Thor (thôr), god of thunder

Tyr (tir), god of battle

Ull (ül), a god, one of the Aesir

Vali (vä′lē), a god, one of the Aesir, a son of Odin

Vidar (vē′där), a god, one of the Aesir, a son of Odin

THE HORSES

Edwin Muir

Barely a twelvemonth after
The seven days war that put the world to sleep,
Late in the evening the strange horses came.
By then we had made our covenant with silence,
5 But in the first few days it was so still
We listened to our breathing and were afraid.
On the second day
The radios failed; we turned the knobs; no answer.
On the third day a warship passed us, heading north,
10 Dead bodies piled on the deck. On the sixth day
A plane plunged over us into the sea. Thereafter
Nothing. The radios dumb;
And still they stand in corners of our kitchens,
And stand, perhaps, turned on, in a million rooms
15 All over the world. But now if they should speak,
If on a sudden they should speak again,
If on the stroke of noon a voice should speak,
We would not listen, we would not let it bring
That old bad world that swallowed its children quick
20 At one great gulp. We would not have it again.
Sometimes we think of the nations lying asleep,
Curled blindly in impenetrable sorrow,
And then the thought confounds us with its strangeness.
The tractors lie about our fields; at evening
25 They look like dank sea-monsters couched and waiting.
We leave them where they are and let them rust:
'They'll moulder away and be like other loam.'
We make our oxen drag our rusty ploughs,
Long laid aside. We have gone back
30 Far past our fathers' land.

                              And then, that evening
        Late in the summer the strange horses came.
        We heard a distant tapping on the road,
        A deepening drumming; it stopped, went on again
        And at the corner changed to hollow thunder.
35   We saw the heads
        Like a wild wave charging and were afraid.
        We had sold our horses in our fathers' time
        To buy new tractors. Now they were strange to us
        As fabulous steeds set on an ancient shield
40   Or illustrations in a book of knights.
        We did not dare go near them. Yet they waited,
        Stubborn and shy, as if they had been sent
        By an old command to find our whereabouts
        And that long-lost archaic companionship.
45   In the first moment we had never a thought
        That they were creatures to be owned and used.
        Among them were some half-a-dozen colts
        Dropped in some wilderness of the broken world,
        Yet new as if they had come from their own Eden.
50   Since then they have pulled our ploughs and borne our loads,
        But that free servitude still can pierce our hearts.
        Our life is changed; their coming our beginning.

John Frederick Nims

Once on the gritty moon (burnt earth hung far
In the black, rhinestone sky—lopsided star),
Two gadgets, with great fishbowls for a head,
Feet clubbed, hips loaded, shoulders bent. She said,
5 "Fantasies haunt me. A green garden. Two
Lovers aglow in flesh. The pools so blue!"
He whirrs with masculine pity, "Can't forget
Old superstitions? The earth-legend yet?"

7

SOME
NEWER
STORIES

EVE
IN DARKNESS

Kaatje Hurlbut[1]

THAT LITTLE MARBLE NUDE was so lovely. She was the loveliest thing I had ever seen. In a corner of my grandmother's dim, austere living room she stood on a pedestal like a small, bright ghost.

I was about five when I used to stand and gaze up at her with admiration and delight. I thought that her toes and fingers were as beautiful as anything about her: they were long and narrow and expressive. She stood slightly bowed and the delicate slenderness of her emphasized the roundness of her little breasts, which were like the apple she held in her fingers.

I wonder now who she was. I think she may have been Aphrodite and the apple was the golden prize, "for the fairest"—the fateful judgment of Paris.[2] But Victoria, my cousin, who was older than I, said that she was Eve. And I believed her.

We observed the quietness of that room, Eve and I, as though we were conspirators. I never talked to her or even whispered to her (as I did to the blackened bronze of Pallas Athene[3] in the hall), but in the quietness I considered many things standing before her and she received my congratulations with a faint, musing smile I found infinitely satisfying.

---

1. *Kaatje Hurlbut*, (kät′yə hėrl′bət). 2. *Aphrodite . . . Paris.* All the Olympian gods (see note page 70) were invited to a marriage feast except the goddess Eris, or Discord. Enraged, she threw a golden apple marked "for the fairest" into the midst of the guests. Three goddesses claimed it—Hera, Athena, and Aphrodite (af′rə di′tē), the goddess of love. Zeus decided that peace could be restored to Olympus if a mortal was to be the judge. Paris (par′is), son of the king of Troy, was chosen. He awarded the apple to Aphrodite, who had bribed him with the promise of the most beautiful woman in the world as his wife. This was Helen, who was already married to the king of Sparta. Paris's abduction of Helen was the cause of the Trojan War. 3. *Pallas Athene* (pal′əs ə thē′nē), Athena, goddess of wisdom.

Others came into the room and talked as though the quietness was nothing. Molly, the Irishwoman who cleaned, bustled about with a dustcloth, muttering and sighing. Victoria even shouted there. Only my grandmother did not shatter the quietness because she had the kind of voice that only brushed against it. Callers were the worst for, sitting with teacups and smelling of strange scents, they threatened never to leave but to sit forever and say in old continuous voices, "We really must go now" and "My dear, promise you will come soon" and "Where have I put my gloves?"

But leave they did. And after the teacups had been removed and the carpet sweeper run over the crumbs I would go back to the room alone and stand before Eve to consider, often as not, the reason for one of the callers wearing a velvet band around her wrinkled old throat. My cousin Victoria said that it was because her throat had been cut by a maniac and she wore the velvet band to hide the terrible scar. I suspected that this was not the truth. But it was interesting to consider. Eve smiled. It might have been true.

Eve smiled because of the things she knew. She knew that I had handled the snuffboxes I had been forbidden to touch: some of them were silver but some were enamel with radiant miniatures painted on the lids and when I looked closely at the faces the eyes gazed back at me, bold and bright. Eve knew that at four-thirty I went to the front window to stick out my tongue at the wolfish paper boy, to whom I had been told to be very kind because he was so much less fortunate than I. She knew that I was deathly afraid of the ragman, who drove over from the East Side now and then, bawling, "I cash old clothes." You couldn't really tell what he was saying but that was what he was supposed to be saying. Victoria told me that he took little girls when he could get them and smothered them under the mound of dirty rags and papers piled high on his rickety old cart. I laughed at Victoria and hoped she didn't know how afraid I was. But Eve knew.

Sometimes I only considered Eve herself because of her loveliness. When the room was dim she gleamed in the shadowy corner; but when the sun came into the room in the morning she dazzled until she seemed to be made of light pressed into hardness. And the cleanness of her was cleaner than anything I could think of: cleaner than my grandmother's kid gloves; cleaner than witch hazel on a white handkerchief.

As I stood before Eve one afternoon Victoria came up behind me so silently I did not hear her.

"What are *you* doing?" she asked suddenly.

I jumped and turned to find her smiling a wide, fixed smile, with her eyes fully open and glassy.

"Nothing," I said, and an instinctive flash of guilt died away, for it was true: I was doing nothing. But she continued to stare at me and smile fixedly until I lowered my eyes and started to move away.

"Wait."

"What?"

"Do you know what that is?" she asked slyly and touched the apple Eve held in her fingers.

"An apple."

"No," she said, smiling more intensely. "That," she thrust her face close to mine and almost whispered, "that is the forbidden fruit." She enunciated each syllable slowly and somehow dreadfully.

"What kind of fruit?" I asked, backing away.

She stopped smiling and looked steadily at me, her eyes growing wider and wider. And then with a kind of hushed violence, as when she would tell me about the murders in the Rue Morgue[4] and about an insane man who howled and swung a club in a nearby alley on moonless nights, she told me about the Garden of Eden; and about the tree and the serpent; and about the man, Adam, and the woman, Eve.

"And the forbidden fruit," she said at last in a harsh flat whisper, "is *sin!*"

"Sin." She whispered the word again and gazed balefully at the little marble statue of Eve. I followed her gaze with dread, knowing all at once that sin was not any kind of fruit but something else: something that filled me with alarm and grief because I loved Eve. And as I stared she only looked past me with her blind marble eyes and smiled.

I suppose it was the first time in my life that I experienced sorrow. For I remember the strangeness of what I felt: regret and helplessness and a deeper love.

"Sin."

My mind tried to embrace the word and find its meaning, for it belonged to Eve now. But I could not grasp it. So I said the word to myself and listened to it.

"Sin."

It was beautiful. It was a word like "rain" and "sleep": lovely but of sorrowful loveliness. "Sin": it was lovely and sorrowful and it belonged to Eve.

Victoria, who had been watching me, asked with a sudden, writhing delight: "Do you know what sin is?"

"No," I said, wishing fiercely that she would go away.

"And I won't tell you," she said slyly. "You're much too little to know."

For a time after that I was so preoccupied with the vague sorrow that surrounded Eve that I went to the room only out of a reluctant sense of

---

4. *the murders in the Rue Morgue,* the subject of a story by the American writer Edgar Allan Poe (1809–1849).

duty. I felt that I might somehow console her. And there she would be, holding the apple in her delicate fingers, smiling. And I wondered how she could be smiling with sorrow all around her. I looked long at her, until her smile almost hypnotized me, and all at once it occurred to me that she did not know about Sin. Poor little Eve. She didn't even know that Sin was all around her, belonging to her. She was only white and beautiful and smiling.

But as Christmas drew near I went to her again as I had gone before: out of need. I went to consider the curious and wonderful things I had seen in the German toy store over on Amsterdam Avenue. There was the old German himself, fat and gentle and sad. My grandmother had told me people had stopped going to his store during the First World War because the Americans and the Germans were enemies. And I hoped earnestly that he did not think I was his enemy. Eve smiled. She knew that I wasn't. And she smiled about the bold colors of the toys trimmed in gold: and about the ugly laughing faces of the carved wooden dolls, too real for dolls' faces but more like the faces of dried shrunken little people, as Victoria said they were.

Someone who had made the grand tour[5] had brought home, along with the laces and lava carvings and watercolor scenes of Cairo, an exquisitely small manger in which the Infant Christ lay wrapped in swaddling clothes. His arms were flung out bravely and his palms were open. He was always taken from the box at Christmastime and placed on a low table where I might play with him if I did not take him from the table. But he was so small and beautiful and brave-looking that I could not bring myself to play with him as I would a toy. Overcome with enchantment one afternoon, I took him up and carried him across the room to Eve. I held him up before her blind marble eyes and she smiled. It was a tremendous relief to have her smile at him.

I looked regretfully at the apple and turned away from her. I held the baby Christ close to my lips and whispered the lovely sorrowful word to him.

"Sin."

But little and brave as ever, with his arms flung out and his palms open, he seemed not to have heard me.

That night I wandered aimlessly down to the basement where the kitchen was and when I approached the kitchen door in the darkness of the hall I bumped into Victoria, who was standing at the closed door listening to the hum of voices that came from inside the kitchen.

She grabbed me and quickly clamped her hand over my mouth.

"Go," she whispered fiercely. "Go back."

But I was frightened and clung to her helplessly. Still holding her hand over my mouth, she led me back down the hall and up the dark

---

5. *the grand tour*, an extended tour of continental Europe, formerly considered an essential part of the education of young men of the British aristocracy.

stairs, stumbling, into the hall above. By that time I was crying and she tried to quiet me, still whispering fiercely.

"Listen," she hissed, "if you won't tell you saw me there I'll tell you something *horrible.*"

"I won't tell," I said into her palm. I hadn't thought of telling; I was too frightened.

"Do you know who that was in the kitchen? It was Molly."

Molly, I remembered, was to come that night: my grandmother had put crisp new bills in an envelope and had said Molly was coming for her Christmas present.

"Molly," said Victoria, "was crying. A horrible thing has happened. Her daughter—" she stared at me with wide frightening eyes that I wanted to turn from but couldn't, "—her daughter *sinned!*"

"What do you mean?" I asked in alarm, thinking of Eve. I was afraid I was going to cry again and I clenched my fists and doubled up my toes so that I wouldn't.

"She had a baby!" She looked hard at me, fierce and accusing. I backed away from her.

"You won't tell you saw me there?"

"How did she sin?" I asked, thinking of the brave baby and Eve gleaming in the dark corner smiling at him.

"She had a baby, I told you," she replied impatiently. And then, as she looked at me, an expression of evasive cunning crept into her eyes.

"King David sinned also."

"King David in the Bible[6]?" I asked.

"Yes. Now promise you won't tell you saw me."

"I promise," I said.

I tried to remember something about King David, but all I could think of was the beginning of a poem: "King David and King Solomon[7] led merry, merry lives."

He sounded happy and grand like Old King Cole was-a-merry-old-soul. I tried to imagine how the sadness of Sin belonged to him: I wondered if he held an apple, like Eve; I didn't think he could have a baby, like Molly's daughter.

I thought about Sin when I lay in bed that night sniffing the lavender scent of the sheets. I whispered the word to myself, carefully separating it from other words and considering all that I knew about it: Eve held Sin in her slender fingers and looked past it with blind marble eyes. Molly's daughter sinned (I wondered if she was as beautiful as Eve); she sinned and had a baby: a little brave baby with his arms flung out and his palms open. Sin. Why, it was hardly sorrowful at all.

When my grandmother came in to say good night I sat up to kiss the

---

6. *King David in the Bible.* David (died 970? B.C.) was the second king of Israel, ruling forty years. The story of his life is told in the First and Second Books of Samuel. **7.** *King Solomon*, David's son and successor.

fragrant velvet cheek and whispered privately: "What did King David do?"

"What did King David do? King David played his harp!" she answered gaily, and it sounded like the beginning of a song:

King David played his harp! He sinned and played his harp! Lovely, lovely Sin: he played his harp!

Slowly at first and then swiftly, the remains of the vague sorrow spiraled out of sight and rejoicing came up in its place.

Over and over I beheld them, bright in the darkness on a hidden merry-go-round, swinging past me, friendly and gay: King David holding aloft his harp; Molly's daughter's little baby with his arms flung out so bravely; and brightest of all came Eve with her apple, smiling and shining with Sin.

THE ULTIMATE THRESHOLD

Herman Maximov[1]

On orders from Lak-Iffar-shi Yast, a House of Death was erected. This House existed one and a half periods. When a Ling who wore the red badge testifying that he had attained his majority wished to cut the thread of his life, he came there. And he was never seen by anyone again . . . This House had been built by a Master Mechanic by the name of Velt. And it was he who destroyed it.

History of the Planet Sym-Kri,
Section 76, Paragraph 491.

Is your decision final?"

The inscription ran across the width of the door, from right to left. The letters, once painted yellow, had peeled and darkened. The all-pervasive dust had settled on them in a thin crust. The plastic-coated door frame was covered with hurried notes and names, scratched out by those who had entered the door, never to return. In the corner there was a pile of things discarded by the thousands who had passed through—devices for telling time, bracelets, metal pill-boxes for cana grains.

"Is your decision final?"

He had to answer the question. A single word. Velt hesitated a moment, trying to still his hammering heart. Then he breathed, just audibly:

"Yes."

The door did not stir. Its green electric eye watched every movement he made. The tunnel smelled of damp. The light bulb, shrouded in cobwebs, burned dimly. A lifeless silence hung in the stagnant air.

"The Ultimate Threshold" by Herman Maximov. From THE ULTIMATE THRESHOLD, A COLLECTION OF THE FINEST IN SOVIET SCIENCE FICTION, edited and translated by Mirra Ginsberg. Published by Holt, Rinehart and Winston, 1970. Reprinted by permission of Gunther Stuhlmann, author's representative.

1. *Maximov,* (mäk′si môf).

Only up above, somewhere along the circular road, the one-seat chitoplatforms were chattering far, far away: clack, clack, clack . . . Against his will, Velt strained to catch the faint sounds penetrating into the underground passage from the surface. They meant movement, and hence, life. Clack, clack, clack—as though someone pitiless were driving nails into his head, his breast, his heart. Velt stood, listening to the distant sounds of life, and felt that he was almost drained of resolve. In a moment he would back away, turn from the dreadful door, and run. Run, driven by terror. Run until his heart was bursting with blood and he had flung himself upon the sun-warmed grass and smelled the welcoming earth.

And then? Then the past would come back. While he was here, the pangs of conscience, the waking nightmare, the nights filled with thoughts as heavy as stone—all these were behind him. The tears of mothers, the cold hatred of fathers and brothers, the last curses of those before whom this door, and the twenty other doors to the House of Death had opened—all these were behind him. While he was here. But all of it would return with daylight, with life. And something new would be added—self-contempt for the moment of weakness.

Velt stretched his hand and touched the raised, discolored letters. They were cold and rough: "Is your decision final?"

"Yes!" he said loudly and distinctly, although every nerve, every cell of his body shrieked "No." "Yes!"

The steel door noiselessly slid up, opening the way. A cold light spilled into the passageway. Velt tore his disobedient feet from the ground and entered the bright space. The heavy door slid softly down behind him.

It was difficult to guess the dimensions of the room. It was seen at the same time as infinitely vast and infinitely small. This effect was produced by mirrors. Space, compressed and endlessly reflected by the mirrors on the walls, floors and ceilings, became an illusion. It seemed that even time, weary of tossing from wall to wall, stopped still and thickened, thrown back to the center of The Room of the Last Confession. Velt's reflections stared at him from all sides—thousands of Velts, with gaunt faces and bewildered eyes. A clumsy, incorporeal host, they crowded the smooth walls. Broken, they hung from the ceiling and crumpled themselves underfoot, as though fused into the floor. Velt was alone with himself. The mirrors splintered him into a multitude of fragments, and each fragment—he sensed it almost palpably—robbed him of another minute of his life, another particle of his dreams and fleeting hopes. So little remained in him that there was no longer any reason for regrets or fears. And this sensation of sudden emptiness within passed over into calm indifference. The calm of the doomed. Velt walked to the corner and lowered himself into the single chair by a low metal table. The chair was shabby, with a sagging seat.

And the confessor machine began at once:

"Life will go, but the holy fire of the great Chimpo will continue to burn," the machine uttered the ritual formula. "Who are you, who have stepped across the ultimate threshold?"

The voice was soft and gentle and so familiar that Velt started and involuntarily glanced around, looking for the only one to whom this voice belonged. His senses lied to him: the room was empty, and only thousands of silent reflections looked back at him. His senses lied, but he could not and did not wish to resist the deception. He leaned back against the chair and plunged into the bottomless pool of memory. The cold squares of the floor dissolved, scattered into the soft, warm dust of a country road, and Velt himself became a small boy in a short ati, just above his scratched knees. His mother was calling him, and he ran, hopping and skipping, to his house, raising fountains of dust.

"Who are you?"

He ran up to her, threw his arms around her, and hid his face against her warm, soft stomach. And she stroked his disheveled head and spoke to him. He could not remember what she said, but her words were tender and a little sad.

"Who are you?"

By an effort of will he shook off his numbness. The ghosts of the past melted and vanished. Childhood disappeared in the abyss of time.

"I am Velt-Nipr-ma Gullit, Master Mechanic, Honorary Ling of Sym-Kri."

"Where and when were you born?"

"In the village of Ikht, on the seventh knot of the Great Canal, in the year of the blooming of the sky blue rea. It was four periods and seven revolutions ago."

The machine was silent for a moment, as though weighing his words. Then something squeaked and quavered in the apparatus concealed in the vault of the ceiling, and the mechanical confessor . . . broke into song.

This little ling
Has twelve misfortunes.
He laughs,
But don't believe him . . .

The machine sang in a gruff, old man's voice, shouting the words with reckless abandon. Frenzy, animal terror, despair and devil-may-care gaiety were all mixed up in the hoarse flow of song blared out by the mechanical throat. In the belly of the machine something cracked, squeaked, crunched, as if someone invisible were driving over broken glass. Velt felt as though someone had punched him on the chin. He jumped up and stared at the ceiling with terror-stricken eyes. Thousands of reflections jumped up with him, staring up. The machine sang. It was unexpected and absurd. It was like delirium. The machine could pray with the one preparing to die, it could weep with him, console him. But it should not sing. He knew that very well.

He has no other home
But the House of Death . . .

The song broke off, and the machine asked in the official tone of an interrogator: "Did you say good-bye to those with whom you are bound by blood ties?"

Velt could not speak. His lips trembled. He stood in the middle of the room and saw the doomed rushing about in terror in this mirrored crypt, hammering their fists on the steel door, forgetting that it could not open while they were alive. And the machine, gone berserk, howled street songs intermingled with sacred psalms. Confession, turned into torture.

"But how could I have known it's gone out of order?" he said aloud, as though justifying himself before his reflections. "How could I have known?"

The reflections were silent. Velt felt in his pocket, brought out several grains of cana, and threw them into his mouth. The narcotic acted immediately; a light veil dimmed his consciousness, his nervous tension subsided, and his muscles relaxed.

"How could I have known?" he repeated, sinking into the chair.

"Did you say good-bye to your relatives?"

"I have no relatives," Velt replied wearily. "I am the last of the Gullits."

"Your friends?"

"There are few honest Lings left in Sym-Kri. I have no friends."

"Friend, friendly, friends," said the machine. "To make friends, to befriend, friendship . . . Whom shall I notify?"

"The Supreme Keeper. He will be pleased."

Yes, the Supreme One would be pleased. He did not know how to forgive insults. And the letter that Velt had sent him was demanding, and therefore insulting to a tyrant. Velt's imagination, stimulated by the narcotic, obligingly painted for him a picture of the short fat Lak-Iffar-shi Yast examining a small black cardboard square with the symbol of the House of Death and Velt's name punched on it, then turning with feigned sorrow to the officials accompanying him: "What a loss! Our best Mechanic, Velt, has killed himself." "It should have been expected," one of the officials, most likely the lanky Kut-Mu, would respond. "He behaved rather strangely of late." And everyone would smile. Just faintly, so as not to violate propriety.

"What good did you do in life?"

The confessor machine calmed down as if it, too, had chewed some of the red cana seeds. Its voice was sound intimate again, despite the occasional notes of concealed anxiety.

Velt shrugged his shoulders, forgetting that the machine would not understand his gesture. Had he done anything good? He must have. It is difficult to live through four long periods without having done anything worthwhile. But what? Velt closed his eyes: it was easier to remember that way. Well, for example, he had designed the "hard triga," a whole system of machines that made it possible to extract the rich deposits of the Second Material. That was good. Or why would they have raised his statue on the shore of the White Lake, next to the statues of the great thinkers and mechanics of Sym-Kri? He had discovered the Law of the Wave. His work had been appreciated: he became the three hundred and seventy-sixth Honorary Ling of the Planet. He had staged a colossal experiment with Flying Darns and had won in the debate with the Dogmatists, who had brought the Science of Things to a dead end. But this was not the main thing. He was simply evading the question, trying to deceive himself. The main thing . . .

"I created you!"

"Me?"

"Yes. You, and the whole House of Death."

The silence lasted an eternity. The machine was thinking over the answer.

"Are you telling the truth?"

"No one lies at the last confession."

"They lie," the machine said with conviction.

"But I am telling the truth. I, Master Mechanic Velt of the Gullit family, built this House."

"Very well," the machine said in a conciliating tone. "If this is so, you must know what awaits you."

"I know."

"Tell me."

Velt thought, with a wry grin: It's testing me. Like a teacher, with a bragging schoolboy.

"When the confession is over, you will open the door to the Stairway. Forty-two steps. One of them—I don't know which one you will select this time—carries a high electric charge. A sudden shock, and you will throw me, no longer alive but not yet dead, into a pool filled with a solution of Quatre. In seven seconds, nothing will remain of the Honorary Ling."

"The plastic buttons will remain," the machine said, and it seemed to Velt that its tone was aggrieved. "They don't dissolve. I've had to clean my drain pipes three times already because of them."

Velt suddenly wanted to laugh. He felt more gay than ever before in his life. He was simply bursting with merriment. He felt the tickling lump of laughter roll irresistibly from chest to throat, from throat to lips. So it had worries too! Plastic buttons! It cleans its drain pipes and probably grumbles at its task like an old woman mending her grandson's old ati. It isn't concerned about the destinies of those who knock at the doors of the House every day, it doesn't give a damn for them at all. . . . If only their buttons aren't made of plastic.

"You laugh," said the machine. "This happens with many. I understand—nerves."

Something gulped again in the mechanism. Some incomprehensible struggle went on inside it. Inarticulate sounds—muttering, whistling, hissing—were trying to break out of it. The machine almost shouted the next question, trying to drown out the noises.

"And now tell me, what were the evil things you did in life?"

The noise mounted. The sounds came in waves and, finally, spilled out into the room. They filled it to overflowing, they screamed out some pain of their own and beat against the mirrored ice of the walls. And suddenly there was silence. The sounds died out all at once. And only a single gong was striking brassily.

"They are always like that," said the machine. "They won't lie peacefully in the repository."

"Who?" Velt asked, puzzled.

"The diagrams I make of everybody after confession. There are too many of them, and they are always trying to break into the speech circuit. Sometimes I cannot control them and they scream through the speaker. But you did not answer my question."

"Yes," said Velt. "I have done evil too."

"What?"

"I created you."

"I don't understand it," said the machine. "You contradict yourself. You have just called it a good act."

"Good can be evil, and evil can be good."

"This is contrary to logic."

"But it is so."

"I cannot understand," said the machine. "I am tired. Every Ling is a new problem, and two blocks are out of order in my problem-solving mechanism."

"You will not understand this even if you have a thousand functioning blocks instead of six."

"But I want to understand."

Velt found the last grain of cana in his pocket. Stupid machine. What, in fact, is it seeking to understand? Life? But life is above logic. Love and hate, joy and sorrow, happiness and disillusionment—can these equations be solved without error? Who can determine where one ends and the other begins? In the tangle of thoughts and feelings one can lose his way as easily as in the forests of Katonah. And wander, lost, for an entire lifetime. Like himself. And, finally, come out upon the open road and realize that it leads to the House of Death. Stupid machine.

"I want to understand," the machine repeated.

"What?" asked Velt.

He bent over the table and pressed the yellow button on the side. A round lid flipped open in the center of the table, and the automat served up a tall slender goblet. It was filled to the rim with the juices of wine fruits and the tuck tree.

"Why you said that you had done a good thing when you created me?"

Velt took his first sip and listened within, waiting for the moment when the pleasant warmth of intoxication began to spread through his body.

"I was convinced that I was doing something good and necessary. I felt that it would help Lings . . ."

"To die?"

". . . to live."

"I don't understand."

Of course. It was useless trying to explain this to a machine. How could it ever understand that true freedom was, first and foremost, the freedom to dispose of one's own life? Why should a Ling go on living if he no longer wanted to? Why could he not follow the example of the sainted Chimpo who, when his work was finished and his life was no longer needed by anyone, mounted the bonfire? These were his thoughts when he, the best Mechanic of the Planet, was developing the project. And these were his thoughts for some time after the House of Death had been built. And others constantly supported and reinforced him in this view. The Supreme Keeper himself had discussed this subject with Velt many times. He spoke of the crisis plaguing the Planet's economy for almost six periods. He spoke of the millions of unemployed Lings who would have chosen to commit suicide but dared not for fear that their funerals would place too heavy a burden of expense upon their loved ones. To them and others like them, he said, the House of Death would be a blessing. And the aged? The helpless old with trembling hands and eyes expressing nothing? They were like a stone around the neck of their families, extra mouths supported by society. "When I am old," Lak-Iffar would say, "and my hands tire of holding the Sacred Sceptre, I shall go to the House of Death myself." And he also said, "A Ling who has lost interest in life but goes on living is not only useless but is also harmful to society. Such Lings sow the seeds of disorder: they do not value their own lives, and therefore they do not value the lives of others. The forty-two classes into which our rational society is divided are a ladder by which generations enter history. And each successive rung of this ladder rests on the preceding one. Those who have lost interest shake the foundations of our order, hoping that the ladder will collapse over their heads. They want to die, and we must help them." Velt nodded in agreement and marveled at the wisdom and humanness of the Keeper.

But not everyone understood the Supreme One's wisdom. Many were against the idea. They condemned it.

They said: it is a lie.

They said: it is blasphemy.

They said: it is a crime.

Perhaps there was some truth in these words, but it was the petty truth of those who are unable to look into the future, the truth of cowards. It did not declare itself loudly and in everyone's hearing. It slipped into the ears as a timid whisper, it clothed itself in the transparent vestments of hints, it retreated and hid itself as soon as one attempted to take a closer look at it. It was too fragile, this truth, and the Supreme One destroyed it with two words—*social demagogy.*

Lings spoke. They whispered from around corners. And he, Velt, went on with his work. He chose a good place—a little valley among the Obsidian Cliffs. He carved the House in the heart of the black rock, with twenty-one tunnels leading into it from the surface. He built an automatic circular road that precluded the possibility of anyone meeting another seeker of death at the ultimate door. He foresaw everything. He surrounded the House with a protective field, he devised foolproof machines; together with psychologists, he developed the program for the confessional. He was building for the centuries, hoping somewhere deep in his heart that he was building a monument to his genius.

"Did you make life easier for the Lings by building the House?"

Velt started. He had forgotten the machine. He had forgotten where he was and why he had come. Very little juice remained in the goblet. He shook it, and a grayish, muddy sediment rose from the bottom.

"No," said Velt. "Everything turned out contrary to expectation."

Yes, everything had turned out contrary to expectation. Fighting for a false humaneness, he had challenged true humaneness. The appearance of the House of Death legitimized suicide and even encouraged it. The promise of an easy end tempted Lings who were oppressed by the burdens of living. And they came to the steel doors and said "Yes." And the doors to nonbeing opened before them. Many came—not only those who were driven by suffering but also those who were led by petty grievances and momentary delusions. And then death became fashionable.

The House became a symbol of fate, a symbol of defeat. Its existence paralyzed the will and robbed struggle of meaning. It drew a sharp line between desire and possibility of realization. It brought, not freedom to live, but only freedom to die. A lie instead of hope, confession instead of food, indifference instead of hatred. That which he had hoped would be a healing balsam for sufferers had turned into salt corroding their wounds. And the timid truth that had been trampled into dust raised its head and filled Velt's nights with ringing whispers. Whispers that were screams, whispers that were weeping. So cries the night bird Shoon over the roof of a house visited by misfortune.

It cried: a lie!

It cried: blasphemy!

It cried: crime!

It cried that he, obedient to an evil will, had brought the Planet sorrow, that he was living like a blind man, afraid to open his eyes.

It is terrible to lose faith in oneself from day to day. It is the same as walking toward an abyss blindfolded. The letters he received burned his hands, thousands of letters filled with curses. And the mountains of black cardboard squares delivered to him daily by pneumomail. He did not know the names stamped on them. But they screamed at him, those silent cardboard squares, neatly engraved with two letters known to everyone: "HD." It was impossible to hide from them.

He tried to hide. He escaped to the Second Continent, buried himself in the wildest, remotest region, worked to the point of stupefaction. He put space between him and the black squares and shut himself off behind a dozen secretaries. But he could not escape from himself and from his Shoon bird.

A period and a half away from society. He should have been forgotten: time erases a great deal from the mind. But the first person to speak to him when he stepped out of the superplane and walked down the ladder reminded him of the House. It was an old woman with a face that was all wrinkles. She touched his sleeve and asked, "Tell me, most respected sir, it isn't frightening?"

"What?" he did not understand her question.

"Oh—out there, in your House . . ."

He recoiled from her. But she clung to his clothes and spoke rapidly.

"He was just a boy, he had just received his red badge . . ."

He broke away and ran, pushing others aside.

And in the evening he had a visit from Uram-Karakh, who had told him about the tablets. "They're infinitesimal," Uram whispered, "like specks of dust. One is enough to produce an irresistible longing to die. Var-Lush, Kam-Dan, Fot-Grun—you didn't think they went voluntarily? Who can tell Lak-Iffar now that he violates the Nine Rules? No one. Do you understand?"

Velt finished the juice, carefully placed the goblet back on the table, and said to himself, It's time to finish.

"You still have four minutes," said the machine. "The time for confession is not up."

"Let eternity which awaits me be four minutes longer."

"You are in a hurry to die?"

"No, I am in a hurry to destroy you."

"Destroy me? But you cannot do it."

"I created you."

"You have no weapons."

"I am myself the weapon."

He rose, smoothed his clothes, and smiled: force of habit.

"How do you intend to do it?"

He knew that it would not be able to prevent him. If he had carried weapons, it would not have opened the door to him; it would have foiled any attempt to destroy it from outside. The House was too well protected from without. But by letting him in, the machine had signed its own death warrant. The program did not provide for defense against a living bomb, and he had turned himself into one.

"Before coming here," he said, "I swallowed two small portions of Sitane."

"What is Sitane?"

"A substance. A powder. When I fall into the pool, the Sitane will come into contact with the Quatre, and . . ."

"Explosion?"

"Of colossal force."

"I see," said the machine. "You have devised a clever plan. But there will be no explosion; I will not let you out upon the Stairway."

"Everyone who comes here must go down the Stairway. Even if you do not want him to."

He approached the inner wall and said loudly, "I am ready!"

The mirrors slid apart, opening a narrow passage. Directly beyond it was the first step of the Stairway leading down. Velt raised his foot.

"Wait," the machine almost shouted. "Wait! It is so terrible to die. If you want, I'll let you out of here."

"You cannot do this. I know it."

"That is true. Good-bye, then. I have switched on the Planet-wide Requiem. After all, you are an Honorary Ling."

"Good-bye."

He glanced back and waved his hand to his reflections. They answered him with his own gesture.

IDIOTS FIRST

Bernard Malamud[1]

THE THICK TICKING of the tin clock stopped. Mendel, dozing in the dark, awoke in fright. The pain returned as he listened. He drew on his cold embittered clothing, and wasted minutes sitting at the edge of the bed.

"Isaac," he ultimately sighed.

In the kitchen, Isaac, his astonished mouth open, held six peanuts in his palm. He placed each on the table. "One . . . two . . . nine."

He gathered each peanut and appeared in the doorway. Mendel, in loose hat and long overcoat, still sat on the bed. Isaac watched with small eyes and ears, thick hair graying the sides of his head.

"Schlaf," he nasally said.

"No," muttered Mendel. As if stifling he rose. "Come, Isaac."

He wound his old watch though the sight of the stopped clock nauseated him.

Isaac wanted to hold it to his ear.

"No, it's late." Mendel put the watch carefully away. In the drawer he found the little paper bag of crumpled ones and fives and slipped it into his overcoat pocket. He helped Isaac on with his coat.

Isaac looked at one dark window, then at the other. Mendel stared at both blank windows.

They went slowly down the darkly lit stairs, Mendel first, Isaac watching the moving shadows on the wall. To one long shadow he offered a peanut.

"Hungrig."

In the vestibule the old man gazed through the thin glass. The November night was cold and bleak. Opening the door he cautiously thrust his head out. Though he saw nothing he quickly shut the door.

Reprinted with the permission of Farrar, Straus & Giroux, Inc. and A. M. Heath & Company Ltd. for Bernard Malamud and Eyre Methuen, from IDIOTS FIRST by Bernard Malamud, copyright © 1961, 1963 by Bernard Malamud.

1. *Malamud*, (mal′ə mŭd′).

"Ginzburg, that he came to see me yesterday," he whispered in Isaac's ear.

Isaac sucked air.

"You know who I mean?"

Isaac combed his chin with his fingers.

"That's the one, with the black whiskers. Don't talk to him or go with him if he asks you."

Isaac moaned.

"Young people he don't bother so much," Mendel said in afterthought.

It was suppertime and the street was empty but the store windows dimly lit their way to the corner. They crossed the deserted street and went on. Isaac, with a happy cry, pointed to the three golden balls. Mendel smiled but was exhausted when they got to the pawnshop.

The pawnbroker, a red-bearded man with black horn-rimmed glasses, was eating a whitefish at the rear of the store. He craned his head, saw them, and settled back to sip his tea.

In five minutes he came forward, patting his shapeless lips with a large white handkerchief.

Mendel, breathing heavily, handed him the worn gold watch. The pawnbroker, raising his glasses, screwed in his eyepiece. He turned the watch over once. "Eight dollars."

The dying man wet his cracked lips. "I must have thirty-five."

"So go to Rothschild."[2]

"Cost me myself sixty."

"In 1905." The pawnbroker handed back the watch. It had stopped ticking. Mendel wound it slowly. It ticked hollowly.

"Isaac must go to my uncle that he lives in California."

"It's a free country," said the pawnbroker.

Isaac, watching a banjo, snickered.

"What's the matter with him?" the pawnbroker asked.

"So let be eight dollars," muttered Mendel, "but where will I get the rest till tonight?"

"How much for my hat and coat?" he asked.

"No sale." The pawnbroker went behind the cage and wrote out a ticket. He locked the watch in a small drawer but Mendel still heard it ticking.

In the street he slipped the eight dollars into the paper bag, then searched in his pockets for a scrap of writing. Finding it, he strained to read the address by the light of the street lamp.

As they trudged to the subway, Mendel pointed to the sprinkled sky.

"Isaac, look how many stars are tonight."

"Eggs," said Isaac.

"First we will go to Mr. Fishbein, after we will eat."

---

2. *Rothschild*, (roth′chīld, roths′chīld), a famous family of bankers and financiers.

They got off the train in upper Manhattan and had to walk several blocks before they located Fishbein's house.

"A regular palace," Mendel murmured, looking forward to a moment's warmth.

Isaac stared uneasily at the heavy door of the house. Mendel rang. The servant, a man with long sideburns, came to the door and said Mr. and Mrs. Fishbein were dining and could see no one.

"He should eat in peace but we will wait till he finishes."

"Come back tomorrow morning. Tomorrow morning Mr. Fishbein will talk to you. He don't do business or charity at this time of the night."

"Charity I am not interested—"

"Come back tomorrow."

"Tell him it's life or death—"

"Whose life or death?"

"So if not his, then mine."

"Don't be such a big smart aleck."

"Look me in my face," said Mendel, "and tell me if I got time till tomorrow morning?"

The servant stared at him, then at Isaac, and reluctantly let them in.

The foyer was a vast high-ceilinged room with many oil paintings on the walls, voluminous silken draperies, a thick flowered rug at foot, and a marble staircase. Mr. Fishbein, a paunchy bald-headed man with hairy nostrils and small patent leather feet, ran lightly down the stairs, a large napkin tucked under a tuxedo coat button. He stopped on the fifth step from the bottom and examined his visitors.

"Who comes on Friday night to a man that he has guests, to spoil him his supper?"

"Excuse me that I bother you, Mr. Fishbein," Mendel said. "If I didn't come now I couldn't come tomorrow."

"Without more preliminaries, please state your business. I'm a hungry man."

"Hungrig," wailed Isaac.

Fishbein adjusted his pince-nez. "What's the matter with him?"

"This is my son Isaac. He is like this all his life."

Isaac mewled.

"I am sending him to California."

"Mr. Fishbein don't contribute to personal pleasure trips."

"I am a sick man and he must go tonight on the train to my Uncle Leo."

"I never give to unorganized charity," Fishbein said, "but if you are hungry I will invite you downstairs in my kitchen. We having tonight chicken with stuffed derma."[3]

---

3. *stuffed derma*, intestine stuffed with a mixture of flour fat, onion, and seasonings, and then roasted.

"All I ask is thirty-five dollars for the train ticket to my uncle in California. I have already the rest."

"Who is your uncle? How old a man?"

"Eighty-one years, a long life to him."

Fishbein burst into laughter. "Eighty-one years and you are sending him this halfwit."

Mendel, flailing both arms, cried, "Please, without names."

Fishbein politely conceded.

"Where is open the door there we go in the house," the sick man said. "If you will kindly give me thirty-five dollars, God will bless you. What is thirty-five dollars to Mr. Fishbein? Nothing. To me, for my boy, is everything."

Fishbein drew himself up to his tallest height.

"Private contributions I don't make—only to institutions. This is my fixed policy."

Mendel sank to his creaking knees on the rug.

"Please, Mr. Fishbein, if not thirty-five, give maybe twenty."

"Levinson!" Fishbein angrily called.

The servant with the long sideburns appeared at the top of the stairs.

"Show this party where is the door—unless he wishes to partake food before leaving the premises."

"For what I got chicken won't cure it," Mendel said.

"This way if you please," said Levinson, descending.

Isaac assisted his father up.

"Take him to an institution," Fishbein advised over the marble balustrade. He ran quickly up the stairs and they were at once outside, buffeted by winds.

The walk to the subway was tedious. The wind blew mournfully. Mendel, breathless, glanced furtively at shadows. Isaac, clutching his peanuts in his frozen fist, clung to his father's side. They entered a small park to rest for a minute on a stone bench under a leafless two-branched tree. The thick right branch was raised, the thin left one hung down. A very pale moon rose slowly. So did a stranger as they approached the bench.

"Gut yuntif,"[4] he said hoarsely.

Mendel, drained of blood, waved his wasted arms. Isaac yowled sickly. Then a bell chimed and it was only ten. Mendel let out a piercing anguished cry as the bearded stranger disappeared into the bushes. A policeman came running, and though he beat the bushes with his nightstick, could turn up nothing. Mendel and Isaac hurried out of the little park. When Mendel glanced back the dead tree had its thin arm raised, the thick one down. He moaned.

They boarded a trolley, stopping at the home of a former friend, but he had died years ago. On the same block they went into a cafeteria and

4. *Gut yuntif* (gùt yùn′tif), "Good holiday." [*Yiddish*]

ordered two fried eggs for Isaac. The tables were crowded except where a heavyset man sat eating soup with kasha.[5] After one look at him they left in haste, although Isaac wept.

Mendel had another address on a slip of paper but the house was too far away, in Queens, so they stood in a doorway shivering.

What can I do, he frantically thought, in one short hour?

He remembered the furniture in the house. It was junk but might bring a few dollars. "Come, Isaac." They went once more to the pawnbroker's to talk to him, but the shop was dark and an iron gate—rings and gold watches glinting through it—was drawn tight across his place of business.

They huddled behind a telephone pole, both freezing. Isaac whimpered.

"See the big moon, Isaac. The whole sky is white."

He pointed but Isaac wouldn't look.

Mendel dreamed for a minute of the sky lit up, long sheets of light in all directions. Under the sky, in California, sat Uncle Leo drinking tea with lemon. Mendel felt warm but woke up cold.

Across the street stood an ancient brick synagogue.

He pounded on the huge door but no one appeared. He waited till he had breath and desperately knocked again. At last there were footsteps within, and the synagogue door creaked open on its massive brass hinges.

A darkly dressed sexton, holding a dripping candle, glared at them.

"Who knocks this time of night with so much noise on the synagogue door?"

Mendel told the sexton his troubles. "Please, I would like to speak to the rabbi."

"The rabbi is an old man. He sleeps now. His wife won't let you see him. Go home and come back tomorrow."

"To tomorrow I said goodbye already. I am a dying man."

Though the sexton seemed doubtful he pointed to an old wooden house next door. "In there he lives." He disappeared into the synagogue with his lit candle casting shadows around him.

Mendel, with Isaac clutching his sleeve, went up the wooden steps and rang the bell. After five minutes a big-faced, gray-haired bulky woman came out on the porch with a torn robe thrown over her nightdress. She emphatically said the rabbi was sleeping and could not be waked.

But as she was insisting, the rabbi himself tottered to the door. He listened a minute and said, "Who wants to see me let them come in."

They entered a cluttered room. The rabbi was an old skinny man with bent shoulders and a wisp of white beard. He wore a flannel nightgown and black skullcap; his feet were bare.

5. *kasha* (kä′shə), a mush made from various grains.

"Vey is mir,"[6] his wife muttered. "Put on shoes or tomorrow comes sure pneumonia." She was a woman with a big belly, years younger than her husband. Staring at Isaac, she turned away.

Mendel apologetically related his errand. "All I need more is thirty-five dollars."

"Thirty-five?" said the rabbi's wife. "Why not thirty-five thousand? Who has so much money? My husband is a poor rabbi. The doctors take away every penny."

"Dear friend," said the rabbi, "if I had I would give you."

"I got already seventy," Mendel said, heavy-hearted. "All I need more is thirty-five."

"God will give you," said the rabbi.

"In the grave," said Mendel. "I need tonight. Come, Isaac."

"Wait," called the rabbi.

He hurried inside, came out with a fur-lined caftan, and handed it to Mendel.

"Yascha," shrieked his wife, "not your new coat!"

"I got my old one. Who needs two coats for one body?"

"Yascha, I am screaming—"

"Who can go among poor people, tell me, in a new coat?"

"Yascha," she cried, "What can this man do with your coat? He needs tonight the money. The pawnbrokers are asleep."

"So let him wake them up."

"No." She grabbed the coat from Mendel.

He held on to a sleeve, wrestling her for the coat. Her I know, Mendel thought. "Shylock,"[7] he muttered. Her eyes glittered.

The rabbi groaned and tottered dizzily. His wife cried out as Mendel yanked the coat from her hands.

"Run," cried the rabbi.

"Run, Isaac."

They ran out of the house and down the steps.

"Stop, you thief," called the rabbi's wife.

The rabbi pressed both hands to his temples and fell to the floor.

"Help!" his wife wept. "Heart attack! Help!"

But Mendel and Isaac ran through the streets with the rabbi's new fur-lined caftan. After them noiselessly ran Ginzburg.

It was very late when Mendel bought the train ticket in the only booth open.

There was no time to stop for a sandwich so Isaac ate his peanuts and they hurried to the train in the vast deserted station.

"So in the morning," Mendel gasped as they ran, "there comes a man that he sells sandwiches and coffee. Eat but get change. When reaches California the train, will be waiting for you on the station

6. *Vey is mir* (vā is mir), "Woe is me!" [*Yiddish*] 7. *Shylock* (shī′lok), a vengeful moneylender in Shakespeare's play *The Merchant of Venice.*

Uncle Leo. If you don't recognize him he will recognize you. Tell him I send best regards."

But when they arrived at the gate to the platform it was shut, the light out.

Mendel, groaning, beat on the gate with his fists.

"Too late," said the uniformed ticket collector, a bulky, bearded man with hairy nostrils and a fishy smell.

He pointed to the station clock. "Already past twelve."

"But I see standing there still the train," Mendel said, hopping in his grief.

"It just left—in one more minute."

"A minute is enough. Just open the gate."

"Too late I told you."

Mendel socked his bony chest with both hands. "With my whole heart I beg you this little favor."

"Favors you had enough already. For you the train is gone. You shoulda been dead already at midnight. I told you that yesterday. This is the best I can do."

"Ginzburg!" Mendel shrank from him.

"Who else?" The voice was metallic, eyes glittered, the expression amused.

"For myself," the old man begged, "I don't ask a thing. But what will happen to my boy?"

Ginzburg shrugged slightly. "What will happen happens. This isn't my responsibility. I got enough to think about without worrying about somebody on one cylinder."

"What then is your responsibility?"

"To create conditions. To make happen what happens. I ain't in the anthropomorphic business."

"Whatever business you in, where is your pity?"

"This ain't my commodity. The law is the law."

"Which law is this?"

"The cosmic universal law, goddamit, the one I got to follow myself."

"What kind of a law is it?" cried Mendel. "For God's sake, don't you understand what I went through in my life with this poor boy? Look at him. For thirty-nine years, since the day he was born, I wait for him to grow up, but he don't. Do you understand what this means in a father's heart? Why don't you let him go to his uncle?" His voice had risen and he was shouting.

Isaac mewled loudly.

"Better calm down or you'll hurt somebody's feelings," Ginzburg said with a wink toward Isaac.

"All my life," Mendel cried, his body trembling, "what did I have? I was poor. I suffered from my health. When I worked I worked too hard.

When I didn't work was worse. My wife died a young woman. But I didn't ask from anybody nothing. Now I ask a small favor. Be so kind, Mr. Ginzburg."

The ticket collector was picking his teeth with a match stick.

"You ain't the only one, my friend, some got it worse than you. That's how it goes in this country."

"You dog you." Mendel lunged at Ginzburg's throat and began to choke. "You bastard, don't you understand what it means human?"

They struggled nose to nose, Ginzburg, though his astonished eyes bulged, began to laugh. "You pipsqueak nothing. I'll freeze you to pieces."

His eyes lit in rage and Mendel felt an unbearable cold like an icy dagger invading his body, all of his parts shriveling.

Now I die without helping Isaac.

A crowd gathered. Isaac yelped in fright.

Clinging to Ginzburg in his last agony, Mendel saw reflected in the ticket collector's eyes the depth of his terror. But he saw that Ginzburg, staring at himself in Mendel's eyes, saw mirrored in them the extent of his own awful wrath. He beheld a shimmering, starry, blinding light that produced darkness.

Ginzburg looked astounded. "Who me?"

His grip on the squirming old man slowly loosened, and Mendel, his heart barely beating, slumped to the ground.

"Go." Ginzburg muttered, "take him to the train."

"Let pass," he commanded a guard.

The crowd parted. Isaac helped his father up and they tottered down the steps to the platform where the train waited, lit and ready to go.

Mendel found Isaac a coach seat and hastily embraced him. "Help Uncle Leo, Isaakil. Also remember your father and mother."

"Be nice to him," he said to the conductor. "Show him where everything is."

He waited on the platform until the train began slowly to move. Isaac sat at the edge of his seat, his face strained in the direction of his journey. When the train was gone, Mendel ascended the stairs to see what had become of Ginzburg.

THE
APOTHEOSIS[1]
OF KI

Miriam Allen DeFord

KI BECAME A MIGHTY MEDICINE MAN because he encountered a god and the god entered into him.

He was hunting alone; there were no longer enough young strong men in the tribe to hunt in groups. Every year the snow came farther south. Where his father had killed horses and bison still, there roamed the woolly mammoth and the reindeer. Of animals that one man can attack, few were left, and often the people were hard put to it to subsist on the grubs and eggs, the roots and berries and nuts, gathered by the women in the summer and put by. For more and more of the year, there was no living except in the caves, and a fire had to be kept going constantly outside, for comfort as well as for protection.

Ki found himself now crossing a wide plain he knew well. Once it had been a prized and precious hunting ground; now he had searched for hours and found no living creature but himself. His heart was low within him, and in despair he glanced upward into the sky for help.

And then suddenly there was a noise like innumerable thunder-bolts, and a flash like innumerable lightning-darts, so that he threw himself on the ground to hide his eyes. In the very midst of the plain something shaped like a giant egg had crashed to earth and burst into flames.

Dazed, Ki stood up and gaped at it. A crack in it opened and . . . somebody? something? crawled out and ran toward him, away from the blaze.

It was like a human being in shape, but vastly tall—taller even than the Terrible Men from the Sunrise before whom Ki's own people fled in fear. Instead of the fur or hide garments which men wear, he (it was male from its contours) was clad in some unknown material that was smooth and shiny, and around his head, resting on his shoulders, was a

1. *Apotheosis* (ə poth/ē ō/sis, ap/ə thē/ə sis), the raising of a human being to the rank of a god.

globular object that threw back glints from the winter sun, as if it were a giant misformed icicle. Then the being reached up and drew this from him, and his face was no human face, not even the weird unholy face of the Terrible Men. There were no ridges at all above the brow, but only a high pale dome; the chin, instead of retreating as does a man's, thrust outward; and the eyes, Ki saw, awed, were the color of river water.

Then Ki knew it was a god—though whether Akku of the Sky or Ber the Fire God or Hegag the God of Storms it was not given to mortal man to guess. Ki sank trembling to his knees, and the god walked nearer to him, and spoke. His voice was like the voice of wind in the trees, and Ki understood not a word he said. But Ki spoke also, if in no answer.

"O great god," he cried, "you have come! You have come as our fathers foretold to us, as our shaman[2] promised us before he died and left us with no medicine man to mediate for us. You have come to help the tribe of Ki-ya, lest the young men die off beneath the cold, and the women and children starve in the caves, and the mighty and glorious people cease to be."

But the god stood and shook his strange head, and Ki understood then that the gods do not speak the language of men, any more than men can speak the language of the gods.

Yet still it seemed to him, as he knelt trembling in his worn furs that had been his father's and his father's father's, that in some manner beyond speech the god comprehended what he had said. For he raised an arm and pointed above him.

And Ki went on speaking to the god in his own tongue, which was the only tongue he knew.

"I see now that you are Akku of the Sky," he said. "Or if not Akku himself, then one from among his sons. I hear and obey, great god. Tell me now how we shall find sufficient food, so that we may live and grow strong again as once we were."

And as if he had known the meaning of the word *food*, the god opened his own mouth and pointed to it with his finger, and then pointed to his belly, where men feel hunger.

But gods do not eat and do not hunger, so Ki understood that it was he and his tribe whose need to eat was known to the god.

"True, but how?" Ki persisted. And the god gestured further. He swayed on his long legs like a man weak from fasting, and closed his eyes, and staggered as if he would fall.

And all the while the huge egg which had fallen from the sky and from which the god had emerged continued to blaze and crackle as if something more than wood fed it, though it is well known that only wood can burn.

---

2. *shaman* (shä′mən), a priest or holy man, with various magical powers.

"I am but a poor weak mortal," Ki pleaded desperately, "and the thoughts of the gods are too far beyond my thoughts. If it be your will, give me to understand how it is that our help is to come from you, and what I must do to carry out your commands."

Then with a stab of anguish it came to him that the god had meant by his pantomime that only by sacrifice could the tribe be saved, and that he desired Ki to lie down in the snow and die, as the god had feigned a man's doing.

Ki was a man full-grown; sixteen times the winter had come since he was a bawling infant at his mother's breast. But he was young still, and the juice and protest of youth were in him. Through his mind flashed thronging memories—memories of a child at play with his brothers, memories of the good years when the tribe had been strong and had feasted, memories of women he had had and of women he had wanted.

When men die, they sleep, the old medicine man had told them—all his class of boys gathered in the forest to be readied for their initiation. This was one of the mysteries that women and children must never hear. They sleep, and we lay them under the earth on a bed of branches, or in a dark inner corner of a cave, with flint flakes for their pillow. And around them we lay their weapons and tools, and the bones of the animals we have burnt and eaten in their honor so that when at last they awaken—and only the gods can know when that will be—they may have near at hand weapons to defend themselves, and the reminders of sacrifice with which to uphold their dignity.

And Ki reflected that now the tribe had so fallen away that even the mightiest warriors and hunters died, and there were no animals to sacrifice to them. More still: when children died, or old women— great-grandmothers who had seen the changes of forty years or more—and even old men who left no descendants to fight for them, instead of being sacrificed to, they themselves became perforce their own sacrifice; and the tribe stilled its hunger by feeding on its own, so that only the bones were left to bury—and those blackened by fire and split to obtain the marrow and smeared with red earth so that when the dead awakened they might think the blood still ran through them. Worse: these two years past, only those who had been killed by beasts or by the Terrible Men from the Sunrise (for they no longer had warriors enough to raid other tribes of their own kind) still were taboo[3] and must be buried as they fell.

That taboo had been ordained before the old medicine man felt himself close to death by some poison or ill-thinking—as death always comes that is not by direct killing. Ki remembered how one night around the fire the shaman had said, "This is the law which the people must obey even if they perish. For if even those killed by beasts or men were not taboo, then men would slay their own fellowmen of the tribe,

3. *taboo* (tə büʹ), forbidden by custom or tradition.

only to feed on them." So he saw to it, when some evil-wisher from some other tribe had put weakness into his own body, that a young man of the tribe should strike him with his cudgel until he fell. It was done in full assembly before them all, that men might know it was by the shaman's own will, and the slayer be innocent.

It was Ki himself who had been chosen for that rite. It was the very cudgel he carried now, in sight of the god, with which he had done the deed.

All these things Ki remembered, and his heart did not wish to die. Least of all to die here, alone before the god. Who then of all the people would know of his sacrifice? Who would ever come to bury his body, and to know that it was worthy of honor?

But man is as nothing before the will of the gods, who rule breath and light and warmth and all that men must have, and rule also the wicked complaints and rebellions of the hearts of men.

So he rose and stood before the god and said, "If this be your will, I am ready. Slay me that the tribe may grow strong again."

But the god did not move to strike him. He had indeed in his hand, as Ki saw now, something, of some unknown divine shape and nature, too small for a cudgel and too large for a hand-ax, that might serve him as a weapon. But he did not raise it; instead he cast it from him, and let it lie where it fell in the snow, and he came nearer to Ki and held out his empty hands; and then once more he pointed to his mouth and to his belly. And he spoke again, in his tongue that no man could understand; and in his tone, had he been a man and not a god, was what would have seemed a note of pleading.

And Ki trembled, trying beyond his power of thought to comprehend.

And the god pointed again upward to the sky, and then to himself, and then, turning, to the sunrise and the sunset, and to the north and last to the south. And his voice was a question, asked with resignation but with the shadow of hope.

And so at last Ki understood.

With his cudgel he struck the god full on the head, and the god fell. And Ki struck him again and again until he lay still and his blood was on the snow.

Then he cast the dead god on the flames that still rose from the burning egg, and when the holy flesh was roasted he drew it forth, and when it was cool he hung it by a thong across his shoulders.

But first he ate the heart.

Before the sun was low in the sky, he reached the cave, and he threw his burden down before him as they came crowding out to see.

"Here is food," he said. "It is the body of a god, of a son of Akku of the Sky, who died that the people might live.

"And I have eaten his heart, and the god has entered into me and given me wisdom. Now I shall be your medicine man, and I shall guide you and teach you, and while you obey me I shall lead you to good hunting grounds, so that the people may wax fat again, and be many, as they once were, and be strong. And with tomorrow's sun, with the vigor that this meat will give us, we shall turn southward, for that is the last direction in which the god pointed.

"All this the god told me without words, before he commanded me to strike him dead. And if any doubt me, let him go to the plain beyond the dark forest, and he will find there what fire has left of a huge and monstrous egg, in which the god rode down from the sky, and appeared before me, Ki, to ransom and redeem the tribe of Ki-ya."

And two young men who did not believe went as he commanded, and found that it was so. And they ate of the sacrifice, and at the next dawn they traveled southward.

Thus it was that Ki became a mighty medicine man. The god had entered into him, and he was as a god. And far to the south, where the snow and ice had not yet come, the tribe found good hunting, so that they grew strong again, and many children were born and did not die, and the tribe of Ki-ya raided and slew their enemies of many other tribes, and so became great once more upon the earth.

That all this is true, is certain. For it was not until Ki had grown weak and very old—nearly fifty years still alive in the world—and his son's son, who envied him his wealth of flint and furs and women and meat and power, had cleft open his head with a stone ax and slain him, that the tribe of Ki-ya was overwhelmed and destroyed by a wandering horde of the Terrible Men from the Sunrise.

A SIBERIAN
SHEPHERD'S REPORT
OF THE ATOM BOMB

Dino Buzzati[1]

AMONG US SHEPHERDS of the tribe there is a very old legend that says when Noah gathered all the animals of creation in his ark, the animals from the mountains and from the valleys made a truce among themselves and with man, recognizing Noah as their master for the time they were to remain in the ark—all, that is, except Moma, the huge tigress that snarled when Noah approached her and the only animal Noah feared. That was why the tigress found no room in the ark and why the flood caught her in her cave. But she was extremely strong. She remained afloat by sheer strength, swimming for forty days and forty nights and more until the waters subsided, the trees rose out of the sea and the earth reappeared. The tigress Moma was then so tired she fell asleep. She is still asleep in the depths of the great forests of Amga, Ghoi, Tepotorgo, and Urakancha.

The legend also says that when the great tigress wakes up, all the other animals will flee from the forest, for man there will be a good hunting season, and Moma will reign in the great forests until the god Beyal descends from the sky to devour her.

Who among us believes this legend? Since our solitude is so great, so many stories are told around campfires and all of us are accustomed to believing and not believing. Rare and most uncertain is the news that comes to us from distant lands, for our wandering life is entrusted to the will of heaven. What, for example, do we shepherds of the steppe know of the measureless realm that stretches toward the setting sun? Old laws forbid us to go beyond the boundary line, and even if we were to cross it, we should have to travel endless distances through great dangers before reaching the nearest inhabited regions. It is beyond the boundary line that lie the forests of Amga, Ghoi, Tepotorgo, and Urakancha, where the tigress Moma fell asleep at the end of the flood.

1. *Buzzati,* (büz zä′tē).

Sometimes troops of armed horsemen gallop by along the boundary line. Once in a while they stop, look toward us, make measurements, and drive red poles with strange signs into the ground. After a few days the wind of the steppe uproots the poles and carries them God knows where. Sometimes even airplanes, those strange flying machines, fly over us. Nothing else happens.

But what is the use telling all this if not to explain our uneasiness? Recently strange and dreadful things have happened. No serious harm has come to us, but we feel fearful forebodings. We noticed the first unusual happening last Spring. The soldiers galloped by more frequently and they drove heavier poles, which the wind would not be able to uproot, into the ground. The poles are still there.

In the middle of June, two large snakes were killed near our camp. Creatures like these had never been seen before. The following day hundreds were seen. They did not bother us or our flocks—they were all moving toward the East. They were of different kinds and of every size. This strange happening astonished us.

Then we noticed that the snakes were not alone. Rats, moles, skunks, worms, and numberless kinds of insects began to cross the plain, all moving in the same direction. They were strangely mixed together, but they showed no hostility toward each other, even though they belonged to species that are ordinarily enemies.

We saw even rabbits, wild goats, and quite a number of small, four-footed creatures of whose very existence we had not known. Some of them were really very beautiful, with fur that is highly prized. Then came the birds. They, too, were fleeing toward the East, abandoning their old homeland. But what were they running away from? What danger hung over them? Instinct does not easily deceive animals. Even we men were uneasy. Yet what good reason did we have to abandon the region which this year was so good for pasture? No matter how much we wondered, we could not imagine a plausible explanation for this great emigration. An earthquake? How could birds fear an earthquake? A plague? What disease could strike so many different species at the same time, the beetle as well as the marmot, the serpent as well as the wildcat? A fire? No smoke could be seen on the horizon nor did the wind smell of smoke. Someone among us jokingly mentioned the old legend of Moma the tigress. I did not like that joke at all.

Finally, it seemed that the whole forest on the other side of the boundary was empty. The last to come through were the wood pigeons and swarming columns of ants that continued for miles and miles. Some stragglers followed, a few at a time. Then the flow stopped completely. The echo of our guns ceased (these had been days of triumph for the hunters), and a sepulchral silence settled over the Siberian steppe. At night, we would foolishly strain our ears. Could it be that we expected the roar of Moma the tigress?

One day this great uneasiness even took hold of our flocks. It was clear that the goats, sheep, and rams were becoming excited, that they, too, were trying to escape to the East. We had to chase some of our fleeing livestock for a long time on horseback. It was necessary to build heavy enclosures.

Many of us were afraid. For no good reason, many wanted to move camp to the East. There were bitter arguments. We finally agreed to take the advice of the elders. They met and decided—we would depart with the next dawn.

It was a hot July evening. The sun had just set and the refreshing breath of night was descending when the dogs suddenly began to bark. Just after sunset, from the direction of the forest and at a great distance, an extraordinary light was seen. It seemed as if the sun had turned back, as if its burning face had become swollen on the rim of the horizon. The mass wavered a few moments, then burst, shooting forth a whirl of frightful flames—red, white, violet, green, yellow. The sun had blown up!

How long did it last? Instinctively I thought it was the end of the world. But it was not. When it was dark again, I raised my dazzled eyes to the zenith. No, the stars were still there.

Then the thunder came. And with the thunder—so frightful a noise was never heard—came the wind, a hot, suffocating wind that took our breath away and razed everything to the ground. I thought I would not be able to stand it, but the wind, too, passed on.

When we recovered our senses, we again kindled the fires the burning wind had blown out, and set forth in search of our livestock, which were fleeing crazily in every direction because the enclosure had been broken to pieces. At that moment, the necessity of the chase prevailed over every other fear. But suddenly we stopped and stood motionless—even the goats, the sheep, the old people. We were all paralyzed together.

Above the bellowing and bleating, above our excited shouts, another voice was heard. No, it was not so powerful as the thunder of a little while before. Yet in a way it was even worse. Once, twice, three times, mournful and cold, it filled the night and froze our hearts. It was the roar of the tigress.

The fires, the fires! Leaving the flock to its fate, we rushed to gather twigs and weeds to increase the number of our fires. Soon there was an almost unbroken chain of flames to protect us. At last the great tigress Moma had awakened and was coming toward us.

At that very moment a long, deep roar rose on the other side of the fires. In the darkness we could see something move. Suddenly it appeared, illuminated by the red shadows. It was she, Moma. She was not an ordinary tiger. She was a monster of gigantic proportions.

Not one of us fired. We saw that the huge beast hardly moved any longer—she was about to die. Her eyes had turned to shapeless lumps of black pulp. Her hide was scorched. On her right side was an open gash as deep as a cave, from which blood flowed.

Moma the tigress, right in front of our eyes, hunched her back to the height of two horses one standing on top of the other and let out a hellish shriek. I felt that I was done for. I fired my rifle without even aiming. The others did the same.

Her huge body fell with a crash. Was she dead? We continued to fire shot after shot, senselessly. The tigress no longer moved.

These are the strange facts referred to at the beginning of this report. The legendary tigress really existed—and even though we immediately burned her carcass because of its horrible stench, the immense skeleton has remained right there on the spot and anyone can come and measure it. But who awakened her? Who took away her life and her promised reign? What was the terrifying explosion that night? The sun had nothing to do with it—in a few hours it was born again at just the right time and in its usual place. What had happened? Could some infernal power have taken over the forests? And if its flames devoured mighty Moma, could it not capriciously reduce us to ashes too? How then can we live calmly? No one sleeps at night and in the morning we wake up tired.

DISCUSSION QUESTIONS

SOME OLD STORIES

Garfield and Blishen: THE MAKING OF MEN *(page 11)*

1. *(a)* Why does Prometheus try to create people? *(b)* How does he go about it? *(c)* What do you learn about Prometheus from this action?
2. *(a)* How does Prometheus plan to keep Zeus from destroying his people? *(b)* What goes wrong with his plan? *(c)* How does he avoid Zeus's command?
3. *(a)* Who are the Fates? *(b)* Why is Hermes puzzled when the wheel begins to turn?
4. *(a)* How does Pandora differ from ordinary human beings? *(b)* Why does Prometheus curse Zeus when he sees her? *(c)* What happens when Pandora opens the forbidden jar?
5. Prometheus sacrifices himself to save his children. *(a)* In what ways does he offend Zeus? *(b)* What is his punishment?
6. Explain how this tale accounts for each of the following: *(a)* the physical appearance of the human race; *(b)* the origin of death; *(c)* the necessity for religious rituals; *(d)* the contradictory impulses that hold people from perfection; *(e)* the origin of disease, madness, and vice; *(f)* hope.
7. Clearly "The Making of Men" is one account of creation, of how things came to be. There are many others. You will find several in Unit II, "In the Beginning."

Dorsey: COYOTE AND THE ORIGIN OF DEATH *(page 30)*

1. This story opens with a problem. What is it? How do the people try to solve the problem?
2. *(a)* How does coyote "solve" the problem? *(b)* What are the reasons he chooses this solution? *(c)* What punishment does he then suffer?
3. Coyote is a peculiar kind of mythic character known as a *trickster.* Tricksters use cleverness and deceit to achieve their ends, pitting their wits against the will of authority. Often the trickster is partially responsible for making the world the way it is. *(a)* How does coyote change the world? *(b)* What power does he oppose?
4. You will find a collection of trickster stories in Unit III, "Mischief and Invention."

Green: THOR'S VISIT TO UTGARD *(page 32)*

1. Why do Thor and Loki go to Jotunheim, the land of the giants?
2. On the second night of their journey Thor, Loki, and Thor's squire Thialfi sleep in what seems to be a large, abandoned hall. What does this hall tell us eventually about the size of giants?

3. As the Aesir, unhappy about losing their contests with the giants, are about to leave Jotunheim, Utgardhaloki says: "Know then that I have cheated you with false seemings and illusions of the eye." With this in mind explain the following: *(a)* the effect of Thor's three blows with Miolnir on the head of Skrymir; *(b)* Loki's contest with Logi; *(c)* Thialfi's race against Hugi; *(d)* Thor's attempt to empty the drinking horn; *(e)* Thor's struggle to lift the cat; *(f)* Thor's wrestling with old Elli.

4. Consider Thor's personality. *(a)* How does he respond to challenges? to failure? to deception and trickery? In general, what sort of god is he? *(b)* What kind of person might choose Thor as a model and patron?

5. "Thor's Visit to Utgard" describes the testing of a hero. You will find other examples of this kind of tale in Unit IV, "Trials and Combats."

Bruce: URASHIMA TARO *(page 42)*

1. *(a)* Why does Urashima rescue the tortoise? *(b)* What would have happened to him if he had treated the tortoise differently?

2. *(a)* To what alien world does Urashima journey? *(b)* What barriers prevent ordinary people from reaching this world?

3. *(a)* In what ways does the Otherworld differ from our world? *(b)* In what ways is it the same?

4. What special reward does Urashima win in the Otherworld?

5. Why does he want to return to earth?

6. Once he has reached his village again, what additional difference between the Otherworld and Earth does Urashima discover?

7. *(a)* At the end of this story Urashima makes a final mistake. What kind of mistake is it? *(b)* What other mythic character in this unit makes the same mistake? *(c)* What lesson does the fate of each imply?

8. A journey to a strange world or to the kingdom of death is a favorite subject of myth. You will find further examples in Unit V, "Visions and the Other World."

Tennyson: MORTE D'ARTHUR *(page 49)*

1. *(a)* As the poem opens, how many men does Arthur have left? *(b)* At what point in the history of his kingdom do we encounter him? *(c)* At what point in Arthur's own life do we see him? *(d)* Why is this parallel significant?

2. *(a)* What season of the year is it as the poem begins? *(b)* Where is Arthur resting? *(c)* In what ways are these details appropriate for the action of the poem?

3. *(a)* When and how did Arthur first receive his sword Excalibur? *(b)* Why does he now order Bedivere to cast it away?

4. *(a)* What kind of test must Bedivere face? *(b)* How does he respond to that test?

5. *(a)* How does Arthur leave the world? *(b)* Where does he think he might be going?

6. What will life be like for Bedivere once Arthur has gone?

7. A vision of "The End of Things" is common in mythology. You will find other tales of the end of all things in Unit VI.

IN THE BEGINNING

Humphries: *from* THE METAMORPHOSES OF OVID *(page 59)*

1. *(a)* According to Ovid, what were things like in the beginning? *(b)* By what process was the universe formed? *(c)* What parts of Ovid's account of creation might a modern scientist accept? *(d)* What question does Ovid leave unanswered?

2. What are the four stages of early history, according to Ovid? Characterize each.

3. It is clear that Ovid admires the earliest age the most. Considering the things he admires about this legendary age, decide the poet's probable reaction to each of the following: *(a)* travel; *(b)* ownership of property; *(c)* law and the legal process; *(d)* hard work; *(e)* a standing army; *(f)* a system of coinage.

4. During the chaotic Age of Iron a new race of men came into being. *(a)* How was this race created? *(b)* In what way is Lycaon typical of this new breed? *(c)* How does Jove punish him? *(d)* Why is this an appropriate punishment?

5. *(a)* Why does Jove decide to destroy the race of men? *(b)* Why do the other gods protest his decision? *(c)* What makes Jove decide to destroy the world by water rather than by fire?

6. What kind of virtues do Deucalion and Pyrrha practice that make them acceptable to the gods?

7. *(a)* Why does Pyrrha refuse to enact, literally, the instructions of the oracle? *(b)* What does the oracle really mean? *(c)* What kind of new race does Jove create through the agency of Deucalion and Pyrrha?

Gaster: THE WAR OF THE GODS *(page 72)*

1. *(a)* How do Apsu and Tiamat, the oldest gods, differ in their reactions toward the younger gods? *(b)* In your opinion, is the reaction of Apsu or Tiamat toward the younger gods closer to that of parents toward their children? *(c)* What happens to Apsu?

2. *(a)* Who is Marduk? *(b)* Why do the gods, led by Tiamat, turn against him? *(c)* What preparations does Tiamat make for the battle? *(d)* What demand does Marduk make before he will go into battle against Tiamat? *(e)* What weapons does Marduk use in winning the battle?

3. How does Marduk make the world?

4. According to Babylonian myth, why was the human race created? What is the most important duty of every creature?

5. *(a)* From what material did Marduk fashion the first people? *(b)* What characteristics would you expect from people made from this material?

6. Like a human character, Marduk has certain personality traits. What kind of god/person is he? For instance, is he a god of mercy and humility? Describe the nature of the god and consider whether or not you admire him.

Waters: *from* BOOK OF THE HOPI *(page 81)*

1. In paragraph 3 of the creation myth of the Hopi we read: "Then he, the infinite, conceived the finite." *(a)* Who is referred to as "the infinite"? *(b)* Before the process of creation began, what existed? *(c)* Who is Sótuknang and what is his function?

2. *(a)* Why does Sótuknang create Spider Woman? *(b)* Who are the twins and what are their duties in completing and maintaining the world?

3. *(a)* How did it happen that the first people were of different colors? *(b)* What part does Sótuknang play in perfecting them? *(c)* What is the one thing he asks of them?

4. What kinds of mischief do Lavaíhoya the Talker and Káto'ya the Snake bring into the new world?

5. *(a)* How does Sótuknang first destroy the world? *(b)* What characterizes the people he saves for the second world? *(c)* How are they protected while the world is destroyed and recreated?

6. *(a)* How does Tokpa, the Second World, differ from the First World? *(b)* What causes dissension in this world? *(c)* How is the Second World destroyed?

7. *(a)* What goes wrong in Kuskurza, the Third World? *(b)* What peculiar weapon do the people of this world develop? *(c)* How is this world destroyed?

8. *(a)* By what device are the people destined for Túwaqachi, the Fourth World, saved? *(b)* Why does Spider Woman forbid them to remain on the large island rich with food?

9. *(a)* How do the people find their Place of Emergence into the Fourth World? *(b)* What virtue does this part of their story teach the reader?

10. *(a)* What is the name and the number of the present world? *(b)* Why may this selection from *Book of the Hopi* be considered an unfinished tale?

Jeffers: THE GREAT EXPLOSION *(page 96)*

1. *(a)* According to this poem how will the universe end? *(b)* What resemblance do you find between the end of the world as Jeffers describes it and the beginning?

2. *(a)* One particular image, used to describe the universe, recurs at several points in the poem. What is it? *(b)* What effect does use of this image have on the way you feel about this history of the universe?

3. *(a)* According to the poet, what are the qualities of God? *(b)* Why does he think that the nature of God is as he describes it? *(c)* Do you agree with the poet? Explain.

Eiseley: HOW FLOWERS CHANGED THE WORLD *(page 98)*

1. *(a)* Before you began to read this essay, could you take its title seriously? *(b)* Why do you think the author chose a title of this kind? *(c)* What does he include in the term *flowers?*

2. What essential weakness prevented the dinosaurs from developing further than they did?

3. Why, according to Eiseley, was the emergence of birds and mammals necessarily linked to the "soundless, violent explosion" of flowering plants?

4. *(a)* How were the angiosperm's seeds able to travel in ways that the seeds of older plant varieties could not? *(b)* In addition to the ability to travel, what other valuable feature did these seeds have? *(c)* How did these seeds change the face of the earth?

5. How did the new grasses lead to the development of the herbivores like bisons and horses and of carnivores like the saber-toothed tiger?

6. *(a)* What is Eiseley's purpose in this essay? *(b)* How does the essay differ from the other accounts of the beginning of things that you have read in this unit?

7. By the end of the essay has Eiseley convinced you that his title is not an exaggeration? Explain.

Clarke: ENCOUNTER AT DAWN *(page 107)*

1. *(a)* Were you surprised by the last sentence in this story? Explain why or why not. *(b)* Why do you think Arthur C. Clarke saved this bit of information until the very end of his story?

2. What is the meaning of the word *dawn* as it is used in the title?

3. How does Bertrond win Yaan's confidence?

4. Why does Yaan decide that the visitors are gods?

IN RETROSPECT *(pages 58-115)*

1. "The War of the Gods" is a Babylonian creation myth; the selection from the *Metamorphoses* is a Roman telling of a myth that contains many Greek elements; *Book of the Hopi* is American Indian. Compare these three myths, paying particular attention to the following points: *(a)* Which myth or myths imagine a beginning in which nothing exists except a creator? *(b)* Which myth or myths describe the world as being destroyed one or more times as men disappoint the gods? By what means is this destruction brought about? *(c)* Which myth or myths tell of the creation of successive races of men?

2. Compare the Greek myth "The Making of Men" (page 11) with the myths mentioned above.

3. The way a god makes the world suggests a great deal about the nature of that god. What does his act of creation tell us about Marduk? about Taiowa? the god in Jeffers's "The Great Explosion"?

4. What essential difference is there between the old creation myths and Eiseley's "How Flowers Changed the World" in accounting for the development of created things?

5. Arthur Clarke's "Encounter at Dawn" is science fiction. Why do you think it has been included in a unit entitled "In the Beginning"?

6. *(a)* For what reasons, according to these creation accounts, were people created? *(b)* Are the people in these myths characteristically good and obedient, or the reverse? Which stories explain the existence of evil within the human race? How do they account for it? *(c)* How do the divine powers respond to evil?

7. In what ways does our explanation for the creation of our world influence our attitudes and our conduct in everyday life? How do you think the world was made? What does this imply about your relationship to the power that created it?

MISCHIEF AND INVENTION

Gleason: ESHU *(page 117)*

1. Take a second look at the opening dialogue between the two neighbors when they are still friends. Does it sound normal and natural to you? Do you think such an "ideal" friendship could exist?

2. What introduces dissension into their relationship? Does their quarrel sound more real to your ears than their friendship did? Why?

3. *(a)* Who is Eshu? *(b)* Do you consider him a trickster? (See the article on page 160.)

4. How does the chief respond to Eshu's action?

Appiah: HOW KWAKU ANANSE WON A KINGDOM WITH A GRAIN OF CORN *(page 120)*

1. What feelings does Nyame the Sky God have for his creatures? What will he do to anyone who tries to prove himself the wisest, but fails? How do the various chiefs and kings react when Ananse claims to be God's messenger? From all this evidence, how would you characterize Nyame?

2. *(a)* What wrongs does Ananse do in order to fulfill Nyame's challenge? *(b)* Considering the character of Nyame, do you object to what Ananse does? Why or why not?

3. *(a)* What skills does Ananse rely upon to succeed? Does he ever doubt he will win? Is he ever frightened? *(b)* How would you characterize Ananse?

4. Do you admire Ananse? Explain your response.

Macmillan: HOW RAVEN BROUGHT FIRE TO THE INDIANS *(page 130)*

1. Raven brings light and fire into his world. *(a)* How does he obtain them? *(b)* Do his actions show that he is particularly interested in helping people? Explain your answer.

2. *(a)* Though the story tells of remarkable achievements, Raven is no typical hero. Describe his characteristics: Is he brave or cowardly, intelligent or stupid, generous or selfish, satisfied or envious, proud or humble, hardworking or lazy? In determining each characteristic, point out an element in the story to justify your description. *(b)* In what ways does Raven fit the definition of the trickster? (See the article on page 160.)

3. *(a)* Are the other people in Raven's world better morally than he? Explain. *(b)* Are any more clever? If so, who?

Alpers: MAUI-OF-A-THOUSAND-TRICKS *(page 135)*

1. *(a)* How does Maui discover "the world below"? *(b)* How does he get there? *(c)* What persons does he meet there?

2. Hina-the-Old and Tangaroa-of-the-Tattooed-Face are Maui's ancestors. *(a)* Describe how he treats each of them. *(b)* What does he get from each?

3. What means does Maui employ to get what he wants? Consider the way he obtains fire and slows the sun's progress.

4. *(a)* How does Maui change his world? *(b)* Why might he be called a creator?

5. Note the title: "Maui-of-a-Thousand-Tricks." *(a)* What is the first trick that Maui plays? *(b)* Name as many other tricks as you can. *(c)* Do Maui's tricks on the whole harm or benefit others?

Jones: LLEU AND THE FLOWERFACE *(page 144)*

1. *(a)* What are the three unhappy destinies Aranrhod swears on Lleu? *(b)* Why is each particularly cruel to a young man? *(c)* In each case what means does Gwydion use to avoid Aranrhod's curses?

2. *(a)* How does it happen that Lleu is transformed into an eagle? *(b)* How does Gwydion find him in this guise? *(c)* How does he rescue him?

3. Explain the justness of the punishments given Blodeuedd and Gronw.

Green: LOKI AND THE GIANTS *(page 154)*

1. In the first of the two episodes in this selection three Aesir try to save the boy Rogner from Skrymsli. Odin and Honir save the boy but don't solve the problem itself. In what way does Loki solve the problem?

2. In the second tale, why does Loki recommend that the Aesir give their oath to the mason? Is he interested in fair play? If not, what is his motivation?

3. *(a)* In what way does the mason's rapid progress endanger Loki? *(b)* How does he save himself?

4. Although Loki is accepted as one of the Aesir, he differs from them in various ways. *(a)* What is his origin? (See the chart on page 333 for information.) *(b)* What do the two episodes in this story show you about the way he differs from the Aesir in the way he solves problems?

Elkin: A POETICS FOR BULLIES *(page 161)*

1. Why is Push so nasty? Does acting as he does take planning, intelligence, and patience? Explain your answer.

2. *(a)* Early in the story Push says,"There *is* no magic." What, instead, does he use to control others? *(b)* What is it about John Williams that seems to prevent Push from controlling him?

3. *(a)* What does Push hope to accomplish by drawing Williams into a fight? *(b)* Does it work out as he plans?

4. At the end of the story Push discovers a new power that he calls "the real magic." What is it? Does it work on Eugene? Will it permit Push to conquer Williams?

5. At one point Push says, "Me and the devil, we do God's dirty work." *(a)* What do you think he means by this? *(b)* In what ways can Push and the devil be called tricksters?

IN RETROSPECT *(pages 116-175)*

1. To what extent do the tricksters Ananse, Raven, Maui, Loki, and Push violate conventional moral standards? Why does each turn to evil? Do you consider any of them justified? Why or why not?

2. In "A Poetics for Bullies," Push says: "There *is* no magic. If there were I would learn it. . . . *Then* I'd change things." *(a)* What tricksters enjoy this power that Push seems to lack? *(b)* What different forms does this magic take? *(c)* Do the tricksters use it to "change things"?

3. What quality does the trickster most frequently rely on in gaining his goal?

4. The actions of tricksters frequently benefit others. *(a)* Which of the tricksters in this unit do things that benefit mankind? *(b)* Are these actions performed primarily to help other people or for the benefit of the tricksters themselves? Give examples to illustrate your answer.

5. How much of the trickster do you think is in you?

6. To help their readers or listeners imagine what a trickster is like, some myths describe them as spiders, coyotes, or ravens. As a modern writer, how would you envision and describe a trickster? What would he or she look like? How would a trickster act, move, and speak?

TRIALS AND COMBATS

Kroeber: TESILYA, SUN'S DAUGHTER *(page 177)*

1. *(a)* Why do Ahta and Hotpa set off to look for wives? *(b)* What details in the story convince you that Tesilya will choose Ahta even before she states her preference? *(c)* What is Hotpa's reason for thinking that Tesilya should choose him?

2. *(a)* After Hotpa marries Jaguar's daughter, what are his feelings toward Ahta and Tesilya? *(b)* Because of these feelings, what does he do?

3. *(a)* Why must the uncle deceive Hotpa about the sex of Tesilya's child? *(b)* What characteristics of this child foretell that he will be a hero?

4. What is the significance of the bone doll, the shinny ball, and the shinny stick?

5. *(a)* What becomes the most important task in Ahta-hana's life? *(b)* How does he prepare himself for that task?

6. *(a)* As a fully grown hero, what supernatural powers does Ahta-hana possess? *(b)* Describe the final struggle with Hotpa.

7. *(a)* What is the location of this myth? *(b)* What information does the story give you about the customs, food, and dress of the people of this region?

8. Explain the various ways in which the story of Ahta, Tesilya, and their son is preserved.

9. Ahta-hana is clearly the traditional hero of this tale, but the narrator suggests that Tesilya is also a significant character. Can she be called a heroine? Why, or why not?

Jacobs: JACK THE GIANT-KILLER *(page 187)*

1. *(a)* The nature of giants varies from story to story. What are the giants like in this one? Consider their size, appearance, where they live, what they eat, and their intelligence. *(b)* Do you feel sorry for them when Jack kills them? Explain your response.

2. Jack is the hero of this legend, but a very special sort of hero. *(a)* How does his background differ from that of most heroes? *(b)* Does he, like Ahta-hana, go through a period of testing and training before his combats? *(c)* How does he conquer his ferocious enemies?

3. Rather than tell a single tale, this selection is composed of a series of similar stories. How many separate stories do you count?

Deutsch: THE TRIALS OF LEMMINKAINEN *(page 195)*

1. When Lemminkainen's mother is attempting to bring him back to life, she speaks of him as "the hero." *(a)* What does he possess or what can he do that allows him to be considered a hero? *(b)* How does he differ from what we ordinarily expect of a hero?

2. *(a)* What trials does Lemminkainen endure in trying to win Louhi's daughter? *(b)* What forgotten incident leads to his death?

3. *(a)* How does Lemminkainen's mother save him from the river of death? *(b)* What heroic virtues did she have to possess to succeed in this task? *(c)* Do you think she might be considered a greater hero than Lemminkainen? Explain.

Bruce: LONG, BROAD, AND QUICK-EYE *(page 205)*

1. How does the Prince discover the existence of the Princess in the iron castle?

2. *(a)* Where does the Prince meet his servants? *(b)* What indications do you have that the place is magical?

3. Contrast the three trials. Are they equally difficult or progressively more so? Explain your answer.

4. To whom should credit be given for rescuing the Princess?

5. Characterize the Prince. Do you like or dislike him? Explain.

Huber: JOE MAGARAC, MAN OF STEEL *(page 212)*

1. *(a)* What is the prize for the man who wins the trial of strength at Mary Mestrovich's birthday party? *(b)* Why is sheer strength so important here?

2. *(a)* How does Joe Magarac, the strongest man, treat others? Consider the cases of: the man from Johnstown, Mary Mestrovich, Pete Pussick, and Mrs. Horkey. *(b)* Why does Joe Magarac laugh all the time?

3. What does Joe's last name tell us about his attitude toward life?

4. Why does Joe get angry when the mill is closed for a long weekend? What is his highest ideal?

5. Hero tales are usually full of exaggerations. Explain how exaggeration is used in building up the picture of Joe Magarac.

6. What kind of people do you think created this hero tale?

Salkey: ANANCY *(page 225)*

1. Reread the description of Anancy at the beginning of the story. *(a)* What traits does this description emphasize? *(b)* Are these traits evident at the ghost wrestling match?
2. *(a)* How does Anancy treat his mother? *(b)* What other character in this unit treats his mother in a similar manner?
3. What is the only way the ghost wrestlers can beat Anancy?
4. How does Anancy's spirit redeem itself?
5. Explain the conclusion Anancy and Brother Tacuma reach at the end of their adventure.
6. What is unusual about the way this tale is told? Read aloud a paragraph or two to illustrate the point you are making.

Downing: THE THREE JOURNEYS OF ILYA OF MUROM *(page 231)*

1. *(a)* Is Ilya of Murom a young, a middle-aged, or an old man? *(b)* What is he seeking? *(c)* Did you expect an attitude of this kind from a hero? Explain your answer.
2. Explain Ilya's three trials and the abilities he displays in winning each one.
3. *(a)* At the end of the three trials what has Ilya won for himself? *(b)* Is this the typical ending of a hero tale? Explain your answer.

IN RETROSPECT *(pages 176-233)*

1. There are many different kinds of heroes and heroines in this unit. *(a)* Characterize each of the following: Ahta-hana; Tesilya; Jack the Giant-Killer; Lemminkainen; Lemminkainen's mother; the Prince of Bohemia; Joe Magarac; Anancy; Ilya of Murom. *(b)* Different audiences admire different kinds of heroes. What kinds of people would admire the various heroes and heroines listed above?
2. The trials the heroes and heroines face are of many different kinds. List as many kinds of trials as you can and the achievements they require. What part does magic play in helping the heroes and heroines overcome the obstacles that face them?
3. After a test of strength or skill there ought to be a reward. But rewards, too, come in many varieties. What kinds of rewards do the successful heroes and heroines receive after they have faced their trials?
4. Imagining heroes and heroic myths remains as vigorous a human activity in our day as it ever was in the past. From sports, politics, movies, etc., list the typical heroes of your generation. What tests must they meet? What rewards do they expect? What do your heroes tell you about yourself and your society?
5. Choose one of the tales in this unit and update the details so that the characters and the action fit into the present time. In doing this you may want to exchange the marvels of science and technology for the old feats of magic. Or you may want to keep the magic.

VISIONS AND THE OTHER WORLD

Thompson: FRIENDS IN LIFE AND DEATH *(page 235)*

1. *(a)* What makes the young bridegroom seek out his dead friend? *(b)* What happens? *(c)* Why does the bridegroom accompany him back to the underworld?
2. *(a)* Characterize the underworld as it appears in this tale. Is it pleasant, gloomy, inviting, frightening, beautiful, harsh? *(b)* What is the significance of the thin kine and the fat kine?
3. *(a)* How long does the bridegroom stay in the land of the dead? *(b)* From the time the bridegroom decides to go with his friend to the underworld, the story gives clues that he will be gone a long time. What are these clues?
4. Is the end of the story inevitable? Why or why not?
5. *(a)* In what ways does this story resemble the Japanese myth "Urashima Taro" (page 42)? *(b)* What favorite American story closely parallels parts of this one?

Colum: HOW ORPHEUS THE MINSTREL WENT DOWN TO THE WORLD OF THE DEAD *(page 238)*

1. *(a)* Why does Orpheus decide to go down to the world of the dead? *(b)* How do you know that he realizes the journey will be dangerous?
2. How does Orpheus find the way to the great gate of Aidoneus's realm?
3. What two arguments does Orpheus use to persuade Aidoneus and Persephone to free Eurydice? Which convinces them?
4. What does Orpheus see in the realm of the dead? How would you characterize that world?
5. Why does Orpheus violate the sole condition imposed upon Eurydice's release?
6. *(a)* What is life like for Orpheus after his second loss? *(b)* What happens to him?

Lewis: FORMS OF THINGS UNKNOWN *(page 241)*

1. *(a)* Though Jenkin believes he is no longer troubled by his rejection by a girl, he admits that he is worried about the present state of his emotions. How does he describe that state? *(b)* In what way is that description an ironic foreshadowing of his own fate?
2. *(a)* What makes Jenkin feel that the trip to the Moon was "worse than he had ever anticipated"? *(b)* Why did the absence of atmosphere become a terrifying experience?
3. How does Jenkin misinterpret the three figures he finds on the Moon?
4. In Greek myth Medusa was a horrible monster with snakes for hair. Anyone who looked upon her was turned to stone. Relate this myth to the story you have just read. How does it explain *(a)* the messages, *(b)* the figures Jenkin finds, *(c)* Jenkin's fate?

5. When "Forms of Things Unknown" was written, men had not yet reached the Moon. Does the fact that men have since walked on the Moon affect your reaction to the tale? Explain.

Radin: THE GIRL WHO WAS SACRIFICED BY HER KIN *(page 248)*

1. *(a)* Why is Wanjiru sacrificed? *(b)* Why do the people bring goats to the sacrifice?
2. Wanjiru blames her family for her death. Is this fair?
3. How does her young lover find and rescue Wanjiru?
4 *(a)* Recount the sequence of events before the lover marries Wanjiru. *(b)* Do you think the lover should have forgiven Wanjiru's family?

Kroeber: THE MAN'S WIFE *(page 251)*

1. *(a)* What is the man's psychological state following his wife's death? *(b)* How does this free him to follow her?
2. *(a)* What is the wife's first action on rising from the grave? *(b)* What evidence do you have that she is now a spirit?
3. Describe the series of barriers between the world of the living and that of the dead. What is their purpose?
4. *(a)* What is life like for the spirits in the land of the dead? *(b)* Why do they find the living man's presence distasteful?
5. *(a)* Why does the chief of the land of the dead decide to allow the man's wife to return to the land of the living? *(b)* What one condition does he impose? *(c)* What earlier events in the story forewarn the reader that the man will not abide by his condition?
6. Would you say that this legend has a "happy ending"? Explain your answer.

Briggs: THE FAIRY DWELLING ON SELENA MOOR *(page 256)*

1. How does Mr. Noy happen to arrive at the fairy dwelling?
2. Who is Grace Hutchens and what advice does she give Mr. Noy?
3. *(a)* In what ways are the fairies different from mortals? Consider their age, agility, size, religion, and fertility. *(b)* Does Grace think that they lead a happy life?
4. *(a)* How do the fairies snare mortals? *(b)* What do they want them for? *(c)* Why do other human beings assume that the fairy captives are dead?
5. *(a)* How does Mr. Noy escape the fairy dwelling? *(b)* What happens to him subsequently? *(c)* What warning to the reader is implied in his experience?

Neihardt: THE GREAT VISION *(page 259)*

1. *(a)* How old was Black Elk when this vision came to him? *(b)* What was his physical condition? *(c)* These facts might cause some readers to question the validity of the vision. Do they bother you?
2. *(a)* Describe the four groups of horses. What does each group stand for? *(b)* What happens after the horses have begun dancing? What do you think this represents?

3. *(a)* What does each of the six old men stand for? *(b)* What powers do they give Black Elk?

4. *(a)* What does the blue man who lives in the flames represent? *(b)* How is he defeated?

5. What is the significance of the red road? the black road?

6. *(a)* What are the four ascents that Black Elk describes? *(b)* In the account of the ascents, what indications do you find that the people are in trouble? *(c)* Can you find any correspondence between this prediction and the history of Black Elk's tribe during his later years?

Bates: RITE OF ENCOUNTER *(page 274)*

1. *(a)* Where is young Singing-owl when the story opens? *(b)* What is he waiting for? *(c)* What means has he employed to bring about this happening?

2. *(a)* In what way does the pistol that Singing-owl takes from the dead white man warn him of how the white men have died? *(b)* Why, a little later, does he drop this same pistol "with a trembling hand"?

3. In the light of later events, what is the significance of the fact that the white men's camp is a short distance upstream from where Singing-owl drinks and bathes?

4. What happens to Singing-owl's vision?

5. How does Singing-owl try to trick Black Smallpox?

6. *(a)* At one point Smallpox says to Singing-owl, "There are but a few I cannot kill. You are one." Later the voice says, "We still walk together. I am a part of you. I will be with you always." Explain these statements in the light of medical science. *(b)* How does Singing-owl react to what he learns from the voice?

IN RETROSPECT *(pages 234–281)*

1. The otherworlds described in this unit are of different kinds. To reach any of these worlds a man or woman must make a journey. List the individuals who venture out of the everyday world and explain the kind of journey each takes.

2. Consider the individuals who travel to the land of the dead. *(a)* What barriers must they pass in order to enter this world? *(b)* Why do these barriers exist? *(c)* How is it that the people in these stories are able to pass the barriers?

3. *(a)* Which individuals find themselves in a strange world without making an attempt to go there? *(b)* How does this happen?

4. The experiences of the questers vary greatly. *(a)* What do the various individuals learn? *(b)* Which receive a special reward for the dangers they have faced? *(c)* Why do others fail to gain a reward?

5. A number of these stories describe the land of the dead. *(a)* What kinds of afterlife do they imagine? *(b)* Why do you think people imagined these various kinds of afterlife?

6. How do you imagine life after death might be? Write an account of your imaginary trip to that otherworld, describing your journey, the appearance of that world, what you learned there, and your return.

7. People of all ages and times have told stories of otherworlds. What do you think is the fascination of this particular kind of myth?

THE END OF THINGS

Sutcliff: THE BATTLE OF GAVRA *(page 283)*

1. *(a)* What action on the part of Cairbri, the High King, leads to the Battle of Gavra? *(b)* Do you think Cairbri knows what will happen? *(c)* Why does he have this deed performed?

2. *(a)* What causes the fighting between Clan Morna, led by Fer-tai, and Finn MacCool and the Clan Bascna men? *(b)* Why does Cairbri order Clan Morna to break off the fight? *(c)* Explain how this interrupted fight between clans leads directly to the great battle.

3. Who kills Cairbri? What happens to this killer of a king?

4. Finn MacCool describes Osca's death as "a hero's death." Would you consider Finn's own death equally heroic? What is it about these deaths that makes them worthy of a hero?

5. Why would a valiant Irish warrior look upon the story of this battle as a legend about "the end of things"?

Radin: THE WONDER-WORKER OF THE PLAINS *(page 289)*

1. *(a)* Why does the young man refuse to let his parents choose a wife for him? *(b)* What warnings do they give him? Are they right?

2. When the young man finds the girl he wants to marry, both act unconventionally. Explain.

3. *(a)* Why do the people of the girl's village so treasure the Wonder-Worker of the Plains? *(b)* What does he do for the young woman? *(c)* How does his life in the unfamiliar village differ from his former life?

4. Why does the young man kill the Wonder-Worker of the Plains?

5. *(a)* How does it happen that the young man and his mother both interrupt the wife's efforts to resuscitate the buffalo? *(b)* If the wife had told them the truth, do you think the end of the story might have been different? Explain.

6. Can you name any element of our modern world so vital to us that its loss would mean the destruction of everything? What would it be?

7. Why is the death of the Wonder-Worker of the Plains "the end of things" for the wife's tribe?

MacLeish: THE END OF THE WORLD *(page 296)*

1. The first seven lines of this poem describe an unusual circus. Point out some of the most unusual things about it.

2. Why do you think the poet describes such a bizarre circus? Considering what follows, why did the poet choose to describe a circus at all?

3. What is it that hovers, "hung over/Those thousands of white faces"?

4. *(a)* What was the experience of the crowd as this event occurred? *(b)* Did you have much the same experience as you read the last line of the poem for the first time? Why or why not?

5. *(a)* What two words are repeated several times in the last six lines? *(b)* How do you explain this repetition?

Dunsany: CHARON *(page 297)*

1. What is Charon's reaction to individual events? Why is this so?
2. What reasons might there be that the dead come for awhile in great numbers?
3. *(a)* How does Charon react to the message of the solitary shade? *(b)* Why does he react in this way?

Asimov: NIGHTFALL *(page 298)*

1. Theremon 762 is a young newspaper man. What event does he come to the Observatory to cover?
2. Explain the essential differences between the planet Lagash and Earth.
3. *(a)* Who are the Cultists? What are their beliefs? *(b)* Why does the young Cultist try to destroy the cameras?
4. Archaeologists on Lagash have determined that its history has had a cyclic character, with at least nine civilizations being destroyed by fire at the height of their culture. Explain this fact.
5. *(a)* Why is it impossible for the astronomers to believe in the existence of Stars? *(b)* What hypothesis does Beenay, the telephotographer, advance to suggest that Stars might exist? *(c)* No one, including Beenay himself, takes this idea seriously. Why?
6. Sheerin, the psychologist, has a theory that darkness causes madness. *(a)* What effects does the advancing of the eclipse have on him and on the various occupants of the Observatory? *(b)* Why do you think these reactions occur?
7. What is the significance of the title?

Green: RAGNAROK *(page 328)*

1. *(a)* Who is Haid? *(b)* What causes Odin to turn to her for help?
2. How does the end of things begin?
3. What destructive powers belong to the Wolf Skoll and the Midgard Serpent?
4. *(a)* How do the chief gods die? *(b)* Are their deaths appropriately heroic? Explain your answer.
5. Why does the second vision, the vision of Odin himself, console him?

Muir: THE HORSES *(page 335)*

1. *(a)* What brought the old world to an end? *(b)* How long, according to the poem, had this occurred before the horses came?
2. *(a)* What has happened to human society since the end of the old world? *(b)* How does the speaker live? *(c)* How would the speaker feel if there were a possibility of returning to a world like the one which has ended?
3. *(a)* How do the people react when the horses return? *(b)* Why does the speaker say that the presence of the horses "can pierce our hearts"?
4. Why do the horses return?

Nims: AD 2267 *(page 337)*

1. What has happened to the earth?
2. In what way is this poem about beginnings?

IN RETROSPECT *(pages 282–337)*

1. The selections in this unit, both prose and poetry, envision various kinds of endings. Identify these different kinds of endings and explain the cause of each.

2. *(a)* Which selections describe only an ending? *(b)* How do the characters in each of these selections react to the absolute end of the world they have known? *(b)* Which characters, faced with this ultimate crisis, do you admire? Which would you call heroic? Why?

3. *(a)* Which tales contain, as well as an end of things, at least a suggestion of a new beginning? *(b)* What hope does each imply?

4. In Unit II you read a number of Creation accounts. *(a)* Did any one of them contain an episode in which the world was destroyed? *(b)* What kinds of endings did such selections consider?

5. In what ways does the time and place at which a story was created influence a people's idea of how things will cease?

SOME NEWER STORIES

Hurlbut: EVE IN DARKNESS *(page 339)*

1. Victoria's consciousness differs sharply from the narrator's. *(a)* What does Victoria think the statue represents? *(b)* How does she interpret other things, for example, the character of the ragman and the origin of the carved dolls in the German toy shop? *(c)* Is her interpretation of things usually trustworthy? Do you think she could be wrong about the statue?

2. *(a)* How old and how mature is the narrator? *(b)* How does she react to ideas given her by others? What does she do about most of Victoria's terrifying suggestions? *(c)* Does Victoria have any real power over her mind? Explain your answer.

3. If there were a truly innocent consciousness, a kind of mind still in Paradise, which would it be? Why?

Maximov: THE ULTIMATE THRESHOLD *(page 345)*

1. In designing the House of Death, what problems did Velt hope to solve?

2. Compare Velt with Coyote (page 30). *(a)* What common problem faces them? *(b)* What particular abilities does each use in creating his solution? *(c)* How do others respond to this attempt at solving the problem? How do they treat Velt and Coyote?

3. Why has Velt decided to destroy his creation?

4. *(a)* What must Velt suffer in order to achieve his purpose? *(b)* To what extent is he then like Prometheus?

Malamud: IDIOTS FIRST *(page 355)*

1. Why is Mendel so urgent about getting Isaac on the train that same night?

2. *(a)* Who is Ginzburg? Consider that, as Mendel puts it, "Young people he don't bother so much," and that at the station Ginzburg himself tells Mendel, "You shoulda been dead already at midnight. I told you that yesterday." *(b)* Are there other times during the evening that Ginzburg appears? If so, what are they?

3. How does Mendel conquer Ginzburg?

4. *(a)* What is Mendel seeking? *(b)* What kinds of tests does he endure in order to gain the reward? *(c)* What heroic virtues must he demonstrate in order to succeed?

DeFord: THE APOTHEOSIS OF KI *(page 363)*

1. The first sentence of this tale says that Ki "encountered a god and the god entered into him." *(a)* Is this literally true? *(b)* Why does the author say this?

2. *(a)* What has been happening to the land of Ki's people? *(b)* What clues do you find as to the period of human history in which this story is set?

3. *(a)* Why is Ki sure the person he meets is a god? *(b)* What does he assume is the god's purpose in coming?

4. Ki recalls that he killed the tribe's medicine man at his own request. *(a)* Why had the medicine man requested that he be killed? *(b)* As Ki faces the god, why does he recall that incident? *(c)* What does it suggest to him?

5. Ki claims the god has given him wisdom. Is this true?

Buzzati: A SIBERIAN SHEPHERD'S REPORT OF THE ATOM BOMB *(page 368)*

1. What is the legend of Moma, the tigress?

2. At the beginning of the story the narrator says of the legend of Moma, "Who among us believes this legend?" At the end of the tale he says, "The legendary tigress really existed . . ." What has happened to change his opinion?

3. Relate the title to the story itself. *(a)* Do any details of the story suggest aspects of an atomic explosion as they might appear to a primitive people? *(b)* How do you account for attaching the legend of the tigress to this event?

IN RETROSPECT *(pages 338–371)*

Myths give us gods, heroes, and tricksters; they explain the beginning and the end of all things; they tell us how people received the gifts that make life possible and how evil came into the world.

The patterns of mythic stories keep recurring in modern writing. Push in "A Poetics for Bullies" is a modern trickster figure; "the end of things" occurs as surely in "Nightfall" as in "Ragnarok." Sometimes these mythic story patterns are strong; often they are only suggested or alluded to.

Consider the five selections of this last unit. Which ones come closest to a basic, mythic story pattern? Do any of them contain god or hero figures? Do any of the characters face a modern-day version of the trials encountered by heroes of old? Explain your answers.

AUTHOR BIOGRAPHIES

Antony Alpers (1919–   )

Antony Alpers was born in New Zealand, where he worked as a journalist and editor on a variety of newspapers and magazines. He went to the University of British Columbia as a visiting lecturer in 1962. Since 1966 he has been a professor of English at Queen's University in Ontario. His published works include *Dolphins: The Myth and the Mammal* (1961) and *Maori Myths and Tribal Legends* (1965).

Peggy Appiah (1921–   )

Born in England, Peggy Appiah now lives in Ghana, where she is involved both in working with children and with the culture of the Ashanti people. She has headed the advisory committee of the Kumasi Children's Home since 1968. Her published collections of Ashanti folk tales include *Ananse the Spider* (1966), *Tales of an Ashanti Father* (1967), and *The Pineapple Child and Other Tales from Ashanti* (1969).

Isaac Asimov (1920–   )

Isaac Asimov's fame as a science-fiction writer began with the *Foundation* trilogy (1951–1953), an epic thousand-year chronicle of humanity's star empires. He now has more than 125 books to his credit. These include fiction, criticism, anthologies, and books on science, history, Shakespeare, and the Bible. He is also an associate professor of biochemistry at Boston University, although since 1958 he has chosen to lecture only occasionally, devoting the bulk of his time to writing.

Russell L. Bates (1942–   )

Russell Bates began writing as therapy while recovering from an injury suffered in a military accident. He drew on his own ethnic background (he is himself a Kiowa) in producing "Rite of Encounter." He has written several children's books, in addition to numerous short stories.

Edward Blishen (1920–   )

Edward Blishen worked as a journalist in London for several years before the Second World War. After the war he became a teacher in preparatory and secondary schools, finally joining the department of education at the University of York. Since 1965 he has been a full-time writer. In addition to his collaborations with Leon Garfield on Greek myth, he has assembled several anthologies of literature for young people and has written on the teaching of English.

Katharine M. Briggs (1898–   )

Katharine Briggs was born in London and educated at Oxford. For many years she headed an amateur dramatic company, writing and producing plays. Her major work, however, is as a folklorist. She has produced a number of studies and collections of English folklore, including the four volumes of *A Dictionary of British Folktales in the English Language* (1970).

Marjory Bruce

Marjory Bruce is the author of *A Treasury of Tales for Little Folks* (1927) and *The Book of Craftsmen: The Story of Man's Handiwork Through the Ages* (1936).

Dino Buzzati (1906–   )

When as a Milanese newspaperman, Dino Buzzati began publishing his fantastical stories in 1933, his readers were unsure whether they were intended as children's literature or morality tales for the more mature. He has published novels, but has had more success with his short fiction, "metaphysical fables" that have been compared to the work of Franz Kafka.

Arthur C. Clarke (1917–   )

During the Second World War Arthur Clarke served with the Royal Air Force. After the war he attended graduate school for a time, but finally abandoned this to become a writer in 1951. When his novel *Childhood's End* was published two years later, critics praised it for combining serious philosophy with science-fiction adventure. He is best known for the filmscript of *2001: A Space Odyssey,* which he coauthored with director Stanley Kubrick.

Padraic Colum (1881–1972)

Within Ireland Padraic Colum was well known for the plays dealing with peasant life which he wrote for the Irish National Theatre. Outside of his homeland he is best known for his masterly retellings of folk tales. In 1923 he went to Hawaii at the invitation of the legislature in order to study Hawaiian folklore. The result was two collections of folk tales, *At the Gateways of the Day* (1924) and *The Bright Islands* (1925). In addition he published collections of Greek, Norse, and Irish myths.

Miriam Allen DeFord (1888–   )

During a long career as a writer, Miriam Allen DeFord has worked at a variety of occupations—journalism, advertising, editing, lecturing—while continuing to produce books of an equally varied sort, including histories, biographies, reference works, mysteries, science fiction, and translations.

Babette Deutsch (1895–   )

Since she began publishing her verse in 1919, Babette Deutsch has written eight books of poetry, as well as numerous translations of Russian, German, and French verse, novels, literary criticism, and children's books. She was born in New York City and educated at Barnard College and Columbia University, where she has taught since 1944.

George A. Dorsey (1868–1931)

George Dorsey was an anthropologist and taught at Harvard, the University of Chicago, and from 1925 until his death, the New School for Social Research in New York City. During his years at the University of Chicago, he was also curator of anthropology at the Field Museum of Natural History, for which he traveled extensively.

Charles Downing

Charles Downing is the author of *Russian Tales and Legends* (1956) and *Tales of the Hodja* (1964).

Lord Dunsany (1878–1957)

Edward John Moreton Drax Plunkett, 18th Baron Dunsany, was born in London and educated at Eton and Sandhurst. He served in the Boer War and the First World War, and became involved in the suppression of the Easter Rebellion in Dublin in 1916, where he was wounded and captured by the rebels. He published his first book of stories, *The Gods of Pegana,* in 1905. His first play, *The Glittering Gate,* was produced by the Abbey Theatre in 1909. He was a prolific writer, producing dozens of plays and short stories, as well as novels, travel books, and three volumes of autobiography.

Loren Eiseley (1907–   )

Loren Eiseley is an anthropologist who has taught at the University of Pennsylvania since 1947. He has written a number of books on historical and philosophical topics in science, including *The Immense Journey* (1957), *Darwin's Century* (1958), *The Firmament of Time* (1961), and *The Mind as Nature* (1962).

Stanley Elkin (1930–   )

Stanley Elkin is a novelist and short-story writer whose work is usually characterized with the phrase "black humor." He has taught English at Washington University in St. Louis since 1960. His published work includes *Boswell* (1964), *Criers and Kibitzers, Kibitzers and Criers* (1966), *A Bad Man* (1967), *The Dick Gibson Show* (1970), and *Searches and Seizures* (1973).

Leon Garfield (1921–   )

Leon Garfield is a writer who admires the literature and music of the eighteenth century and likes to employ the period as a setting for his novels. In addition to his evocations of the eighteenth century, he has collaborated with Edward Blishen on two retellings of Greek myth, *The God Beneath the Sea* (1971) and *The Golden Shadow* (1973).

Theodor H. Gaster (1906–   )

Theodor Gaster is a linguist, a folklorist, and a cultural historian whose specialty is the ancient Near East. He has been a professor of religion at Barnard College in New York City since 1966. His published work includes *Thespis: Ritual Myth and Drama in the Ancient Near East* (1950) and an abridged edition of Sir James Fraser's classic study of myth, *The New Golden Bough* (1960).

Judith Gleason (1929–   )

Judith Gleason has published a number of books dealing with the culture of West Africa, including *This Africa: Novels by West Africans in English and French* (1965), *Agotime, Her Legend* (1970), and *Orisha: The Gods of Yorubaland* (1971).

Roger Lancelyn Green (1918–   )

Roger Lancelyn Green has been an actor, a bookseller, a librarian, an editor, and the author of many books of poetry, mythology, and fairy tales. His interest in the mythology, history, literature, and archaeology of ancient Greece is reflected in such books as *Mystery at Mycenae* (1957), *Ancient Greece* (1960), and *Tales of the Greeks and Trojans* (1964).

Charlotte Huber

Since graduating from Barnard College in New York City, Charlotte Huber has worked as a journalist and broadcaster as well as writing a number of children's books, including *Skippy, the Monkey, The Princess with the Dirty Face, They Were Brave and Bold,* and *These Are The Tales They Tell.*

Rolfe Humphries (1894–   )

Rolfe Humphries was a teacher for over fifty years, mostly at the secondary level. He has published numerous translations, including *Poet in New York* (1940) by Federico Garcia Lorca, as well as the works of the Latin poets Virgil, Ovid, Juvenal, Martial, and Lucretius. He has also published a number of books of his own poetry.

Kaatje Hurlbut

Kaatje Hurlbut was born in New York City and now lives in Connecticut, where she divides her time between her family and her writing.

Joseph Jacobs (1854–1916)

Joseph Jacobs was a tireless folklorist who had as his ambition in the collections of folk tales which he edited "to write as a good old nurse will speak when she tells fairy tales." One-time editor of the journal *Folk-Lore,* he published the collection *English Fairy Tales* in 1890, bringing out a second collection, *More English Fairy Tales,* in 1894. Jacobs' retellings have been enduringly popular and are the form in which most children know such traditional tales as *Jack the Giant-Killer.*

Robinson Jeffers (1887–1962)

When Robinson Jeffers and his wife arrived in Carmel, California, in 1914, they knew they had found the place where they wanted to settle. So Jeffers built a house of the shore granite on a cliff above the ocean, where they lived out their lives and where he did all his writing. Feeling that poetry must become more realistic, he drew the subjects of his narrative poems from the life of the part of California where he lived. Although Jeffers is often accused of misanthropy, the photographer Edward Weston once said that Jeffers' poetry rather reflects a despairing love of humanity.

Gwyn Jones (1907–   )

Gwyn Jones is a writer and teacher who has published novels, translations of medieval Welsh romances and Icelandic sagas, and collections of folk tales. He has been a professor of English at University College, Wales, since 1940.

Theodora Kroeber (1897–   )

Theodora Kroeber began writing only in her fifties, publishing her first book, *The Inland Whale,* a collection of California Indian tales, in 1959. She has also written two books, *Ishi in Two Worlds* (1961) and *Ishi, Last of His Tribe* (1964), on the association between her husband, the anthropologist Alfred Kroeber, and Ishi, the sole survivor of a California Indian tribe.

C. S. Lewis (1898–1964)

C. S. Lewis was born in Belfast and educated at Oxford. Wounded during World War I, he returned to Oxford, where he taught for most of his life. Lewis is well known both for his scholarship in the field of medieval literature and for his Christian apologetics, especially the allegorical fantasies beginning with *Out of the Silent Planet* (1938).

Archibald MacLeish (1892–   )

Archibald MacLeish abandoned a prosperous law practice in 1923 and left for Paris with his wife and children to become a writer. After returning to America in 1928, he traveled in Mexico, following the route of Cortez. The result was the narrative poem *Conquistador,* which won the Pulitzer Prize in 1933. In 1953 he was awarded both the National Book Award and a second Pulitzer Prize for his *Collected Poems 1917–1952.* And in 1959 he won a third Pulitzer Prize, this time for drama, for his verse play, *J.B.*

Cyrus Macmillan (1880–1953)

Cyrus Macmillan is the author of *Canadian Wonder Tales* (1918) and *Canadian Fairy Tales* (1922), reprinted as *Glooskap's Country and Other Indian Tales* (1956).

Bernard Malamud (1914–   )

Bernard Malamud was born and raised in Brooklyn, the son of Russian immigrants. He wrote his first novel, *The Natural* (1952), while a member of the English department of Oregon State University, where he taught for twelve years. *The Magic Barrel* (1959), a collection of short stories, won the National Book Award. *The Fixer* (1966) won both the National Book Award and the Pulitzer Prize.

Herman Maximov

Herman Maximov is a young writer who lives in Alma-Ata, a city in Kazakhstan, in southeastern Russia. He began to publish science-fiction stories in 1965.

Edwin Muir (1887–1959)

Edwin Muir was born in the Orkney Islands, off Scotland's northeast coast. It was during a period of residence in Prague, Dresden, and Austria during the early twenties that he began to write, producing criticism, *Latitudes* (1924), *First Poems* (1925), and his first novel, *The Marionette* (1928). He also began doing translations of European writers, introducing Kafka to English readers. Later books of poems were *Journeys and Places* (1937), *The Narrow Place* (1943), *The Voyage and Other Poems* (1946), and *One Foot in Eden* (1956).

John G. Neihardt (1881–1973)

When as a young man John Neihardt lived on the edge of the Omaha Indian Reservation in Nebraska, he came to know the Indians well, sharing their memories and learning to see and feel as one of them. In 1911 he began to plan five book-length narrative poems on the West, the last one dealing with the battle of Wounded Knee— the final Indian resistance on the Plains. *A Cycle of the West* was completed in 1949. It was in the course of writing this poem that he encountered the Sioux holy man Black Elk. The result was *Black Elk Speaks* (1932).

John Frederick Nims (1913–   )

John Frederick Nims has taught and traveled widely in the United States and Europe. During the 1940's he was an editor of *Poetry* magazine. Since 1965 he has been a professor of English at the Chicago Circle Campus of the University of Illinois. His first book of poems, *The Iron Pastoral* (1947), was in graceful revolt against the prevailing modernism of American verse. Since then he has published *A Fountain in Kentucky* (1950), *Knowledge of the Evening* (1960), and *Of Flesh and Bone* (1968).

Paul Radin (1883–1959)

Paul Radin was an anthropologist who made an outstanding contribution to the contemporary understanding of the folklore, religion, and language of primitive peoples. He considered the response of the primitive mind to basic human problems to be profound, sophisticated, and comprehensible, differing in degree, but not in kind, from that of modern man. Among his published works are *The Autobiography of a Winnebago Indian* (1920), *Primitive Man as Philosopher* (1927), *Primitive Religion* (1938), and *The Trickster: A Study in American Indian Mythology* (1956).

Andrew Salkey (1928–   )

Andrew Salkey was raised in Jamaica and now lives in London, where after a brief career as a teacher, he makes his living as a free-lance writer. He has written a number of novels and short stories with Jamaican settings, including *West Indian Stories* (1960), *Drought* (1966), and *Riot* (1967). He has also edited several collections of West Indian writing.

Rosemary Sutcliff (1920–   )

Rosemary Sutcliff has written a number of books for children dealing with the past, both of the historians and of the romancers. An example of the former is *The Eagle of the Ninth* (1954), which takes place in Roman Britain; and of the latter *The Hound of Ulster* (1963), a retelling of the story of Cuchulain, the great hero of Irish romance. She has also written several novels for adults, including *Sword at Sunset* (1963), a novel based on the story of King Arthur.

Stith Thompson (1885–   )

Stith Thompson spent most of his academic career at Indiana University, where he was professor of English and folklore. He published a number of fundamental studies in the field of folklore, among them (with A. Aarne) *The Types of the Folktale* (1928), the six volumes of the *Motif-Index of Folk-Literature* (1932–1937), and *The Folktale* (1946).

Alfred, Lord Tennyson (1809–1892)

The publication in 1850 of his long philosophical elegy, *In Memoriam,* brought Alfred Tennyson fame, and in the same year he was appointed poet laureate to succeed Wordsworth. During the years he spent completing this poem, Tennyson was also producing his second major work, *The Idylls of the King* (1859), a series of twelve narrative poems which retell the Arthurian tales collected centuries earlier by Sir Thomas Malory.

Frank Waters (1902–   )

All his life Frank Waters has lived in and written about the Southwest. He was born in Colorado and educated as an engineer, spending nearly ten years working for the Southern California Telephone Co. before beginning to write. He has written a number of novels, including *The Man Who Killed the Deer* (1942). He has also written several books on the Indian cultures of the Southwest, among them *Masked Gods: Navajo and Pueblo Ceremonialism* (1950) and *Book of the Hopi* (1963).

PRONUNCIATION KEY

The pronunciation of each word is shown just after the word, in this way: **ab bre vi ate** (ə brē′vē āt). The letters and signs used are pronounced as in the words below. The mark ′ is placed after a syllable with primary or heavy accent, as in the example above. The mark ′ after a syllable shows a secondary or lighter accent, as in **ab bre vi a tion** (ə brē′vē ā′shən).

Some words, taken from foreign languages, are spoken with sounds that do not otherwise occur in English. Symbols for these sounds are given in the key as "foreign sounds."

a	hat, cap	o	hot, rock	ə	represents:
ā	age, face	ō	open, go		a in about
ä	father, far	ô	order, all		e in taken
		oi	oil, voice		i in pencil
b	bad, rob	ou	house, out		o in lemon
ch	child, much				u in circus
d	did, red				
		p	paper, cup		
e	let, best	r	run, try		
ē	equal, be	s	say, yes		
ėr	term, learn	sh	she, rush		
		t	tell, it		
f	fat, if	th	thin, both		
g	go, bag	ŦH	then, smooth		
h	he, how				
		u	cup, butter		
i	it, pin	ù	full, put		
ī	ice, five	ü	rule, move		
j	jam, enjoy				
k	kind, seek	v	very, save		
l	land, coal	w	will, woman		
m	me, am	y	young, yet		
n	no, in	z	zero, breeze		
ng	long, bring	zh	measure, seizure		

foreign sounds

Y as in French *du.* Pronounce (ē) with the lips rounded as for (ü).

à as in French *ami.* Pronounce (ä) with the lips spread and held tense.

œ as in French *peu.* Pronounce (ā) with the lips rounded as for (ō).

N as in French *bon.* The N is not pronounced, but shows that the vowel before it is nasal.

H as in German *ach.* Pronounce (k) without closing the breath passage.

The pronunciation key is from the *Thorndike-Barnhart Advanced Dictionary,* copyright 1974 by Scott, Foresman and Company.

INDEX OF AUTHORS AND TITLES